IIIA	IVA	VA	VIA	VIIA	VIIIA
								2 **He** Helium 4.003
			5 **B** Boron 10.81	6 **C** Carbon 12.01	7 **N** Nitrogen 14.00	8 **O** Oxygen 15.9994	9 **F** Fluorine 18.998	10 **Ne** Neon 20.183
IB	IIB		13 **Al** Aluminum 26.98	14 **Si** Silicon 28.09	15 **P** Phosphorus 30.97	16 **S** Sulfur 32.06	17 **Cl** Chlorine 35.45	18 **Ar** Argon 39.95
28 **Ni** Nickel 58.71	29 **Cu** Copper 63.54	30 **Zn** Zinc 65.37	31 **Ga** Gallium 69.72	32 **Ge** Germanium 72.59	33 **As** Arsenic 74.92	34 **Se** Selenium 78.96	35 **Br** Bromine 79.91	36 **Kr** Krypton 83.80
46 **Pd** Palladium 106.4	47 **Ag** Silver 107.9	48 **Cd** Cadmium 112.4	49 **In** Indium 114.8	50 **Sn** Tin 118.7	51 **Sb** Antimony 121.8	52 **Te** Tellurium 127.6	53 **I** Iodine 126.9	54 **Xe** Xenon 131.3
78 **Pt** Platinum 195.1	79 **Au** Gold 197.0	80 **Hg** Mercury 200.6	81 **Tl** Thallium 204.4	82 **Pb** Lead 207.2	83 **Bi** Bismuth 209.0	84 **Po** Polonium (210)	85 **At** Astatine (210)	86 **Rn** Radon (222)

63 **Eu** Europium 152.0	64 **Gd** Gadolinium 157.3	65 **Tb** Terbium 158.9	66 **Dy** Dysprosium 162.5	67 **Ho** Holmium 164.9	68 **Er** Erbium 167.3	69 **Tm** Thulium 168.9	70 **Yb** Ytterbium 173.0	71 **Lu** Lutetium 175.0
95 **Am** Americium (243)	96 **Cm** Curium (247)	97 **Bk** Berkelium (249)	98 **Cf** Californium (251)	99 **Es** Einsteinium (254)	100 **Fm** Fermium (252)	101 **Md** Mendelevium (256)	102 **No** Nobelium (254)	103 **Lw** Lawrencium (256)

Environmental Chemistry
AN INTRODUCTION

Lucy T. Pryde

SAN DIEGO MESA COLLEGE
SAN DIEGO, CALIFORNIA

CUMMINGS PUBLISHING COMPANY

Menlo Park, California · Reading, Massachusetts
London · Amsterdam · Don Mills, Ontario · Sydney

To the memory of Merle R. Tripp,
my first chemistry teacher.

Acknowledgments

Cover photograph by Richard G. Chafian. Photographs appearing on the following pages are by Richard G. Chafian and Michael J. Pollard: 88, 94, 96, 176, 235, 251, 280, 281, 300, 310, 316. Photographs appearing on the following pages are by Philip R. Pryde: 10, 21, 34, 53, 59, 63, 65, 66, 67, 69, 88, 114, 119, 136, 137, 146, 153, 154, 155, 158, 172, 173, 180, 186, 196, 206, 207, 210, 211, 216, 223, 226, 346.

ISBN 0-8465-5850-5
DEFGHIJKLM-HA-798765

Cummings Publishing Company, Inc.
2727 Sand Hill Road
Menlo Park, California 94025

Preface

This text has been written for students who are primarily interested in the arts, the humanities, and the social sciences. These students look forward to a great variety of professions—business, law, politics, social work, the creative arts—and yet each of them shares a common role as an informed and responsible citizen. Therefore this text is designed to be the basis of a vital and relevant course based on the environmental problems of our society. Chemistry is basic to the understanding of the nature of these problems and the planning to alleviate them. The chemical nature of substances and their transformations from the viewpoint of the environment bring both the possible solutions and the fundamental chemistry into sharper focus; an examination of the alternatives can be no more valid than the understanding of the underlying principles. The text recognizes that science itself is not sufficient to solve environmental problems but that each individual must participate in society's value judgments leading to economic and political action.

Special features of this book are:

Regarding *level*, the text assumes no prior knowledge of chemistry and very minimal use of mathematics.

The text encourages *flexibility of approach*. Students are familiar with and concerned about nuclear energy and the energy crisis in general. Therefore this topic is treated very early in the course (in Chapter 3) as an immediate environmental application. However, once Chapters 1, 2, and 4 have been discussed, all of the other chapters can be presented in any order desired.

Diagrams and illustrations, including photo essays, are used more extensively than usual to present scientific concepts and phenomena.

While *socioeconomic considerations* are introduced, including action at the federal level, polemics are avoided. Rather, facts are presented objectively with consideration given to the complexity of underlying variables.

At the end of each chapter, two types of *study questions* are included, technical ones to check comprehension of chemical concepts and a set of more qualitative ones to provoke further study and thought.

Chapter-end *bibliographies* are keyed to the study questions for directed research. For further exploration of topics in the text, an extensive bibliography is included at the end of the book along with a glossary of environmental and chemical terms.

A *laboratory manual* containing twenty-three experiments accompanies the text.

My appreciation is extended to my colleagues at San Diego Mesa College for their encouragement and support while pursuing this project. To all those teachers and students who participated in offering helpful suggestions, I am deeply indebted. A special thanks is extended to my husband, Philip R. Pryde, whose patience and understanding during the preparation of this text is truly appreciated. In addition, his photographic skills have contributed greatly to the value of the text. Lastly, I wish to acknowledge the enthusiasm and guidance of the Cummings team who turned this book into reality.

Lucy T. Pryde

Contents

CHAPTER SIX. CHEMISTRY OF THE WATER ENVIRONMENT

CHAPTER SEVEN.   PESTICIDES: CHEMICAL CONTROLS AND THEIR ALTERNATIVES

CHAPTER EIGHT.   CHEMICALS IN THE INTERNAL ENVIRONMENT: FOOD AND DRUGS

Chapter 1
Introduction

Part One: WHAT IS ENVIRONMENTAL CHEMISTRY?

As we look around us, it is not difficult to find evidence of our deteriorating environment and the need to do something about it. As a result of this need, a new field of emphasis is now emerging from within the discipline of chemistry, environmental chemistry. What special contribution can chemistry make towards solving our environmental problems? These problems must be understood — their causes, their effects, their interrelations with each other — before we can find satisfactory solutions, and chemistry gives us one way to understand.

Chemistry and Technology

Chemistry has traditionally been regarded as the study of the composition of substances and the transformations they undergo. This rather broad definition covers an amazing variety of activities, but perhaps the unifying theme of all chemistry, indeed of many sciences, is to find the underlying principles necessary to interpret and predict correctly natural physical phenomena. The resulting theories can then be tested by planned experimentation.

Extending the boundaries of understanding is a pursuit common to many fields of human endeavor and is a goal worth pursuing in itself. Yet chemistry is much more than that, for any pure science establishes the groundwork for accompanying technology, the practical application of scientific principles. The technological applications of chemistry have the most direct bearing on the general public, since chemical theories have led to the development of many new processes and products which reach throughout our society. Plastics, fabrics, drugs, exotic metal and ceramic materials, insecticides, improved gasolines, and many other products which were unknown twenty years ago, and which directly affect our lives today, have come into being through applications of chemistry. Also, many of these same areas of chemical technology are precisely the factors that are implicated in our present environmental problems.

At the outset, the distinction should be drawn between basic chemistry and the resulting technology, so that the proper target for our concern can be identified. A research chemist may be motivated by basic curiosity and carry out his experimental plan with great objectivity, with little concern for "practical" consequences. His results may open new areas of interpretation and applications, with far-reaching consequences that he may never have predicted. In any application, the positive virtues of a new technology are always more immediately obvious than its potential drawbacks. Chemistry and its applications are human activities and, as such, hold the same possibilities for error and shortsightedness that plague other areas of life.

Technology, therefore, must be subject to constant review and re-evaluation. This does not mean that it and the basic research that preceded it must stop. It does mean that chemists must be increasingly aware of their role in managing and interpreting the natural world for the common good. The period of unquestioned growth and innovation has ended, and the implications of new technology will be subject to critical review in advance rather than after the fact.

Environment

The environment was once considered to be an appropriate field of study for those interested in the climate, topography, and resources (such as the minerals or water) of a certain location. This purely physical study of the environment has since broadened to include all the factors in our surroundings that influence man, such as the available space, the noise, and the quality of the resources available to us. We are coming to realize more and more that all of these factors are interrelated. This realization is one of the most important aspects of learning to live successfully on our spaceship planet, for it means that it is not possible to work exclusively on any one aspect of the environment at a time.

The science of ecology specifically deals with the study of the interrelationships of biological systems as they interact with their surroundings. This term, which has now been popularized, is used to emphasize the connections among soil, water, air, plants, animals, man, and man's technology.

Environmental Chemistry

From the vast scope of chemistry and environmental study, several overlapping areas of importance can be seen. For example, the quality of our air is closely related to the way in which we choose to produce electric power. We can use nuclear fuel or fossil fuels such as oil, gas, and coal. Each type has specific advantages and disadvantages which must be understood as part of the decision-making process. The impact of each choice must be evaluated, and this can be done most effectively by first understanding the chemistry involved.

How we control automobile emissions is closely related to the chemistry of combustion processes. Photochemical smog resulting from combustion is the product of a chain of chemical reactions taking place in our air spaces. A similar example occurs when we study the quality of our water resources and the methods to purify and reuse this important component of our life-support system. Our internal environment is drastically affected by the drugs we use and the food we eat, which possibly contains pesticide residues left from our attempts to control insect populations. New materials with many excellent properties may develop into large-scale problems, as in the disposal of vast amounts of plastics.

Environmental chemistry deals with those aspects of our environment that can be clarified by understanding the basic physical and chemical principles involved. This provides a foundation for a more intelligent approach to questions of alternatives and appropriate controls to reduce the widespread abuses of our planet. Solution of environmental problems will require a scientifically literate public as well as socially aware scientists. The next section explores the relationships that must function between these groups.

**Part Two: THE ROLE OF ENVIRONMENTAL CHEMISTRY
          IN PROBLEM SOLVING**

It is generally agreed that there are three main causes of our present pollution levels: (1) increasing population, (2) increasing per capita consumption, and (3) the kinds of technology we employ.[1] All of these causes involve a complex of interlocking problems, and even experts do not agree as to the relative importance of these factors. Chemistry has a role to play in finding solutions to all of these problems.

Development of "the pill" and newer biochemical discoveries make it physically possible to control our population if the matching will to

---

[1] For a complete discussion of these factors, see Commoner, Barry, *The Closing Circle* (New York: Alfred A. Knopf, 1971).

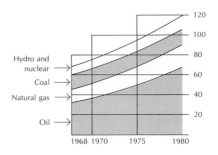

Richard F. Conrat

Changing technology is symbolized by this petroleum storage and refinery complex. In 1900, petroleum products furnished only 6.5 percent of the nation's need for industrial energy; they now provide nearly three quarters of this demand. The vast storehouse of petroleum provides fuel for homes, industry, and transportation. The versatility of both petroleum and the industry which processes it provides materials used to create the modern chemical world: plastics, pesticides, detergents, industrial solvents and lubricants, and synthetic textiles.

Some environmental effects of increased petroleum consumption are the increase in spillage from drilling or transportation and increased air pollution at the refineries due to dust, smoke, oxides of sulfur, carbon monoxide, and escaping hydrocarbons. Evaporative losses occur at every step of the cycle. The products have also created their own environmental impacts, such as widespread distribution of chlorinated hydrocarbon pesticides.

Since petroleum is a finite resource, there is an increasingly serious conflict over its use for fuel versus its use as an intermediate in the production of other chemicals, for if all known supplies are recovered and used at current rates, our crude oil resources will last only about thirty years.

Two factors connected with population contribute to the density of this residential area. The trend towards urbanization in the United States as well as the increasing total population of our country make growing demands on our available resource base. Larger population also means more total wastes added to the environment.

Per-capita consumption is another factor in our present pollution levels. The power lines typical to most communities are visual reminders of the growth in power consumption on an absolute and also on a per-capita basis in the United States. The same growth is evident in other indices; oil consumption is estimated at 55 barrels per capita in 1970 but is expected to grow to 74 barrels per capita in 1980.

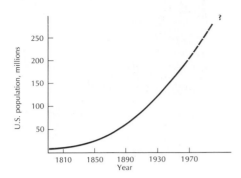

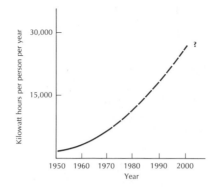

do so is present. Increasing consumption is linked to the availability of energy as well as to rising expectations for the "standard of living." Unfortunately, it is becoming clear that "standard of living" and "quality of life" are not always the same goal. Perhaps the most important area for the application of chemistry to environmental problems is in the kinds of technology we use, for here we do have conscious choices to be made which must be based on available evidence.

Environmental Education

For solution of any or all of these three causes of pollution levels, increased public understanding of science is necessary. It is not enough for the scientific and governmental experts to understand the chemical basis for solving a particular problem. Unless the public understands a regulatory decision, it will earn little support. The full range of opinion must be examined in the public forum, and therefore any concerned citizens must have access to environmental education. It is hoped that this exposure will produce changes in attitude as well as in specific knowledge. Too often a lack of scientific understanding has led to either fear or apprehension on the part of the public, sowing the seeds of mistrust. The scientifically literate person will be better equipped to understand our world, for, like it or not, the twentieth century is marked by rapid technological change. The scientifically literate person will also have a heightened awareness of the interdependency of all facets of our surroundings. The truly international nature of pollution problems will become obvious and lead to consideration of solutions in a wider perspective.

Increased public education is essential too if the citizen is not only to understand decisions, but also to influence the decision-making process. In this context, environmental chemistry establishes a foundation for informed public action.

The *automobile* would be high on any list of technological changes leading to serious environmental deterioration. Once the symbol of affluence, automobiles are increasingly used to symbolize the environmental problems associated with our changing technology and increasing population. The results of our dependence on the automobile have been serious air pollution, unpleasant and harmful noise levels, inefficient utilization of raw materials, and questionable land-use policies whereby highways take precedence over parks and open space. Ever-increasing numbers of automobiles have made new highways obsolete even before they are completed. In your area, do you observe many automobiles with more than one occupant? What choices are available in our application of transportation technology?

It is not only the urban roadways which suffer from the woes of too many automobiles. The ultimate planned obsolescence of the automobile with no universally accepted or enforced method of recycling the materials have produced the all-too-familiar scene of automobile junkyards. The chemical complexity of the automobile, composed of many metals, glass, and plastic materials, makes any recycling plan difficult. How can this visual insult be avoided?

Elihu Blotnick

Richard F. Conrat

Criteria versus Standards

The role of an educated public in helping to bring about and maintain a clean environment cannot be underestimated, for although scientists must find suitable criteria for the quality of our surroundings, the public and their agencies must set and enforce the standards. The difference between these two concepts is considerable. Criteria are statements of predicted effects at specified levels of a pollutant, based on experimental results. Standards are legal limits based on the criteria but also on judgments of benefit versus risk. For example, automobiles produce large amounts of carbon monoxide, a serious health hazard. Criteria can be determined from experiments showing the concentrations of carbon monoxide necessary to produce harmful effects on animals. Standards can then be established, but several choices are available. Automobiles could simply be outlawed or emission standards set at zero, which would have the same effect. Instead, some compromise is reached after weighing the benefits of continued automobile use (reaching places of employment, for example) against the risks (harm from carbon monoxide). There are many such decisions to be made, and the public must play an increasing role in helping with this process. Furthermore, only public demand and support can produce effective enforcement of established standards.

Public participation in decisions based on scientific evidence is a somewhat new idea. In the past such decisions were often made by government officials after private consultation with representatives of the scientific community. Now there is pressure to bring evidence into the open so that it can be cross-examined by other scientists and the public as well. Such an interplay of ideas before a final decision is reached helps to ensure that the citizens themselves have a say in judgments which affect the quality of their own lives. This process has been greatly enhanced by the passage of some landmark federal legislation.

Part Three: WHERE'S THE ACTION?

Federal Organization: NEPA and CEQ

Assuming an informed and concerned citizenry, what are the channels available to bring about environmental improvement? The last few years have produced major federal legislation to help in the fight. The National Environmental Policy Act of 1969 (known as NEPA) has far-reaching purposes.

To declare a national policy which will encourage productive and enjoyable harmony between man and his environment; to promote

The business of *modern agriculture* is another prime example of our changing technology. The amount of harvested land has been decreasing in the United States, while per-capita farm production has remained nearly constant. How has this been accomplished? Farming methods have been drastically changed. Fertilizers assume a more important role. Feedlots rather than open ranges are used to raise cattle, which results in organic wastes being confined in a small area. Natural processes cannot utilize the amount of nitrogen available, and thus excess nutrients enter the water supply and cause problems.

Increasing population and economic pressures have combined to create huge monoculture farms, an open invitation to devastation by pests. The response has been to protect crops with increasing doses of chemical pesticides. The persistent chemical pesticides such as DDT have made their way into the far reaches of our world, even showing up in the middle of oceans and polar environments.

Once the crops leave the farm, the requirements of storage, processing, and distribution of such large amounts of food have introduced many chemical additives into our foods. Changing life-styles create a demand for convenience foods, one more step in our modern food technology.

efforts which will prevent or eliminate damage to the environment and biosphere and stimulate the health and welfare of man; to enrich the understanding of the ecological systems and natural resources important to the Nation.[2]

One of the most important consequences of NEPA is that all policies, regulations, and public laws of the United States must be interpreted and administered in light of their environmental significance. The responsible agency must prepare an "environmental impact statement" in which the effects of the project both in the short run and long term are analyzed. All reasonable alternatives which might minimize environmental damage are also to be considered. Any irreversible and irretrievable commitment of resources must be clearly given. The environmental impact statement must be made available to state and local agencies and to the public for review at least ninety days before any action is taken. In effect then, NEPA is an open disclosure act, making federal decision-makers responsible for their decisions. The policy of preparing such an impact study applies to pending federal legislation as well as to any project in which the federal government is substantially involved such as projects on public lands, U.S. Corps of Engineers plans, or federally financed housing developments. The public has both the opportunity and the responsibility to see that the statements are filed and are adequate in light of the intent of NEPA.

Another purpose of NEPA was to establish the Council on Environmental Quality (CEQ). The CEQ is a three-member advisory council created in the Executive Offices of the President. The members are appointed by the President and have responsibilities to gather, analyze, and interpret environmental trends and information. They must advise the President on the broad spectrum of environmental quality problems such as land use, wildlife conservation, and population growth. CEQ can recommend new national policies and help to coordinate and investigate existing environmental guidelines. Their advice enables the President to submit the Environmental Quality Report to Congress as required by NEPA each July 1. Final environmental impact statements are all filed with the CEQ.

The Environmental Protection Agency

CEQ has been helped in its mission by the establishment of the Environmental Protection Agency (EPA) in 1970. Primarily a regulatory agency, this agency is the most comprehensive pollution-fighting group now in the federal system. The EPA has major responsibilities in such areas as air, water, noise, and radiation pollution, as well as the control

[2]Public Law 91-190, 91st Congress, S.1075.

of pesticides and solid waste disposal. In many cases the new agency is now coordinating various efforts that were already underway in a myriad of different departments. Some of the transferred programs are shown in Table 1.

By combining most of the federal pollution control efforts into one agency, it is hoped that the effectiveness of all programs will be improved and that industry will have its responsibilities clarified. The EPA's role includes setting and enforcing standards, conducting research on the effects of pollution and the means of control, funding such research in other institutions, and providing technical assistance to state and local pollution control units. EPA operates through ten regional offices in attempting to achieve close cooperation between federal and local programs (see Figure 1). Since the EPA is a relatively new agency, it remains to be seen exactly how effective it really becomes in carrying out its mission, but early activities seem to be encouraging. The first director, William Ruckelshaus, has provided strong leadership for the new agency.

To a large degree, the eventual success or failure of EPA will depend on the degree of public enthusiasm and support for its activities. Unless

Table 1. Programs Transferred to the Environmental Protection Agency

Program	Former agency
Federal Water Quality Administration	Interior
National Air Pollution Control Administration	Health, Education, Welfare (HEW)
Bureau of Solid Waste Management	HEW
Bureau of Water Hygiene	HEW
Bureau of Radiological Health (portions of)	HEW
Pesticide research and standards setting of Food and Drug Administration and Interior	HEW and Interior
Pesticides registration authority	Agriculture
Authority to conduct ecological research	Council on Environmental Quality
Federal Radiation Council	Executive Office of the President
Environmental radiation protection standard setting	Atomic Energy Commission (AEC)

Source: Document 91–364, House of Representatives, 91st Congress, 2nd Session.

Figure 1. Federal Regions of the Environmental Protection Agency

UNITED STATES
ENVIRONMENTAL PROTECTION AGENCY
WASHINGTON, D.C. 20460

Regional offices	Phone	States covered
I Boston, Massachusetts 02203	617–223–7210	Connecticut, Maine, Massachusetts, New Hampshire, Rhode Island, Vermont
II New York, New York 10007	212–264–2525	New Jersey, New York, Puerto Rico, Virgin Islands
III Philadelphia, Pa. 19106	215–597–9151	Delaware, Maryland, Pennsylvania, Virginia, West Virginia, D.C.
IV Atlanta, Georgia 30309	404–526–5727	Alabama, Florida, Georgia, Kentucky, Mississippi, North Carolina, South Carolina, Tennessee
V Chicago, Illinois 60606	312–353–5250	Illinois, Indiana, Michigan, Minnesota, Ohio, Wisconsin
VI Dallas, Texas 75201	214–749–2827	Arkansas, Louisiana, New Mexico, Oklahoma, Texas
VII Kansas City, Missouri 64108	816–374–5493	Iowa, Kansas, Missouri, Nebraska
VIII Denver, Colorado 80203	303–837–3895	Colorado, Montana, North Dakota, South Dakota, Utah, Wyoming
IX San Francisco, Calif. 94111	415–556–4303	Arizona, California, Hawaii, Nevada, American Samoa, Guam, Trust Territories of Pacific Islands, Wake Island
X Seattle, Washington 98101	206–442–1200	Alaska, Idaho, Oregon, Washington

people are willing to back their concern with the necessary money and commitment to new patterns of environmental management, the awakening interest in protecting our fragile spaceship may be short lived. Unfortunately, we do not have the luxury of unlimited time to solve all our environmental problems. EPA has recognized this by calling for a national commitment for participation

> in the development of a new environmental ethic — a way of life which will allow us to retain and improve the life-enhancing features of technology without repeating and intensifying the mistakes of the past.[3]

---

[3]*Toward a New Environmental Ethic*, Environmental Protection Agency (U.S. Government Printing Office, 1971), p. 1.

Not all environmental decisions fall under NEPA, CEQ, or EPA by any means. Other important federal legislation will be pointed out as we discuss a specific topic, for example the Clean Air Act of 1970 in Chapter 5. Many states have excellent programs in one or more areas of environmental protection; for the most part it will be left to the readers to check on state and local regulation in their own areas.

Group Action

At all levels of government, the necessity and ability of individual citizens and citizen groups to make their views known is becoming more and more important. Although public access to information has been enhanced by NEPA and other acts requiring agencies to reveal information, there are still too many cases where background data are hard to obtain. For example, industries are not required to disclose to the public any data relevant to environmental protection. Because of the power of numbers, one important place to find the action in making your opinion count is within any number of established groups or clubs. The advantages of dealing with environmental problems by belonging to such groups are many. You will receive current news by reading the group's

Table 2. National Organizations with Strong Interests in Environmental Protection[a]

Common Cause 2100 M St., NW Washington, D.C., 20037	National Parks and Conservation Association 1701 Eighteenth Street, NW Washington, D.C. 20009
Consumer Alliance P.O. Box 11773 Palo Alto, California 94306	National Wildlife Federation 1412 16th Street, NW Washington, D.C. 20036
Environmental Defense Fund 162 Old Town Road East Setauket, New York 11733	Sierra Club 1050 Mills Tower San Francisco, California 94104
Friends of the Earth 30 East 42nd Street New York, New York 10017	The Wilderness Society 729 15th St., NW Washington, D.C. 20005
National Audubon Society 950 Third Avenue New York, New York 10022	Zero Population Growth 4080 Fabian Way Palo Alto, California 94303

[a]For a complete guide to environmental groups interested in environmental protection, consult *A Golden Guide to Environmental Organizations* (Golden Press, 1972).

publications. Opinions backed by significant numbers of people cannot be easily ignored, and everyone benefits from the vital interplay of ideas possible between members who share similar concerns. Many of the organizations have been involved in environmental protection for many years and therefore have a great deal of accumulated background material and good organization for tackling current problems. Some national organizations active in the environmental field are given in Table 2. They may have local sections in your area. Also, local organizations exist which are centered on a specific problem. Some investigation may turn up groups studying your local issues; people with a great deal of stamina may wish to consider forming such a group to anticipate or meet a local environmental problem.

On this list you can note several organizations that had their origins in other activities but were forced to actively enter the field of environmental protection as the seriousness of problems increased. The National Audubon Society would be an example of this phenomenon, for their original interest in birds has required them to deal with the problems of diminishing undeveloped land, air and water pollution, and their effects on wildlife. This same realization has been reached by many other organizations not appearing in Table 2. For example, the American Chemical Society also reflects growing concern for environmental problems in its subcommittee on environmental improvement. Many other national professional organizations have similar committees. Church groups and clubs of all kinds commonly have a committee working on some aspect of environmental education.

Environmental Law

Action as a group may also take the form of a class action lawsuit, a concept, it seems, that will be tested with increasing frequency in the future. A "citizen's class action" is a legal suit filed on behalf of the class of citizens who are injured as a group and who expect relief as a group. For example, a group of homeowners whose property values are lowered by noise from an airport can file a suit to gain financial relief. Whether or not this concept can be applied to much larger and less defined groups is not yet clear. Could the citizens of an entire city file a class action lawsuit against a large industrial firm that pollutes the air of that city? Could one city sue another for dumping sewage in a river that then flowed polluted downstream? These and related legal questions will be tested and decided in the future.

The increasingly legalistic approach to environmental problems has spurred the development of another successful merger of fields based on need—environmental law. Many lawyers have been generous in donating their time and expertise to questions of law involved in a given environmental situation and the specialty field is growing rapidly. The Environmental Defense Fund (see Table 2) is an organization of both scientists and lawyers seeking to take specific legal action in order to stop environmental abuses. The Sierra Club similarly engages in legal moves to achieve environmental objectives. Some of the most successful battles have taken place when groups have cooperated in a temporary coalition to work towards a specific goal.

Individual Effort

Even if you have a voice as part of a group, individual action can be of primary importance. Educating yourself is the first step, but your informed opinion must reach others if it is to influence action. The means of communication can be a personal visit, a phone call, a letter, or even a post card, but you can make your ideas known. Letters to government or industry officials or to the editor of your local newspaper all profit from being concise, constructive, and timely. Another very effective way of communicating is by means of personal example. Some suggestions along these lines will be offered in the Epilogue after you have considered the scope of environmental chemistry in Chapters 2 through 9.

Suggested Readings

Brown, Martin, ed. *The Social Responsibility of the Scientist*. New York: Free Press, 1971.

> This is a collection of essays by prominent scientists. Each expert deals with a contemporary issue of science such as federal funding of research projects, chemical warfare, food additives, radiation, population, pesticides, etc. Together the essays help to analyze the role of a scientist in today's society.

Commoner, Barry. *The Closing Circle: Nature, Man and Technology* New York: Alfred A. Knopf, 1971.

> Dr. Commoner is widely regarded as an authoritative and articulate spokesman on environmental problems. This book gives a new look at the nature, causes, and possible prevention of environmental disaster.

Council on Environmental Quality. *Environmental Quality, 2nd Annual Report*. U.S. Government Printing Office, 1971.

> As required by NEPA, the CEQ must submit an annual report to Congress. This report reviews the current status of environmental

programs, discusses economics and legal aspects, and contains a section on environmental problems in the inner city. Contains many useful tables as well as the full text of NEPA and other important federal legislation. Look also for the most recent report.

Ehrlich, Paul and Harriman, Richard L. *How to Be a Survivor*. New York: Ballantine Books, 1971.

Using the analogy of the earth as a spaceship, the authors first put forth the troubles with the craft. The principles of operation, size of the crew, classes of occupants, and effective environmental control systems are analyzed, ending with the characteristics of the spacemen. One of the appendices contains a provocative model for a new United States Constitution.

Chapter 2
Atoms: A Chemist's View of Matter

The most fundamental questions about matter deal with its structure and the search to understand its ultimate composition. At first, the search was purely philosophical. The early Greeks are particularly noted for their contributions towards understanding the structure of matter. Much later, scientific experimentation became the method of extending our knowledge. Together, philosophy and science have brought us many insights into the structure of matter. Although our understanding is far from complete, we are indeed fortunate to be starting the study of chemistry from our twentieth-century perspective. This allows us to use definitions and concepts that have resulted from all the lengthy and gradual development of the past.

All fields of study involve the use of characteristic vocabulary. You have only to try to read any specialized magazine to verify that interest groups develop specialized language, be it psychology, chemistry, mathematics, car racing, or surfing. Chemistry, in addition, shares another characteristic with many other fields—the advantage of using symbols to abbreviate lengthy terms and concepts.

In this chapter some of the fundamentals of language and symbolism concerning atoms will be introduced. First we will focus on the general structure of the atom. The stability and natural reactions of the nucleus form the second major topic, laying the groundwork for the chapters to come.

Part One: ELEMENTS AND ATOMS

Man has always tried to understand the incredible variety of substances he could observe in his environment. This goal has led to a search for basic "building blocks" for all matter. Such units could be linked in many different ways to form the wide variety of observable substances. We have moved a long way from the early Greek idea that all substances are composed of four basic "elements"—air, water, fire, and earth. We now recognize approximately 104 different basic substances that cannot be decomposed by ordinary chemical means. These are known as elements in the modern sense of the word. Some of these elements are well known to you, such as carbon, oxygen, and hydrogen. Other elements may not be familiar to you; many of them are relatively rare in nature, such as dysprosium, niobium, and astatine.

The smallest unit of an element that still retains all significant properties of that element is known as an atom. We again owe the genesis of this idea to the early Greek philosophers who were the first to suggest that matter was ultimately composed of individual particles. Each element consists of a single type of atom (although there can be some variation within that type, as we shall see shortly, in the case of isotopes).

Regions of the Atom

The Electron Cloud. Experimentation within the last few centuries has refined our ideas about the nature of atoms. It is now known that atoms are themselves composed of two regions—a small and densely packed nucleus and an electron cloud around the nucleus. It is hard to get a proper idea of relative size of the parts of the atom. The diameter of an atom averages approximately 10^{-8} cm (0.00000001 cm) whereas the central nucleus has a diameter of only 10^{-13} cm. Thus the nucleus is roughly one one-hundred thousandth the diameter of the entire atom. If the nucleus of an atom were the size of a tennis ball, the diameter of the entire atom would be approximately four miles!

The electrons in the electron cloud which surround the nucleus are responsible by far for most of the volume that an atom occupies. This is not due to the size of electrons, for each electron is an extremely small particle. Rather, the movement of electrons around the nucleus (which will be discussed in more detail in Chapter 4) defines the electron cloud region. An imperfect but useful analogy would be to compare a ball swinging around on the end of a string to the electrons in an atom.

Table 1. Atomic Particles

Name of particle	Position in atom	Discoverer	Electrical charge	MASS Absolute, grams	Relative, amu[a]
Proton	Inside nucleus	Ernest Rutherford 1919	+1	1.672×10^{-24}	1
Neutron	Inside nucleus	James Chadwick 1932	0	1.675×10^{-24}	1
Electron	Outside nucleus	J. J. Thompson 1897	−1	9.107×10^{-28}	5.484×10^{-4}

[a]Atomic mass units (amu) define a relative mass scale based on the most common form of carbon having a mass of 12 amu. 1 amu $= 1.66 \times 10^{-24}$ grams, so the value of 1 amu for a proton and a neutron is in reality a rounded number. These small differences become very important in calculating the energy released in a nuclear reaction. The mass of the electron is so small that its mass is sometimes given as 0 amu; this does not mean it has no mass, but rather that it is much less than that of the proton and neutron if rounded to one significant figure.

Even though the ball itself is quite small, its movement will define an entire region. The electron cloud region, the outermost, exposed part of an atom, is responsible for the chemical behavior of atoms as they interact with each other.

We have noted that electrons are extremely small. In addition to their small size, electrons are characterized by their negative electrical charge and by their extremely small mass; they contribute very little to the total mass of an atom.

Mass and weight are not the same thing, although you may often find these terms used interchangeably. The difference lies in the fact that the *weight* of an object is a measure of the gravitational pull on the object, whereas the *mass* of the same object measures the tendency of the object to stay at rest if it is stationary or to continue in motion if it is already moving. Mass can be thought of as the quantity of matter present compared with a standard set of masses. This means that mass is a more fundamental measurement than weight, for mass does not change as position changes. For example, a bar of lead would *weigh* less out in space than it does on the surface of the earth, but its *mass* would be the same.

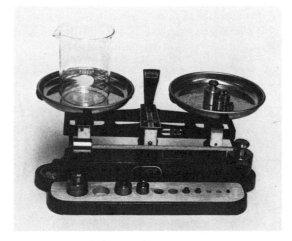

Weight   Mass

The Nucleus. The extremely dense core of an atom is known as the nucleus. It contains a concentration of almost all of the atom's mass. Although over a hundred different particles have been identified in the nucleus or coming from the nucleus, there are just two main types of particles to consider—the neutron and the proton. Both of these particles have much greater mass than the electron. They also differ from the electron in electrical charge: the proton carries a positive charge, while the neutron is electrically neutral. These two most important nuclear particles, protons and neutrons, are compared with electrons in Table 1.

An atom as a whole is electrically neutral. From the data listed in Table 1, it can be seen that the nucleus of an atom will have a positive charge, due to the presence of at least one proton. The number of negatively charged electrons outside the nucleus balances the number of positively charged protons inside the nucleus. However, the number of electrons can be easily influenced by many external chemical factors. Therefore the number of protons is taken to be the more fundamental characteristic of an atom.

The number of protons in the nucleus of an atom is unique for each type of element. This characteristic number of protons is referred to as the charge number or the atomic number of that atom. The atomic number determines what element is present. We can now define an element more specifically: an element is a sample of matter containing atoms of only one atomic number. For example, every sodium atom has an atomic number of 11; the nucleus of a sodium atom contains 11 protons. Since protons have a positive charge, the nucleus carries a charge of 11+. The most common type of sodium atom also has 12 neutrons in the nucleus; therefore the mass of a sodium atom's nucleus, expressed in amu, would be 23.

We can express all of this information about the sodium atom more compactly by use of the symbol $^{23}_{11}\text{Na}$.

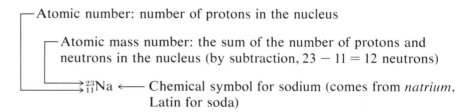

Atomic number: number of protons in the nucleus

Atomic mass number: the sum of the number of protons and neutrons in the nucleus (by subtraction, $23 - 11 = 12$ neutrons)

$^{23}_{11}\text{Na}$ ⟵ Chemical symbol for sodium (comes from *natrium*, Latin for soda)

In this symbol, the atomic mass number is written to the upper left of the chemical symbol; the atomic number (the number of protons) is written to the lower left. This type of symbol specifically represents the nucleus, but if the atom is electrically neutral, the number of electrons would be known, too (11 in this case), the same as the number of protons.

Isotopes

The number of protons (atomic number) determines the type of element. As long as the number of protons is constant, there can be

Table 2. Isotopes of Hydrogen

Symbol	Special names given to isotope	#p	#n	Natural abundance	Nuclear stability
$_1^1H$	"Normal" hydrogen; Protium	1	0	99.985%	Stable
$_1^2H$	"Heavy" hydrogen; Deuterium	1	1	0.015%	Stable
$_1^3H$	Tritium	1	2	a	Unstable

[a]Very rare isotopic form. Only 1 atom of $_1^3H$ occurs for every 10^{17} atoms of $_1^2H$.

variations in the number of neutrons present and still have the same element. Carbon atoms, with an atomic number of 6, exist naturally in seven forms; two important ones are $_6^{12}C$ and $_6^{14}C$. In each case, there are six protons, identifying the element as carbon, but the atomic mass number varies. In ^{12}C, there are six neutrons and in ^{14}C, there are eight neutrons. These two different forms of carbon are called isotopes. Isotopes of an element have the same atomic number but differ in atomic mass due to different numbers of neutrons in their nuclei. All elements have known isotopes, although the relative amounts and stability of these isotopes differ greatly. In this case, ^{12}C is stable and accounts for 98.9 percent of all carbon atoms. ^{14}C, which accounts for less than 0.001 percent of all carbon atoms, naturally emits radiation. This property is utilized in dating objects (see page 34). A set of isotopes for another element is given in Table 2.

Atomic Weight of an Element

A symbol such as $_1^3H$ represents only a single isotope and gives us the mass of that particular type of atom. Since elements occur in mixtures of isotopes, a way is needed to reflect the natural distribution of isotopes for any element. This is given by the element's atomic weight. The concept of an element's atomic weight involves two ideas: the relative abundance of the different isotopes of that element and one isotope of standard mass to use for comparison. Combining these two ideas, the atomic weight of an element is defined as the average relative mass of the isotopes of that element referred to the standard of carbon-12 taken as exactly 12.0000 . . . amu. Because a comparison to a standard mass is made, the atomic weight scale is also referred to as the relative atomic

Table 3. Determining the Atomic Weight of Neon

The element neon naturally occurs in three isotopes: neon-20, 21, and 22. The relative abundance of these isotopes are 90.92 percent, 0.26 percent, and 8.82 percent, respectively. The atomic weight of neon is then calculated from the exact mass of each isotope and its natural abundance in this way:

Isotope	Relative mass, based on ^{12}C as 12.00 amu	×	Of all neon atoms, this isotope accounts for the fractional part:	=	Total mass contribution, amu
Neon-20	19.99	×	0.9092	=	18.17
Neon-21	20.99	×	0.0026	=	.05
Neon-22	21.99	×	0.0882	=	1.94
			1.0000	Atomic weight: 20.16 amu	

To obtain a more accurate result, even more exact figures could be used. The atomic mass of neon-20, for example, is exactly 19.99244 amu. The masses of the other isotopes are also known more precisely, leading to an atomic weight for neon accepted to be 20.183 amu.

mass scale. An example of an atomic weight computation is given in Table 3.

Similarly, oxygen consists of 99.759 percent ^{16}O with a mass of 15.99491 amu, 0.037 percent ^{17}O with a mass of 17.99914 amu, and 0.204 percent of ^{18}O with a mass of 17.99916 amu. This leads to an atomic weight for oxygen of 15.9994 amu. Prior to 1927 it was thought that oxygen existed as only one isotope ^{16}O but subsequent experiments showed the mixture of isotopes to be present. Oxygen had been the standard for the relative mass scale. When it was found to be a mixture, oxygen was abandoned as a standard; the single isotope of the element carbon (^{12}C), a stable, convenient, and easily obtained isotope, was chosen.

Gram-Atomic Weight

Closely related to the concept of atomic weight is the *gram-atomic weight* (GAW or g.at.wt.) of an element. Numerically this is simply defined as the atomic weight expressed in grams. Therefore oxygen, which has an atomic weight of 15.9994 amu, has a gram-atomic weight of 15.9994 grams or approximately 16 grams. This definition has the effect of making the values for atomic weight convenient for use in the laboratory. A certain number of grams are easily weighed out for use, but the atomic mass unit is too small itself to be practical. The gram-atomic weight of an element, such as 16 grams for oxygen, may also be referred to as one *gram atom* or as a *mole of atoms*.

It is clear that 16 grams could not be the mass of a single atom of oxygen; rather it is the mass of a very large group of atoms. Experimental results have shown that in one gram-atomic weight of any element there are 6.02×10^{23} atoms; this number is known as *Avogadro's Number*. This piece of information, together with the gram-atomic weight, allows you to find the weight of an individual atom. For example, for an atom of oxygen:

$$\frac{16 \text{ grams/GAW}}{6.02 \times 10^{23} \text{ atoms/GAW}} = 2.66 \times 10^{-23} \text{ grams/atom}^{[1]}$$

It is obvious why single atoms cannot be weighed and in fact have never been seen even with the most powerful magnifying system.

We will see a parallel to the defined gram-atomic weight for an element in Chapter 4 when we talk about the weights of groups of atoms chemically combined into molecules.

The Periodic Table of Elements

The Periodic Table of Elements, given inside the cover of this book, is a very useful reference for the chemist, for a great deal of information about elements is represented in a compact fashion. The table is formed by an arrangement of the elements in order of their increasing atomic numbers. The chemical symbol for each element and its atomic weight is also shown. Elements with similar properties form groups (also called families), which are the vertical columns in the table. There also are trends in properties associated with any horizontal row of elements (called periods). Knowing the relationships that exist in the orderly arrangement of elements in the periodic table is an important tool for prediction of chemical reactions. Many of the patterns in the table can be explained on the basis of the distribution of electrons in the region outside the nucleus of each atom. In Chapter 4 we will look at some more specific details about the organization of the periodic table.

---

[1]Another way to calculate this same value is to use the definition of an atomic mass unit from Table 1.

$$\frac{16 \text{ amu}}{\text{atom}} \times 1.66 \times 10^{-24} \frac{\text{grams}}{\text{amu}} = 2.66 \times 10^{-23} \frac{\text{gram}}{\text{atom}}$$

Numerically, therefore, the reciprocal of Avogadro's number defines the gram value of the atomic mass unit.

Early attempts to relate elements to each other were based purely on observable properties. Theoretical considerations such as the atomic number or the distribution of electrons are both twentieth-century developments.

One of the first attempts to relate elements was made by Doberiner in 1817. He showed that "triads" of elements could be chosen such that the atomic weight of the middle one, along with the physical and chemical properties, was close to being the average of the other two. One such triad he proposed was:

	Atomic weight	Density (g/ml)	Form at room temperature
Chlorine	35.5	1.56	Gas
Bromine	80	3.12	Liquid
Iodine	127	4.94	Solid

Newlands in 1860 arranged known elements in order of increasing atomic weight and then found that after every 7th element, the properties began to repeat. He then arranged elements with similar properties underneath each other and called his ideas the "Law of Octaves." Unfortunately his essentially correct proposal was greeted with much laughter by chemists at the time.

In 1869–71 Dmitri Mendeleev carried Newlands' idea further and ordered approximately seventy elements into a form of the periodic table very similar to that used today. His success was due in large part to the fact that he was so sure of his systematic arrangement of the elements that he left spaces in his table for what he felt sure were undiscovered elements. He correctly predicted the properties of the "missing" elements based on observable patterns of properties for the known elements. The subsequent discovery and verification of properties for scandium, gallium, and germanium established Mendeleev as the originator of the periodic table.

Part Two: NUCLEAR STABILITY

The Discovery of Natural Radioactivity

The atom was long believed to be the indivisible building block of all matter. Its properties were thought to be constant and fixed by its nature. The first hint that the atom was capable of spontaneous change took place just before the turn of the century. This surprising property was discovered accidentally in 1896 when a French physicist, Antoine

Henri Becquerel (1852–1908), was intending to study a property known as fluorescence. He knew that some materials, after exposure to the ultraviolet radiation present in sunlight, will themselves emit enough light to cause an image on a photographic plate. He had a sample of a compound of uranium and carried out his experimental plan, causing the expected image to appear. However, an image also appeared on a photographic plate that happened to have been stored together with an unexposed sample of the salt in a drawer, away from the sunlight! Even inserting a sheet of paper or glass or silver between the uranium salt and the photographic plate did not change the result. This evidence pointed out the existence of some penetrating natural form of energy coming from the compound, capable of changing the photographic plate. He named the new effect radioactivity and the energy radiation. His discoveries started a scientific investigation that shows little sign of ending. Although we have made great strides in probing the secrets of these natural radiations, there are many things we still do not understand.

This startling discovery led to many new questions. Why do some elements naturally emit radiation and others do not? What is the source of the radiation? Some of the answers lie in examining the structure of atoms themselves in light of modern theory.

Stability of Isotopes — Guide for Prediction

We can observe that even different isotopes of the same element vary widely in atomic stability. Hydrogen, for example, exists in two stable forms which do not emit any natural radiations. The third form, tritium, is a naturally unstable type of atom and will give off radiation. Since the only difference among the three forms of hydrogen is the number of neutrons present, this factor would appear to have a direct bearing on the question of the stability of an atom.

Consider for a moment what would happen if the nucleus contained only protons. As they are all positively charged and like charges repel each other, it is hard to imagine a stable nucleus under those conditions. Indeed, no stable nucleus is known to contain only protons ($_1^1$H has only one proton). The neutrons appear to have a specific function in maintaining the nucleus. As the number of protons increases, the number of neutrons necessary to maintain stability also increases. Therefore for the lighter elements, the ratio of n to p is 1/1, for example, $_2^4$He, $_3^6$Li, $_5^{10}$B, $_6^{12}$C, and $_8^{16}$O. As the atomic number increases, particularly after element 20, calcium, the number of neutrons needed to maintain stability becomes proportionally greater. Stable $_{22}^{48}$Ti, for example, has 26 neutrons for 22 protons. The difference is even more pronounced as you move to element 82, lead, which has as one stable isotope of $_{82}^{208}$Pb with 126 neutrons for 82 protons, for an n/p ratio of 1.54/1, and another stable form $_{82}^{206}$Pb, n/p = 1.51/1.

The exact nature of the forces holding the nucleus together is not known. The force cannot be primarily that of charged particles for neutral particles (one type of electrostatic force), as the particles are too close together. This same reason rules out that the force is gravitational in origin even though every object has a gravitational attraction for all other objects; in this case the calculated magnitude of the force is too small to account for observed energy of the nucleus.

One very recent theory, proposed by the Japanese theoretician Yukawa, is that the nucleus is held together by means of an *exchange force*. The protons and neutrons are thought of as continuously exchanging a third particle called a π meson. The mass of this particle is approximately $275 \times$ that of an electron, and it may be positive, negative, or neutral in charge. The π meson itself has an independent life of only 10^{-8} seconds.

There does seem to be an upper limit to the number of neutrons that can be added, as most of the heavier elements tend to be unstable no matter how many neutrons are present. This same problem of stability for heavier elements is pointed up by the fact that the most abundant elements are those below atomic number 40.

The stable isotopes have been determined for each element. A very interesting graph can be drawn to locate these isotopes, plotting the number of protons against the number of neutrons (Figure 1). The elements fall within a narrow band, sometimes called the "belt of stability." The belt of stability shows stable (nonradioactive) isotopes. If we consider a radioactive, unstable isotope, $^{14}_{6}C$ with 6 protons and 8 neutrons, for example, we can see that it does not fall with the "belt." (The small x plots this isotope in Figure 1.) An isotope not in the stable region will be naturally radioactive and emit radiation to adjust its nuclear structure until it is within the belt of stability.

As other examples of the usefulness of this graph, check the location of $^{6}_{3}Li$, which is stable, and $^{8}_{3}Li$, which is not. Strontium $^{88}_{38}Sr$ is stable, but $^{90}_{38}Sr$, above the stable region on the graph, is radioactive. You may be aware of strontium-90's importance as a component of radioactive fallout as the result of atmospheric testing of nuclear weapons in the early 1960s.

Types of Natural Radiation

Natural radioactivity now is interpreted as the spontaneous emission of particles and rays from the nucleus of an atom. Another use of the graph in Figure 1 is to give a clue as to the type of natural radiation

Figure 1. The Belt of Stability

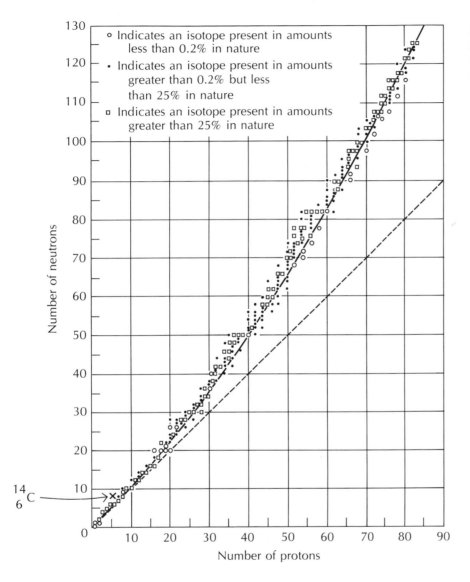

Solid line indicates neutron-proton ratio of naturally occurring elements; dashed line is for a neutron-proton ratio of one.

Source: Alfred B. Garrett et al., *Chemistry, A Study of Matter*. Xerox Corporation, 1968.

emitted as an isotope adjusts to fall within the belt. Carbon-14, for example, falls above the stable region, meaning it has an excess of neutrons. One possible mechanism to return ^{14}C to the stable region would be the simple emission of a neutron, but this is rarely observed. Instead, it is thought that when carbon-14 decays spontaneously, one neutron in the nucleus changes into a proton, an electron, and an anti-neutrino. The fate of the anti-neutrino (an extremely small, uncharged particle that was only proven to exist in 1956) is unclear, but the electron is emitted and the proton remains in the nucleus. The n/p ratio is improved to such an extent that the resulting nucleus comes within the stable region. This internal step can be represented in this manner:

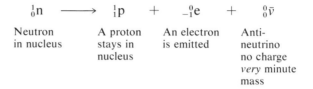

$$^{1}_{0}n \longrightarrow \ ^{1}_{1}p \ + \ ^{0}_{-1}e \ + \ ^{0}_{0}\bar{\nu}$$

| Neutron in nucleus | A proton stays in nucleus | An electron is emitted | Anti-neutrino no charge *very* minute mass |

The element has now undergone a natural transmutation and has actually changed identity as the number of protons has changed. The atom is no longer carbon-14, it is nitrogen-14. The over-all change in the carbon-14 is represented by this nuclear equation.

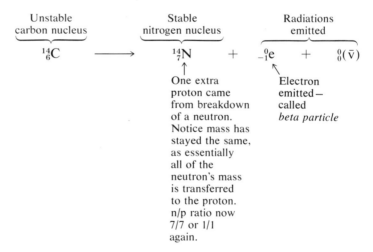

Unstable carbon nucleus   Stable nitrogen nucleus   Radiations emitted

$$^{14}_{6}C \longrightarrow \ ^{14}_{7}N \ + \ ^{0}_{-1}e \ + \ ^{0}_{0}(\bar{\nu})$$

One extra proton came from breakdown of a neutron. Notice mass has stayed the same, as essentially all of the neutron's mass is transferred to the proton. n/p ratio now 7/7 or 1/1 again.

Electron emitted — called *beta particle*

Note that a symbolic representation such as this shows charge numbers and mass numbers for both elements and particles emitted.

When electrons are emitted from the nucleus in this way they are called beta particles (β). The different name does not imply a difference between beta particles and electrons, but rather it reinforces the idea that the source of the particle given off is the nucleus itself; it is not an electron from the electron cloud.

Another type of natural radiation is quite commonly given off by heavy elements in attempting to become more stable. These heavy elements, beyond an atomic number of 83, usually fall above the range of stability. For example, $^{238}_{92}U$ decays by giving off a bundle of two protons and two neutrons known as an alpha particle (α). Since an alpha particle has two protons, it is the same as the nucleus of a helium atom. It is given the symbol ^4_2He. This transmutation can be represented in this way:

$$^{235}_{92}U \longrightarrow \; ^4_2He \; + \; ^{231}_{90}Th$$

Alpha particle given off	Only 90 protons left, identity of element changes to thorium

Note that the algebraic sum of the charge numbers on the right must equal that present on the left. The same is true for the mass numbers, since they are expressed to the nearest whole number. Check this relationship for the ^{14}C decay. It is true in that and every other case of transmutation.

Table 4. Properties of Three Main Types of Natural Radiation

| | SYMBOLS | | Charge | Mass | PENETRATING POWER | |
	Greek letter	Nuclear symbol			Relative	Numerical ratio (as determined through aluminum sheet)
Alpha particle	α	^4_2He	+2	4	•Slowest moving and least penetrating — stopped easily by a few thicknesses of metal sheet	1
Beta particle	β	$^{\;\;0}_{-1}e$	−1	0	•More penetrating than alpha — still stopped by several thicknesses of metal	100
Gamma ray	γ	—	—	—	•Most penetrating — even goes through 10 inches of lead. •Travels at speed of light, 3×10^{10} cm/sec.	10,000

Figure 2. Uranium-235 Natural Decay Series

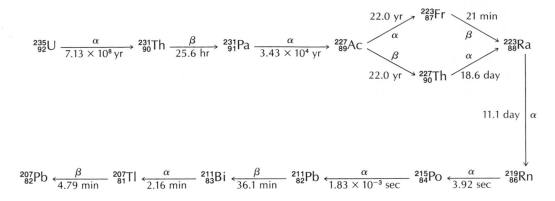

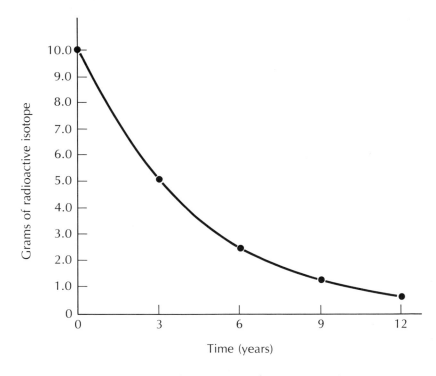

Figure 3. Decay of a radioactive isotope with a half-life of three years

(10.0 grams of an isotope with $t_{1/2} = 3$ years)

Both beta emissions and alpha emission are usually accompanied by emissions of energy bundles called gamma (γ) rays. Gamma rays are similar to very high energy x-rays. Being a form of energy, they have no mass. Gamma radiation is sometimes emitted from unstable nuclei even if no particles are thrown out. Several important properties of the main types of natural radiation are given in Table 4.

Natural Decay Series

Few of the naturally radioactive isotopes of heavy elements achieve stability by means of a single emission. In particular, alpha emission is very rarely successful in producing a stable nucleus. In the case of the ^{235}U decay shown previously, the thorium produced is not stable. It in turn emits a beta particle, producing protactinium. This in turn is unstable and emits an alpha particle to form actinium. This process continues through several steps until eventually a stable isotope is reached. In this case, the disintegration stops when the stable $^{207}_{82}$Pb is formed. This process represents a natural decay series. The course of the series from ^{235}U to ^{207}Pb is charted in Figure 2.

Half-life

The times referred to in Figure 2 are for the half-life of each isotope. Half-life is defined as the average time interval necessary for a radioactive isotope to decay to half the number of atoms of the original isotope. The symbol for half-life is $t_{1/2}$. For example, suppose you start with 10 grams of a radioactive isotope that had a half-life of three years. At the end of three years, 5 grams of the original isotope would remain unchanged. After a total of six years, only 2.5 grams of the original isotope would be present, only 1.25 grams after nine years, and so on. This concept is represented graphically in Figure 3. The curve for any radioactive isotope would have the same shape, whatever the original amount.

The half-lives of radioactive isotopes vary tremendously from small fractions of a second to billions of years. In the ^{235}U series shown in Figure 2, half-lives vary from 1.83×10^{-3} seconds to 7.13×10^8 years. The half-life is an important characteristic used to identify an isotope, as it is impossible to change the observed half-life. None of the usual means which alter a chemical reaction—heat, pressure, acid, or other chemicals—will change the rate of disintegration. There is no way to stop the natural disintegration process; only a continuation of the natural decay process will end the radioactivity of the isotope. This very constancy is responsible for using natural radioactive decay rates to date geologic and archaeologic objects.

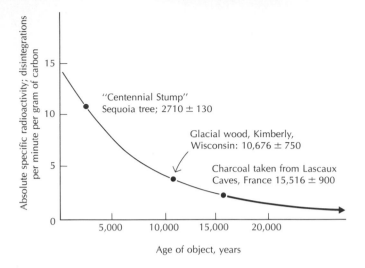

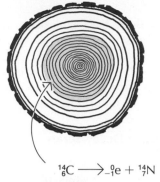

$$^{14}_{6}C \longrightarrow ^{0}_{-1}e + ^{14}_{7}N$$

The graph y-axis is labeled "Absolute specific radioactivity; disintegrations per minute per gram of carbon" with values 0, 5, 10, 15. The x-axis is labeled "Age of object, years" with values 5,000, 10,000, 15,000, 20,000. Data points are labeled:

"Centennial Stump" Sequoia tree; 2710 ± 130

Glacial wood, Kimberly, Wisconsin: 10,676 ± 750

Charcoal taken from Lascaux Caves, France 15,516 ± 900

Radiocarbon dating is one of the most useful tools devised for fixing the age of any object containing organic compounds. The method is based on several physical principles. The first is the change that occurs when high-energy cosmic rays transmute some nitrogen atoms into radioactive carbon-14. Assuming that the cosmic-ray activity has been constant through time (or by applying correction factors to compensate for the slight historical variations), all living material in this giant sequoia tree contains an equilibrium proportion of radioactive carbon-14 to the more plentiful, nonradioactive carbon-12. Both types of carbon behave in the same manner in forming cellulose and the other complicated organic matter of the tree.

As the tree grows a new ring each year, the old growth no longer replenishes its supply of carbon. Therefore, the amount of ^{12}C remains fixed but the ^{14}C continues its naturally radioactive decay by emitting a beta particle. The decay is not affected by any physical or biological force such as heat, pressure, or the chemical form of the carbon. Therefore, by knowing the half-life of ^{14}C (5730 yrs) and comparing the amount present to the equilibrium concentration, the age of the organic material can be determined.

This process has been applied to the "centennial stump" sequoia tree, cut down in 1874, and subsequently found to be 2710 years old by radiocarbon dating. For objects older than 50,000 years, the extremely low levels of radioactivity make detection difficult. Present atmospheric levels of ^{14}C are almost double the reference level of 14 disintegrations per minute per gram of carbon, due to atmospheric nuclear testing. Scientists of the future will have to consider this man-made variation in the natural production of ^{14}C when dating objects from the present age by a radiocarbon method.

General Grant Tree, Kings Canyon

Environmental Exposure to Natural Radiation

Man is continually exposed to radiation from several sources—the sun, outer space, radioactive materials in the earth, and even our own bodies. This natural radiation is referred to as background radiation.

Cosmic rays from space provide a major component of the background radiation. The earth receives a high dose of particles, particularly protons, and gamma rays from outer space. Usually only gamma radiation is received at the surface of the earth. The protons which come to the earth react with the components of the upper atmosphere, producing ^{14}C and a wide array of other possible particles, along with more gamma rays. The amount of cosmic radiation reaching the earth's surface varies with altitude, as the protective shield of the atmosphere changes. Less atmosphere at higher elevations allows more particles to fall on the mountain climber, the aircraft, or space craft. People living at an elevation of 5000 feet in Denver or at 10,000 feet in the Andes receive greater background radiation due to their elevation.

Certain rocks and minerals contain radioactive isotopes, particularly isotopes of uranium and thorium. From time to time, one of these isotopes turns up in clay used to make pottery and unknowingly, the consumer can find himself with a lovely radioactive set of dishes! The important naturally occurring isotopes are given together with their half-lives, in Table 5.

Table 5. Important Natural Radioactive Isotopes

Isotope	Name	Half-life
$^{238}_{92}U$	Uranium	4.5×10^{10} yr
$^{232}_{90}Th$	Thorium	1.39×10^{10} yr
$^{40}_{19}K$	Potassium	1.3×10^{9} yr
$^{87}_{37}Rb$	Rubidium	4.7×10^{10} yr
$^{138}_{57}La$	Lanthanum	1.1×10^{11} yr
$^{147}_{62}Sm$	Samarium	1.06×10^{11} yr
$^{14}_{6}C$	Carbon	5.77×10^{3} yr

Notice that other than ^{14}C each of the isotopes has a very long half-life, at least a billion years. This is responsible for their continued presence on the earth. Since the age of the earth is placed at approximately five billion years, (5×10^9), any isotope with a short half-life (and not being formed as part of a decay series) might have disappeared in that time span. ^{14}C, although it has a comparatively short half-life, is continually being formed by the action of cosmic rays.

What other things in our environment may be sources of natural radioactivity? Different types of building materials vary in radioactive content due to the presence of naturally unstable isotopes. Living in a concrete house exposes the occupant to one and one-half times more radiation per year than living in a brick house, and three times as much as living in a wooden house. The extremely low doses of radioactivity received are regarded as insignificant. However, a U.S. Congressman recently suggested that the office buildings for the Senate and House of Representatives, being composed of granite and brick, were producing above normal background radiation levels, resulting in a variety of symptoms such as fuzzy and illogical thinking, prolonged periods of nonsensical talk, and delusions of grandeur. Needless to say, the scientific evidence supporting the cause of the observed effect is not well established as being due to radiation level!

Potassium ($^{40}_{19}K$) is a very common component of natural background radiation. Potassium-40, together with ^{14}C and ^{226}Ra, is found in our bodies. Of these three, ^{40}K provides us with the largest internal source of radiation as the potassium is distributed throughout our bone structures. Beer has a significant potassium content (25 mg/100g), and therefore drinking beer adds ^{40}K to the body—leading to the rather curious statistic that each individual can of beer contributes the same dose of radiation as that resulting from the nuclear power industry in an entire year! We shall examine some of the assumptions inherent in that statement in the next chapter. In any event, the presence of natural sources of radiation in our bodies should not cause undo concern, as man has managed to coexist with these sources up to now.

Man has added to natural background levels and doses of radiation received by the general public through nuclear weapons testing, all facets of the nuclear power industry, and the many growing uses of natural and artificial radioactive isotopes in industry, agriculture, and medicine. The production and uses of artificial radioactivity will be considered in the next chapter in order to compare the significance of man's radiological impact with that nature has provided.

Study Questions

1. Would you weigh the same on top of a mountain as you do at sea level? Would your mass be the same?

2. Compare the three basic atomic particles as to their electrical charge and mass.

3. Can you suggest a reason why the neutron was the last of the three basic atomic particles to be discovered? (You might want to read about its discovery to see if your guess is close to reality.)

4. Is there any such thing as an element with no protons in the nucleus? Explain.

5. What number of protons and neutrons are present in $^{175}_{71}Lu$? If the atom is electrically neutral, how many electrons will be present?

6. For each of the following nuclear symbols, give the charge number, the mass number, the number of protons, the number of neutrons, and the name of the element.

   a. $^{14}_{7}N$ b. $^{21}_{10}Ne$ c. $^{58}_{28}Ni$ d. $^{254}_{102}No$

7. If an atom contains 13 protons and 11 neutrons, what element would it be? If another atom contained 13 protons and 14 neutrons, would it be the same element? Which of these two atoms would you predict would be more stable and why?

8. What isotopic form of hydrogen accounts for the vast majority of hydrogen atoms?

9. The element chlorine naturally consists of two stable isotopes. One has a mass of 34.97 amu and the other, 36.97 amu. Since the atomic weight of chlorine is 35.45, how can you tell which isotope must be most plentiful in nature? (If your algebra permits, calculate the actual percentage of each isotope.)

10. Which of the following terms refer to the same value? What is that numerical value?

One mole of sulfur	One gram-atomic weight of sulfur
One molecule of sulfur	One gram-atom of sulfur

11. a. What is the gram-atomic weight of magnesium?
    b. What is the weight of one mole of magnesium?
    c. How many atoms are contained in one mole of magnesium?
    d. What is the weight of a single magnesium atom?

12. From the information on page 26, calculate the expected density of bromine if this property were really the average of the values given for chlorine and iodine. How does the calculated value compare with the given density for bromine?

13. Use the "belt of stability" given in Figure 1 to predict which of the following isotopes will be stable and which radioactive.

   a. $^{7}_{2}He$ b. $^{9}_{4}Be$ c. $^{6}_{4}Be$ d. $^{14}_{7}N$ e. $^{17}_{7}N$
   f. $^{40}_{17}Cl$ g. $^{60}_{30}Zn$ h. $^{195}_{78}Pt$ i. $^{148}_{58}Ce$

14. Explain the apparent contradiction in saying that an electron can be emitted from the nucleus of an unstable atom even though the nucleus does not contain any electrons.

15. $^{232}_{90}$Th decays by giving off an alpha particle. Write the nuclear equation for this transmutation.

16. $^{191}_{76}$Os decays by giving off a beta particle. Write the nuclear equation for this transmutation.

17. Each of the following isotopes decays by emitting an alpha particle. What isotope will be formed as the result of the transmutation?

    a. $^{213}_{83}$Bi   b. $^{223}_{86}$Rn   c. $^{225}_{89}$Ac

18. Each of the following isotopes decays by giving off a beta particle. What isotope will be formed as the result of this transmutation?

    a. $^{223}_{86}$Rn   b. $^{209}_{81}$Tl   c. $^{209}_{82}$Pb

19. What is meant by a natural decay series?

20. Which type of radiation has the greatest mass? Why will this also be the particle with the least penetrating power?

21. $^{231}_{90}$Th has a half-life of 24.6 hours. If you isolated 10 grams of this pure isotope, what time would elapse before you were no longer sure of having 2.5 grams of pure substance?

22. If you start with 20 grams of a radioactive substance and find that after two hours you have only 1.25 grams of the original substance, what must be the half-life of that material?

23. $^{128}_{53}$I has a half-life of 25.0 minutes. Assuming you start with six million atoms, how many of these atoms would you expect to have after five hours?

24. What is background radiation? Does man have any control over the amount of background radiation he receives?

25. Radon is a radioactive element. Since it is a gas, radon can enter the lungs and then, of course, continue to emit radioactivity. Explain why it is now illegal in Colorado to use uranium mine tailings as landfill in inhabited areas. *Hint:* Consult Figure 2.

Suggested Readings

Boorse, Henry A. and Motz, Lloyd (eds). *The World of the Atom,* 2 volumes. New York: Basic Books, 1966.

An interesting reference for historical and biographical information concerning discoveries connected with the atom and its structure. Clearly written, with many explanations of basic physical phenomena.

Gamov, George. *The Atom and its Nucleus*. Englewood Cliffs, New Jersey: Prentice-Hall, 1961.

Introductory level book written by a scientist who has been very successful in interpreting science to the layman. Explains basic theories of atomic structure with emphasis on nuclear changes.

Hein, Morris. *Foundations of College Chemistry*. Belmont, California: Dickenson, 1967.

Excellent source for basic chemical information. Several chapters pertaining to topics considered so far, including properties of matter, elements, atomic theory and structure, and the periodic table. This is a text for an introductory level chemistry course.

Chapter 3
Energy From Atoms: Nuclear Power

The most significant scientific event in the last century is probably the release of energy that accompanied the first successful splitting of atoms. The new knowledge and its resulting technology ushered in a new era—in warfare and politics, in peaceful energy sources, and in direct effects on the environment. To understand and control the uses of this new form of energy remains a challenge to all humanity.

To help meet this challenge, we will examine some of the basic nuclear processes and their resulting environmental effects. We will first define and discuss artificial radioactivity, including the important processes of fission and fusion. We will then present two divergent interpretations of the biological damage due to radiation and currently accepted methods of detecting and measuring radioactivity. We will also consider prospects and problems connected with the control and safe utilization of nuclear power. We will end this chapter by looking into the future at two newly developing applications of the energy obtainable from atoms.

Part One: ARTIFICIAL RADIOACTIVITY

It had always been the dream of early chemists to change elements into other elements, particularly base metals such as lead into gold. Little did they realize that elements were constantly changing identity around them due to natural radioactive processes! The first reaction that purposely accomplished such a transmutation took place in 1919 when Ernest Rutherford changed nuclei of nitrogen into oxygen by means of bombardment with alpha particles. This change also produces a proton, which is the nucleus of the normal hydrogen atom. The nuclear equation, shorthand for this reaction, is:

Alpha   Compound nucleus
particle   of fluorine   Proton

$$^{14}_{7}N + ^{4}_{2}He \longrightarrow [^{18}_{9}F] \longrightarrow ^{17}_{8}O + ^{1}_{1}H$$

Protons $7 + 2 = [9] = 8 + 1$
Neutrons $7 + 2 = [9] = 9 + 0$

The compound nucleus of fluorine, given in brackets in the equation, is probably formed for a fraction of an instant (around 10^{-11} second in this case) when the alpha particle is added to the nucleus of the nitrogen. The energy transmitted to the stable nitrogen nucleus by the incoming alpha particle causes the fluorine nucleus to be unstable. It releases a proton, leaving a nucleus of stable oxygen-17.

Artificial Production of Radioisotopes

The first artificial transmutation resulting in a radioactive isotope (also called a radioisotope) as the product was carried out quite accidentally in 1934 by Irene Joliot-Curie. She was continuing the scientific tradition of her famous mother, Marie Curie, who was the discoverer of radium, polonium, and thorium. In an experiment similar to Rutherford's, Irene Joliot-Curie used alpha particles to bombard aluminum nuclei.

$$\underset{\text{Aluminum}}{^{27}_{13}\text{Al}} \ + \ \underset{\substack{\text{Alpha} \\ \text{particle}}}{^{4}_{2}\text{He}} \longrightarrow \underset{\text{Phosphorus}}{[^{31}_{15}\text{P}]} \longrightarrow \underset{\text{Phosphorus}}{^{30}_{15}\text{P}} \ + \ \underset{\text{Neutron}}{^{1}_{0}\text{n}}$$

The surprise was that the phosphorus-30 produced was not stable but itself decayed to form silicon.

From that accidental beginning, man's ability to produce radioisotopes has achieved great sophistication. Many different particles are now used to carry out the transmutations, including protons, neutrons, electrons, and deuterons ($^{2}_{1}\text{H}$). Machinery to accelerate these particles to a very high speed was a necessary technological development for research in this field; the cyclotron, betatron, cosmotron, synchrotron, and linear particle accelerator are results of that need. These instruments are often referred to as "atom-smashers," although the image conveyed by that term is somewhat misleading. The atom is not reduced to a formless splat but rather undergoes a nuclear reaction.

One of the most interesting applications of the ability to carry out artificial transmutations has been in the production of new elements. Element 92, uranium, is the heaviest element that is also stable enough to occur naturally, but by bombarding uranium with neutrons or deuterons, heavier elements can be artificially formed. Taking those elements and in turn bombarding them with alpha particles can produce still heavier elements. These procedures started in 1940. Since that time, a steadily growing list of elements has been made in this way.

To produce even heavier elements, the bombarding particle was changed from neutrons or alpha particles, to the nuclei of light atoms. Element 103 (lawrencium), for example, was first prepared in this way in 1961.

$$\underset{\text{Californium}}{^{250}_{98}\text{Cf}} \ + \ \underset{\text{Boron}}{^{11}_{5}\text{B}} \longrightarrow \underset{\substack{\text{Lawrencium} \\ \text{(Half-life = 8 sec, decays by} \\ \text{giving off } \alpha \text{ particle)}}}{^{250}_{103}\text{Lw}} \ + \ 4(^{1}_{0}\text{n})$$

Recently, even heavier elements have been artifically produced: 104 with suggested name rutherfordium was first prepared in 1969, and 105, suggested name hahnium, in 1970. The means of preparation used by the University of California team at Lawrence Radiation Laboratory for element 105 was:

$$^{249}_{98}\text{Cf} + ^{15}_{7}\text{N} \longrightarrow ^{260}_{105}\text{Ha} + 4(^{1}_{0}\text{n})$$

Californium   Nitrogen   Hahnium
(half-life 1.6 ± 0.3 seconds)

The shortness of half-life for these heavy elements has been thought by some to place a theoretical limit on the number of new elements possible, as identifying such a fleeting element requires greater and greater ingenuity as classical chemical methods become unreasonable to use. However, element 105 had a half-life considerably longer than the millisecond range predicted. There are theoretical reasons to support "islands of stability" in the regions of elements 114, 126, and 164! Some evidence has already been presented for element 112, and new developments seem certain to add to our understanding of fundamental nuclear processes.

Nuclear Fission

Of all the reactions of artificial radioactivity, the most significant discovery was made in 1939 by the German scientists Otto Hahn and Fritz Straussmann who first observed the process of nuclear fission. The reaction was a startling departure from other transmutations. Unlike most nuclear reactions, which produce a product isotope differing only in one or two charge units from the original target nucleus, the products in this case consisted of two medium-weight fragments, as well as excess neutrons, and a great deal of energy. Leise Meitner, another German scientist who was working in Scandinavia at the time, correctly suggested that some of the uranium atoms were able to absorb a neutron temporarily, then split into two roughly equal parts. Compare, for example, the difference between the reactions of ^{238}U and ^{235}U when hit by a neutron.

Artificial transmutation:

$$^{238}_{92}\text{U} + ^{1}_{0}\text{n} \longrightarrow [^{239}_{92}\text{U}] \longrightarrow ^{239}_{93}\text{Np} + ^{0}_{-1}\text{e}$$

Fission, a special type of transmutation:

$$^{235}_{92}\text{U} + ^{1}_{0}\text{n} \longrightarrow [^{236}_{92}\text{U}] \longrightarrow ^{141}_{56}\text{Ba} + ^{92}_{36}\text{Kr} + 3(^{1}_{0}\text{n}) + \gamma$$

This is just one of several possibilities for the fission of ^{235}U, as it can split in several different ways, but in each case the medium weight fragments are similar. Some other possibilities are:

$$^{235}_{92}U + ^{1}_{0}n \longrightarrow [^{236}_{92}U] \longrightarrow ^{144}_{56}Ba + ^{90}_{36}Kr + 2(^{1}_{0}n) + \gamma$$
$$\longrightarrow ^{138}_{56}Ba + ^{95}_{36}Kr + 3(^{1}_{0}n) + \gamma$$
$$\longrightarrow ^{141}_{54}Xe + ^{92}_{38}Sr + 3(^{1}_{0}n) + \gamma$$
$$\longrightarrow ^{133}_{51}Sb + ^{93}_{41}Nb + \gamma$$

Chain Reaction

In all but the last example of uranium fission reactions, neutrons were produced. The neutrons may then enter another ^{235}U nucleus and cause fission to occur there. Since two or three neutrons are produced for each nucleus of ^{235}U, the possibility of a chain reaction arises. A chain reaction can lead to an atomic bomb. This happens if enough uranium atoms are present within a small enough space to quickly produce enormous amounts of energy and an uncontrollably explosive force. When controlled, the chain reaction makes the nuclear reactor possible. In either case, the fission reaction occurs with the release of large amounts of energy. Figure 1 shows schematically the principle of a chain reaction.

Figure 1. The Principle of a Chain Reaction

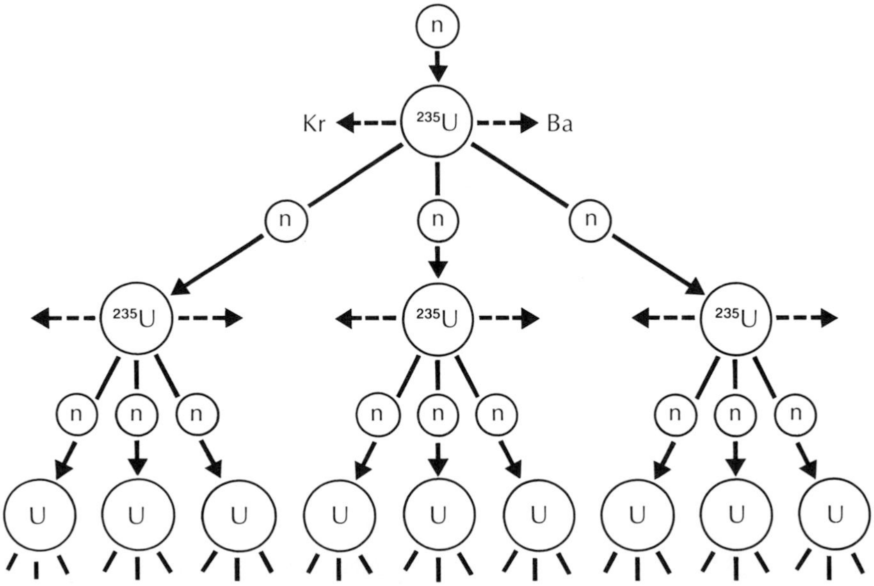

Einstein's Equation: $E = mc^2$

The source of the energy released in a fission reaction is the conversion of matter into energy. $E = mc^2$, the famous relationship proposed by Albert Einstein, mathematically relates the energy released in a nuclear reaction to the mass lost and to the constant c, the speed of light. The immensity of energy released is the most striking thing about this relationship. If one pound of any substance were totally converted into energy in a nuclear reaction, the energy resulting would be eleven billion kilowatt hours—enough to meet the entire electric power needs of the United States for three days!

The energy-mass relationship was proposed by Einstein in 1905 solely on theoretical grounds. It was not until after the discovery of fission in 1939 that the possibility of providing experimental evidence for this remarkable mathematical statement existed. On the basis of measurements taken in the last thirty years, the validity of $E = mc^2$ is now firmly established.

Note that the equations written for the fission of ^{235}U do not appear to show any mass lost during the reaction. Both left- and right-hand sides of the equations have 236 mass units. Remember that these numbers are written as being accurate to the nearest whole number only. In actual fact, there is a mass loss of approximately 0.1 percent which is converted to energy in a fission reaction. Although this percentage does not sound large, keep in mind that a huge amount of energy results, far more than from conventional chemical energy sources of the same mass.

Nuclear Fusion

The mass lost during a different type of nuclear reaction illustrates the same mass-energy relationship. This second type of energy-producing reaction is fusion. In a fusion reaction, lightweight nuclei unite to form heavier particles. In this type of reaction, as much as 0.5 percent of the mass is converted to energy. For example,

$$^{2}_{1}H \quad + \quad ^{2}_{1}H \quad \longrightarrow \quad ^{3}_{2}He \quad + \quad ^{1}_{0}n \quad + \quad \gamma$$

$$\text{Deuteron} \qquad \text{Deuteron} \qquad \text{Helium} \atop \text{nucleus}$$

Other examples of fusion reaction which similarly produce large amounts of energy are:

$$^{2}_{1}H + ^{3}_{1}H \longrightarrow ^{4}_{2}He + ^{1}_{0}n + \gamma$$

$$^{2}_{1}H + ^{6}_{3}Li \longrightarrow 2(^{4}_{2}He) + \gamma$$

Fusion reactions are fundamental in supplying the energy of our sun.

In that case, a proton cycle is thought to occur with the net effect of fusing four protons into one alpha particle with the release of two positrons (positively charged electrons). This over-all reaction gives enough energy to power our solar system.

Part Two: MEASUREMENT AND EFFECTS OF RADIOACTIVITY

Radiation Units

Units in which radiation is measured fall into two basic types. One type of unit describes the intensity of the radioactive source itself. The curie is the only commonly used unit of radiation intensity and is defined in terms of the amount of a radioactive substance necessary to give 3.7×10^{10} disintegrations per second. (This is the number of disintegrations occurring in one gram of radium in one second.) The usefulness of this unit is somewhat limited in dealing with the effects of radiation, as it is important to know not only how many nuclear disintegrations are taking place but also how much radiation is absorbed in sensitive tissue.

Other common radiation units give a measure of absorption of radiation into tissue or air and therefore are a measure of the dosage of radiation received. In understanding this type of unit, the mechanism of ionization is important. As particles and rays from radioactive sources strike atoms in the absorbing material, the electrons from the atom struck are torn away from the electron cloud region. This leaves an imbalance between the positive and negative charges previously associated with that atom. A charged atom, called an ion, is therefore created, and thus arises the term ionizing radiation. This same ionizing power may break apart the chemical bonds between atoms in a complex molecule, altering the expected chemical characteristics. The ionizing power is responsible for observed radiation damage such as skin damage, loss of hair, gastrointestinal disturbance, cancer, and death upon excess exposure. Radiation may also cause damage by altering genetic codes or by changing the DNA molecules in chromosomes which may result in biological mutations. In general, tissues that show the most damage from radiation are those that normally are reproducing at a rapid rate such as bone marrow, blood-forming tissues, lymph nodes, and embryonic tissue. Ironically, this damaging of rapidly reproducing tissue also explains the success of radiation in treating some types of cancer; the fast-multiplying cancerous cells are more easily killed by radiation than are the slower growing, healthy cells surrounding the cancer.

Ionization then, is the key to radiation damage and therefore to units describing radiation absorbed. The three common units of dosage are the *roentgen,* the *rad,* and the *rem.* For many purposes they can be

The *roentgen* is specifically defined as the amount of gamma or x-rays required to produce ions carrying 1 electrostatic unit of charge in 1 cubic centimeter of dry air at standard conditions of temperature and pressure. The unit was named after the German physicist Wilhelm Roentgen who discovered x-rays in 1895.

The *rad* is an absorption of a standard amount (100 ergs) of energy per gram of absorbing tissue. Since the roentgen measures interaction of gamma or x-rays in air, the absorbed dose in tissue as measured in rads can be different numerically from the exposure as measured in roentgens. For example, with moderate energy gamma rays, an exposure of 1 roentgen will produce an absorbed dose in muscle tissue of 0.97 rads. For some cases therefore, it is a fairly good approximation to say that roentgens equal rads, but for exact comparisons, the type of absorbing tissue and nature of the radiation must be considered.

The *rem* is defined as the product of the absorbed dose in rads and the relative biological effectiveness (R.B.E.) of the incoming radiation.

$$rem = rads \times R.B.E.$$

The R.B.E. is a number that is selected to take into account the relative ability of various kinds of radiation to accomplish ionization. The heavy and highly charged alpha particle can form more ions than the lighter and singly charged beta particle. On the other hand, because it forms fewer ions, a gamma ray, for example, has greater penetrating power than an alpha particle. R.B.E. is set at 1 for gamma rays and beta particles, at 10 for alpha particles, and at 20 for some of the heavier nuclear fragments that might result from a fission reaction. Neutrons vary in their R.B.E. depending on their speed and energy, but values range from 2.5 to 10.5. These values imply that if you are considering only x-rays and gamma rays, where R.B.E. = 1, rads are mathematically equal to rems. For this reason the two terms are often said to be equal. If alpha particles, neutrons, or one of the other heavy particles are also involved, the number of rems will be larger than the number of rads for the same absorbed dose, indicating more biological damage has occurred. For this reason, the rem is sometimes referred to as a measure of equivalent biological damage; a dose of 1 rad of gamma rays or 0.1 rad of alpha particles would each be equal to 1 rem and have the same effect, since the R.B.E. of the alpha particle is 10 times greater.

Table 1. Radiological Data (1000 millirems = 1 rem)

A. Sources of radiation dose to persons in the United States.
(All numbers involve a range of values depending on location.)

Natural

Terrestrial radiation; earth's crust, principally U, Th	55 millirems/year
Internal sources; principally ^{40}K, but also ^{87}Rb, ^{14}C, ^{226}Rn . . .	25 millirems/year
Cosmic radiation (add 1 millirem for each 100 feet elevation) .	<u>40 millirems/year</u>
(range: 100–150)	120 millirems/year

Man-made

Medical exposures

Average chest x-ray	100–200 millirems/exposure
Average G–I tract exam	200–500 millirems/exposure
Dental x-rays	20 millirems/exposure
Per capita dose for diagnostic x-rays in the United States . .	55 millirems/year

Television viewing:
Black and white (Multiply number of hours of viewing
per day by 1 mrem to get yearly dose.)
Color (Multiply number of hours of viewing per day
by 2 mrem to get yearly dose.)

Typical operating nuclear power reactor at boundary	1–5 millirems/year
All aspects of nuclear industry	.2–10 millirems/year
Nuclear weapons testing, 1954–61	29 millirems/year
Nuclear weapons testing, present levels of fallout.	<10 millirems/year

B. Radiation protection standards: Doses above natural background

Occupational exposures to individuals employed in the nuclear industry[a]

Whole body (30 year maximum).	5,000 millirems/year
Gonads and red bone marrow	5,000 millirems/year
Skin, thyroid, bone	30,000 millirems/year
Hands, forearms, feet, ankles	75,000 millirems/year[b]
General public	170 millirems/year[c]

[a]The occupational exposure limits are set higher than those for the general public as the workers are all healthy adults who are less susceptible to radiation damage than children. It is also assumed that the hazards can be foreseen and controlled.

[b]The different allowable exposures reflect the different susceptibility of these organs to radiation-induced cancers. Leukemia is the most radiogenic of all human cancers (most easily induced by radiation) and therefore allowed exposures are lower for red bone marrow than for other organs.

[c]This number approximately coincides with the national average of radiation exposure from natural and medical sources. Therefore, the philosophy behind this standard is that no person shall receive more radiation from other artificial sources than from the combination of natural and medical exposure. Recent testimony before the Joint Committee on Atomic Energy (Vol. 1, 1970, p. 1295) outlined the desirability and feasibility of reducing the 170 millirems/year to 22 millirems/year in the future.

considered equivalent. However, they are defined in different ways. In some cases, the numerical values will be quite different, for they depend on the type of radiation and the nature of the absorbing medium. The roentgen is defined with air as the absorbing medium. The rad is a more general unit, applicable to tissue absorption. If the type of incoming radiation is also considered, then the rem is the proper unit.

Each of these units can be used to measure radiation originating from artificial as well as from natural sources, and it is common to combine them with a time factor in quoting standards or dosages received. Some pertinent radiological data standardized in millirems are given in Table 1.

The radiation protection standards listed in Table 1 are the result of work by various national and international organizations. Most of these groups were organized in the late 1920s and have operated to evaluate available data and set appropriate limits of exposure since that time. The first maximum permissible dose (MPD) was set in 1931. This value has subsequently been lowered several times. The reduction is not so much the direct result of positive evidence of the harmful effects of the higher levels but a realistic reevaluation based on current scientific opinion and the realization of the many uncertainties connected with interpreting available information. These organizations have always taken the stand that all exposure to ionizing radiation is probably harmful and therefore all unnecessary exposure should be avoided.

Even in the medical field, it is argued that exposure could and should be reduced to only ten percent of its present value by proper education and certification of medical personnel. Better x-ray equipment, faster films, narrowing of the x-ray beam, and other such measures could bring the benefit more closely in line with the risk. The over-use of diagnostic x-rays (as opposed to therapeutic uses) may have created undesirable exposure levels in the past. For example, many states are no longer encouraging the use of mobile x-ray units. The effectiveness of these units in detecting tuberculosis was not sufficient to justify the exposure to the general public, particularly since tuberculin skin tests are available.

Biological Damage Due to Radiation

Evaluating the risk from exposure to radiation in an exact fashion has been a subject of some controversy. One of the fundamental points in the argument revolves around two hypotheses that have developed concerning the possibility of injury. These will be discussed in some detail here as similar arguments can be advanced not only for radiation, but also for damage from toxic agents such as pesticides, food additives, and components of air pollution or water pollution.

The linear hypothesis holds that all radiation, no matter how low the dose, is harmful, even if the effect cannot be measured or observed in a healthy person. This concept does not lend itself to setting a medically permissible dose, for any dosage has an effect. It can, however, lead to the establishment of a sociologically permissible dose, so that any injury is compensated for by the benefit received. Thus a yearly dental x-ray may be justified, but the use of x-rays to fit shoes or to check on proper throat position for training singers is of doubtful benefit.

The threshold hypothesis holds that low-level doses of radiation are not necessarily harmful below a certain threshold level. Therefore one only needs to find that threshold (which will vary according to type of damage, type of radiation, etc.) and set the permissible dose accordingly. Figure 2 contrasts these two hypotheses.

Unfortunately, the scientific evidence is not clear-cut in helping to decide between the two hypotheses, for most available evidence is for high exposures for which the effect is clearly observable. It is known, for example, that a single dose of 800 rems (800,000 millirems) will be fatal to all those exposed, even with special medical treatment. A single dose of 400 rems will be fatal to fifty percent of the exposed individuals if not treated, and 200 rems produces nausea and fatigue. 100 rems causes these same symptoms in only half of those exposed. One dose of 25 rems can be detected by blood measurements.

Figure 2. How Biological Systems Respond to Radiation: Two Theories

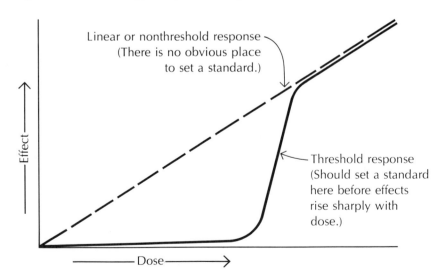

Most scientists now feel that genetic effects exhibit nonthreshold behavior, but possible long-term genetic changes are not easy to measure. For small doses, such as are received from most medical uses, television, or from nuclear power plants, the expected effects would be very subtle and therefore extremely difficult to assess. One might predict slight changes in the rate of genetic birth defects or increased instances of certain cancers and diseases. These are long-term effects and statistically difficult to substantiate. Furthermore, in light of the number of synthetic chemicals in our environment, it would be hard to assign any effect discovered to only one cause such as radiation.

All of these uncertainties mean that the individual opinion of the scientist will unavoidably be involved in interpreting data taken for high exposures and making an informed guess as to the effect at low levels. Thus genuine differences of opinions result, along with considerable emotional involvement. These differences cannot always be settled by doing the appropriate scientific experiment unless more refined methods of detecting damage are to be developed. Even if that requirement were met, the size of a sample population needed and the problems inherent in applying animal data to humans would still leave many unanswered questions.

Another related point in evaluating the risk involved in radiation exposure is the question of fractionation of exposure. Are the effects of one massive dose the same as the cumulative effects of several small doses? In setting limits, the assumption has been made that repeated low levels of exposure over time are not as damaging as a single dose of the same magnitude. It has been assumed that a healthy body can repair low-level radiation damage, but this mechanism has not been demonstrated. Rather, it may be that enough healthy cells remain so no damage is noted. Some researchers now feel that the evidence points to the fact that fractionation of radiation over time does not lessen the carcinogenic (cancer-causing) effects of ionizing radiation. Clearly this would have a much more serious effect on the genetic future of the human race if this were to be the case.

Biological Concentration of Radioisotopes

In addition to numerical standards associated with radioactive emissions, it is also important to consider the specific isotopes involved. The isotopes will differ in the type of radiation emitted, thus changing the R.B.E. factor. They also differ in their behavior once in the body. Some isotopes will lodge in specific tissue such as bones, and some will provide whole body exposure. In general, a radioactive isotope behaves chemically like the stable isotope of the same element and therefore mimics the behavior of the stable form in the body.

Similarity in chemical activity leads to the possibility of biological concentration for certain isotopes. Strontium behaves like calcium in the body. If an organism stores calcium, some radioactive ^{90}Sr may also be incorporated. If another species, higher on the food chain, consumes and stores the calcium and strontium, the over-all concentration of the radioisotope may be increased in the body of the higher species. (This same mechanism also affects the distribution of pesticide residues in the environment.) The net result is that certain organisms may contain concentrations of radioisotopes far greater than those found in surrounding air, water, and soil. In the days when atmospheric testing of nuclear weapons was taking place (ended for most countries by treaty in 1963), the Eskimos of the Arctic were found to be the recipients of unusually large amounts of cesium-137. This unfortunate result was the end of a food chain which started with the unsuspected ability of small lichen plants to collect the radioisotopes and concentrate them. The caribou continued the concentration by grazing on the lichens; finally the Eskimo at the top of the food chain ate the caribou, receiving the accumulation of ^{137}Cs.

Iodine-131 is another case in point. A radioactive isotope released in atmospheric testing and a potential pollutant from nuclear power plants, it can be concentrated in the food chain (plants—cow's milk—humans in one route) and is subsequently taken up by humans and deposited in the thyroid glands. Although ^{131}I has a short half-life (8.05 days), it stays in the body for well over three months. Therefore, ^{131}I can continue its damage from radioactive decay over a considerable period of time.

Detection of Radiation

The property of radiation that causes damage in biological tissue can also be used in detecting radiation. Ionizing properties were responsible for the first indication of radiation in the image on the photographic plate which Becquerel observed, and the use of film badges is a common and inexpensive way of monitoring for radiation today. By measuring the effect of radiation on a sophisticated arrangement of films, dosage can be determined.

The principle originally under study by Becquerel is the basis of a rather new development in measuring radioactivity, the scintillation counter. Ionizing radiations will produce scintillations (flashes of light) in crystals of certain materials, such as sodium iodide with trace amounts of thallium and anthracene added. The light is then detected by appropriate light-sensitive devices, providing a measure of the amount of radiation.

The principle of scintillation also led to one of the earliest applications of radioactive materials; radium chloride was mixed with zinc sulfide and painted onto watch dials. The resulting scintillations produced a "glow-in-the-dark" effect. (In reality, the glow is a series of closely spaced flashes, as the zinc sulfide fluoresced in the presence of the naturally radioactive radium.) Some of the earliest victims of radiation-induced cancers were the young ladies who painted such watch dials, carefully licking their paint brushes to make sharp tips. Luminous watches and clocks now rely on other fluorescent rather than radioactive materials for the same effect.

The Geiger Counter

Another common method of detecting radiation is the Geiger counter, a device that has achieved wide popularity for its ease of operation. (Perhaps another factor has been its use in movies and television as the eager prospector searches for uranium ore in the hills of Canada!) Correctly called the Geiger-Mueller counter (or G-M counter) in honor of the German scientists who developed and improved it, the basis of detection is the G-M tube containing gas under low pressure. A diagram of this apparatus and a picture of a typical laboratory apparatus are shown in Figure 3.

No complete electrical circuit is possible through the tube until incoming radiations cause some of the gas molecules to ionize. The charged ion is then attracted towards the central wire in the tube. The central wire and the outside cylinder are kept at a high voltage (electrical pressure) differential in order to cause the movement of ions. While moving towards the metal wire, the ion collides with more gas molecules

Figure 3. The Geiger Counter

Scaler unit

Geiger-Mueller tube

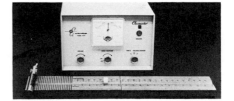

Thin mica window

High-voltage source and necessary circuitry to record counts received

Insulating plug

Metal central wire

Metal cylinder

Argon gas under low pressure

and soon an avalanche of ions are moving in the same direction. This results in a burst of electric current as the circuit is completed in the G-M tube. Supporting electrical circuitry in the scale unit maintains the voltage difference and changes the impulse of current into a flash of light, an audible click, or a reading with a suitable meter, depending on the need of the operator. All of the radiations emitted by the sample do not enter the window, so the observed count rate should be compared with a standard of known radioactivity under the same conditions.

Part Three: THE NUCLEAR POWER INDUSTRY

The United States is now confronting what is described as a crisis in electric power production. Rising expectations in our way of living coupled with rising population have resulted in pressures to produce more electricity. This has traditionally been accomplished largely at the expense of our environment. The need to generate power but at the same time to balance the true need against resulting environmental problems has placed power production into the public view. Some pertinent statistics as they relate to power and population appear in Table 2. These clearly show the increasing role that nuclear power is expected to play.

Table 2. United States Electric Utility Power Statistics Relating to Population and Consumption

	1950	1968	Estimate for 1980	Estimate for 2000
Population (millions)	152	202	235	320
Total power capacity (million of kilowatts)	85	290	600	1,352
KW capacity/person	0.6	1.4	$2\frac{1}{2}$	$\sim 4\frac{1}{4}$
Power consumed per person per year (kilowatt-hours)	2,000	6,500	11,500	$\sim 25,000$
Total consumption (kilowatt-hours)	325 billion	1.3 trillion	2.7 trillion	~ 8 trillion
Nuclear power capacity (millions of kilowatts)	0	2.7	150	940
Nuclear power capacity (% of total)	0%	<1%	25%	69%

Source: Hearings before Joint Committee on Atomic Energy, JCAE, Vol. I, 278.

At present there are 22 nuclear power plants, which produce only 2 percent of the nation's electric power supply, but 93 more plants are now under construction or on order (see Figure 4). By 1980 it is expected that nuclear power may provide 25 percent of our electrical needs. Coupled with the growing number of plants is an increase in the size and capacity of the proposed reactors and a growing tendency for ownership of nuclear facilities to pass from federal to private ownership. It is widely known that radioactivity can cause damage to humans as well as plants and animals, leading to anxiety on the part of many concerned citizens who ask—who is responsible? What are the consequences?

Figure 4. Nuclear Power Reactors in the United States

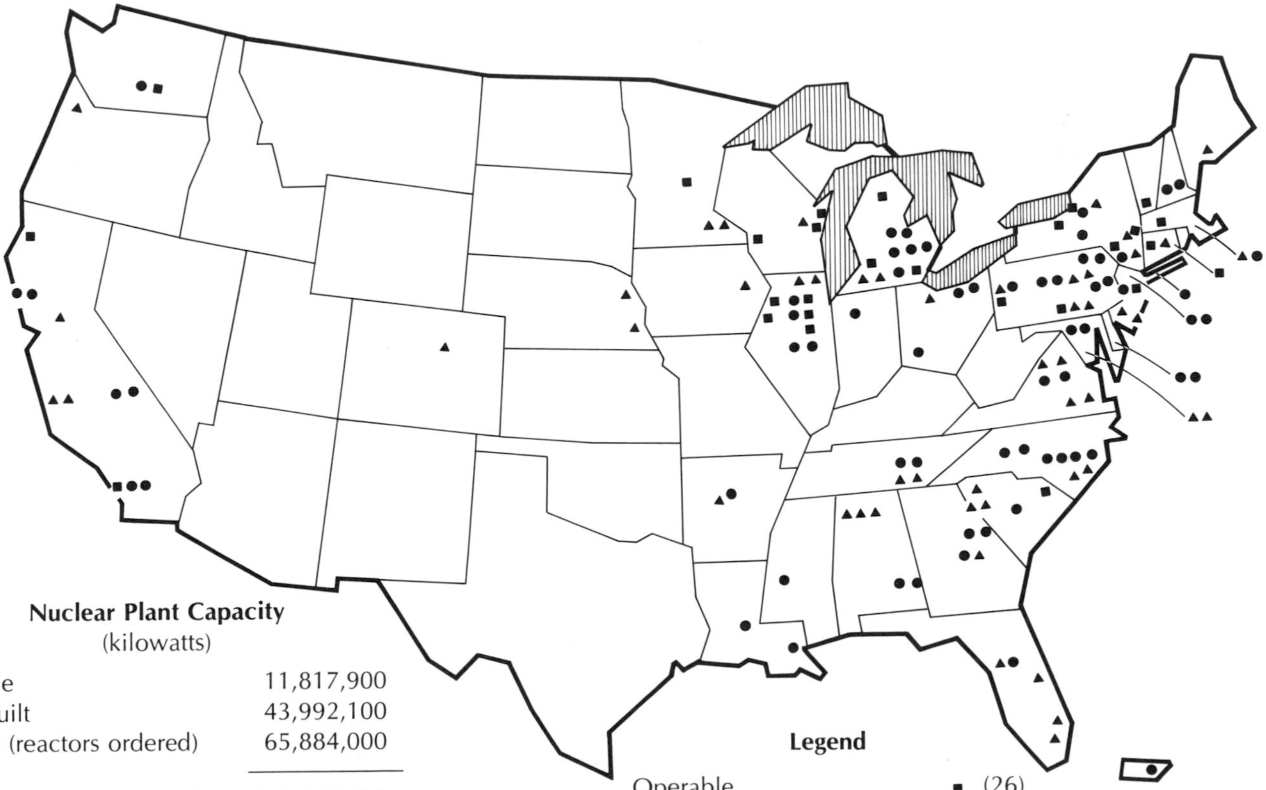

Nuclear Plant Capacity
(kilowatts)

Operable	11,817,900
Being built	43,992,100
Planned (reactors ordered)	65,884,000
Total	121,694,000

Total electric utility capacity as of
March 31, 1972: 369,834,630 kilowatts

Legend

Operable	■	(26)
Being built	▲	(51)
Planned (reactors ordered)	●	(66)

The Role of the Atomic Energy Commission

The Atomic Energy Commission (AEC), since its establishment by Congress in 1946, has held the responsibility for the safe development of atomic energy. Up to that time, atomic energy had been the province of the military. The Manhattan project, established in September of 1942, had been responsible for early development including the first demonstration of controlled fission and the production of both plutonium and hydrogen bombs.

The primary responsibilities of the Atomic Energy Commission are to protect the health and the safety of people from possible radiological damage. To accomplish this, the AEC insists upon superior quality in design, construction, and operation of nuclear power plants. Elaborate systems have been set up to automatically shut down the reactor in case of any accident. Designs must also include such consequence-limiting safety features as the containment shell around the reactor itself. These safety systems continually are tested and limits for emissions reevaluated as deemed necessary. All emissions are kept as low as practicable; as soon as new technology is available, older reactors must be modified to incorporate new safety features.

Under congressional direction, the AEC has the roles of encouraging and subsidizing the design and development of nuclear power plants and also of acting as the regulatory agent deciding on and enforcing necessary safety requirements. This dual responsibility has been the subject of much criticism for a conflict is possible between developing and limiting. Although their record has been impressive so far as the result of a cautious approach to safety, the future development of even larger and more numerous plants should proceed more effectively if the two functions were separate. Even within the AEC many people advocate this move, if only to assure public confidence.

The first self-sustaining nuclear chain reaction was initiated on December 2, 1942 in great secrecy beneath the stands of the University of Chicago athletic stadium. Years of scientific development had been telescoped due to the military significance of the potentially powerful energy source for the reality of wartime. Early in November of 1942, the first main nuclear pile (what we would now call reactor) started to be assembled. Blocks of graphite were alternated with pellets of uranium oxide fuel interspersed with neutron-absorbing control rods. Gallons of cadmium salt solution were ready as an emergency way to absorb neutrons by flooding the pile. As a further neutron-capturing device, the pile was enclosed in a balloon cloth bag, probably the subject of much guessing when made by Goodyear Company, as the call for a square balloon by the Army was rather unusual! However, emergency procedures proved unnecessary. At 3:25 pm the reactor was allowed to become self-sustaining for the first time by slowly with-drawing the control rods until the chain reaction could occur. Even more important, reinserting the control rods stopped the reaction, thus showing the feasibility of man's controlling the process. News of the successful experience was relayed to James P. Conant at Harvard by saying: "The Italian Navigator has landed in the New World." "How were the natives?" replied Conant. "Very friendly," was the response.

The success of this experiment was a tribute to the genius of Enrico Fermi, an Italian-born scientist who came to this country after winning the Nobel Prize in 1938 for his work on the transuranium elements. In leading the team of scientists who built this first reactor, he hoped that what had begun with man's first philosophical speculations about the nature of the universe would end with the release of atomic energy on a large scale for the peaceful benefit and advancement of mankind.

The Nuclear Reactor

At the heart of every nuclear power is the reactor itself in which the controlled fission is carried out. The fuel uranium is in the form uranium dioxide (UO_2), which has been fabricated into pellets about the size of a pencil eraser. These fuel pellets are stacked inside of thin 10-foot-long stainless steel fuel rods (sometimes called fuel pins). The rods are arranged in clusters to assure proper geometry for capturing escaping neutrons. To cause fission, it is necessary to slow down the neutrons coming from the splitting atoms so they will enter other ^{235}U nuclei available. In addition, the number of neutrons must be regulated so they do not trigger additional fissions unless desired.

Moderation and control of the neutrons are accomplished in the core of a nuclear reactor by neutron-absorbing rods and also by water circulating in a closed system through the core. The control rods, usually made of cadmium or boron steel, absorb neutrons when completely inserted. As the rods are withdrawn, the extent of the chain reaction is increased. The constantly circulating water slows the neutrons and additionally serves to remove heat for exchange with the steam generator. The entire fuel assembly is usually located near or below ground level inside the cylindrical containment sphere that often externally marks the presence of a nuclear generating unit.

Once the energy has been produced to generate heat, a nuclear electric generating plant and a conventional steam electric plant are the same; the only basic difference is the method initially used to produce heat so that steam is formed. A diagram of a typical pressurized water reactor

(PWR) is given in Figure 5. A schematic location of the principal components of a PWR is shown together with a picture of the Connecticut Yankee Atomic Power Station for comparison in Figure 6.

Nuclear Reactors: Blessing or Bomb?

One uncertainty that exists in the minds of many people is: "Can a nuclear reactor blow up with the intensity of an atomic bomb?" The answer is no, as the design principle is quite different. In an atomic bomb, two or more masses of 90 percent pure fissionable material are kept at some distance from each other until the desired time of detonation.

Figure 5. Typical Pressurized Water Reactor

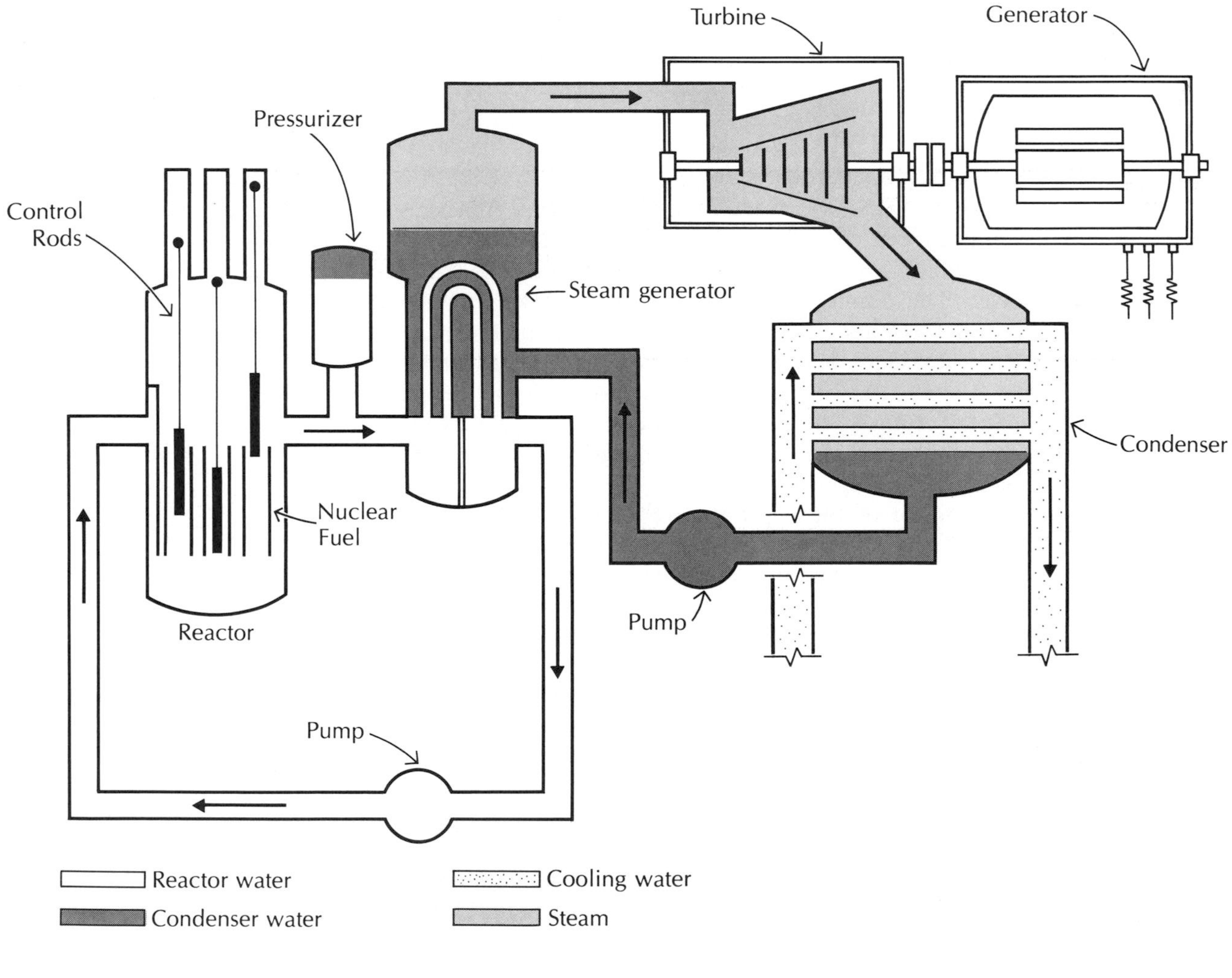

Control Rods
Pressurizer
Turbine
Generator
Steam generator
Condenser
Nuclear Fuel
Reactor
Pump
Pump

▭ Reactor water ▒ Cooling water
▬ Condenser water ▤ Steam

Connecticut Yankee Power Plant, Haddam Neck, Connecticut

Note the three separate water cycles in the diagram on the left— the primary cycle within the reactor, the water and steam cycle, and the cooling water system. Newer reactors may utilize various gases or liquid sodium in the primary cycle, allowing the reactor to operate at a higher chemical efficiency.

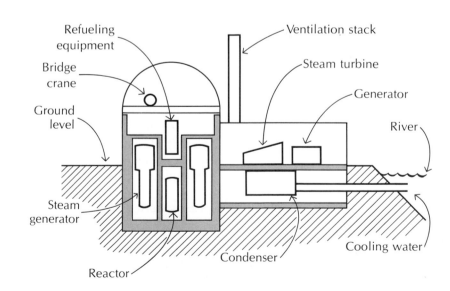

Then they are rapidly brought together so that the critical mass is exceeded (the critical mass is the smallest mass of fissionable material that will support a self-sustaining chain reaction under stated conditions). The masses must be arranged with proper geometry so that neutrons have maximum probability of entering other ^{235}U nuclei. Further, the masses must be held together long enough for an explosive force to build up. These conditions do not exist in a nuclear reactor. The fuel is only 3 to 5 percent ^{235}U, the geometry of the fuel rods is quite different, and there is no force to hold the fuel together even if heat from an out-of-control chain reaction were to melt the core.

Probably the most serious reactor accident imaginable would involve loss of coolant water while at the same time suffering a coolant-carrying pipe rupture (a "blowdown") within the reactor core itself. This could result in a melting core together with steam in the core region. The steam pressure could prevent any emergency cooling water from reaching the core. Water in the core will decompose into hydrogen and oxygen gases in the presence of ionizing radiation. The mixture of gases could explode, creating the possibility of breaking through the shell surrounding the reactor core and possibly breaking the outer containment shell. The probability of such a series of events occurring is extremely low, but if it did happen, large amounts of radioactivity would be released. The damaging results could be widespread if the radioactive materials were carried by prevailing wind currents. Some people have suggested that the impact of such accidents could be minimized by placing special emphasis on locating the plants far from populated centers and possibly locating the entire plants underground.

The potential consequences of such a catastrophic accident led commercial insurance companies to refuse to assume this risk. As a result, a joint assumption of financial liability by the government and the insurance industry was set up by the Price-Anderson Act in 1957. As amended in 1967, the present government contribution is $486 million and the insurance pool fund is $74 million for a total of $560 million as the maximum indemnity available to compensate all victims of a nuclear power plant accident. Although this seems to be a large figure, a government study made in 1957 (when smaller reactors were contemplated) placed projected property damage alone at $7 billion for such a major accident. Your own property damage insurance is sure to contain exemption clauses for both wartime and peacetime nuclear damage.

Atmospheric Discharges

Other than such a catastrophic but remote blowdown, what are the possibilities for environmental contamination associated with a nuclear reactor? Some radioisotopes are discharged from a stack which ventilates the reactor containment structure and the turbine building. The most important of the radioactive products discharged is krypton-85, a beta and gamma emitter with a half-life of 10.4 years. Krypton is one product of the fission reaction and, being gaseous, not all of it will remain in the reactor core. Similarly, isotopes of xenon and iodine are formed and may be discharged, although processes are now in use to absorb the iodine in activated charcoal or to chemically react the iodine-131 so that it forms a solid. In solid form, it can be removed more easily from the effluent gas and added to spent fuel and other solid wastes for disposal. Various commercial systems are now under development for better filtration of these gaseous wastes.

In discussions concerning the safety of nuclear power plants, it is often mentioned by proponents that a conventional fossil-fuel plant discharges relatively greater amounts of radioisotopes into the atmosphere than do nuclear plants of comparable size. One problem in appraising this statement realistically is that the types of exposure are different. Krypton-85 in airborne effluent from a nuclear plant gives whole body exposure, whereas isotopes found in fly ash of a fossil plant, such as thorium, uranium, and radium, are either soluble bone seekers or are insoluble and lodge in the lungs. In addition, comparison is difficult as large variations in radioactivity emitted come about as the result of hold time for the waste gases, tower height, and efficiency of exhaust cleaning devices.

Despite these problems, studies comparing the amount (but not type) of radiation released indicate that a nuclear reactor of the boiling water type gives more atmospheric radiological exposure than a coal burning plant. Such a plant, in turn, gives more exposure than a pressurized water nuclear reactor.

In any case, such a comparison is not really a valid arguing point. For one thing, it should be pointed out that fossil-fuel plants are really distributing naturally occurring isotopes but nuclear power plants are actually creating new radioisotopes to be distributed. Also, it would only be fair to consider the radiological exposure as the result of all activities supporting power production, not just the reactor itself.

Airborne radioactivity released can be minimized by simply delaying the gases as they pass through the ventilation exhaust system, as many isotopes produced have very short half-lives. For example, krypton-89 has a half-life of 3.5 minutes, krypton-90 of 33 seconds. Each of these gaseous isotopes produce solid strontium in decaying, so the particulate material produced can be filtered and added to the other solid wastes. Iodine-131 (8.05 days), xenon-138 (17 minutes), and nitrogen-13 (10 minutes) are other isotopes that will lose their radioactivity rather quickly and therefore profit by delayed release. Pressurized water reactors have a delay time of up to 60 days, but the earlier boiling water type reactors allowed only a 30-minute holdup in gases.

It has been demonstrated that nuclear power plants can operate with a minimum of airborne discharge, with releases well below established limits. A person sitting on the fence at the boundary of a nuclear power plant for 24 hours, 365 days a year, would receive at most 5 millirems. From the radiological data given in Table 1, you can see this accounts for a small percentage compared with background exposure. Even this amount is constantly being monitored and amounts of discharge reduced. Continued efforts to improve the radiological quality of the exhaust gases should be expected.

Activation Products

The nitrogen-13 mentioned as a product of nuclear plants is an example of a radioisotope that is not a primary product of the fission reaction. ^{13}N results instead from neutron bombardment of materials present in the coolant, core, pressure vessel, pumps, piping, and other components in contact with the coolant water. Such isotopes are called *induced radioisotopes* or *activation products*. Most of them are solids or dissolved liquids rather than gases. In some reactors, specific activation products are made purposely by lowering materials into the core; these radioisotopes are then used in medicine, agriculture, and industry. In a power reactor, the activation products are inadvertent and unavoidable but are usually not released to the environment at the reactor site due to their physical form. They do become a problem when it is time to reprocess the fuel in order to recover unused uranium.

One activation product that may be released is tritium, ^3_1H, which can be produced from neutron capture by coolant additives such as boron, lithium, and ammonia. Other modes of production include activation of hydrogen in the coolant water molecules and also the possibility of the tritium itself being a fission fragment. Much of the tritium will be absorbed by the fuel rods and will be released during fuel reprocessing, but some will escape along with the gaseous krypton-85.

Waterborne Discharges

Some of the tritium created in a reactor replaces normal hydrogen in water molecules. This changes H_2O to HTO, or tritiated water. Since its properties are very similar to that of normal water in every way except radiological, it is difficult to separate the HTO from the H_2O, causing a problem in disposal. The coolant water is periodically purified in order to limit the amount of radioactivity it contains due to activation products and small amounts of fission products that leak through minute imperfections in the fuel-element cladding. This waste water, together with water from other areas of the operation, will be concentrated and stored for later disposal, although small amounts are released to the water way serving the plant. Isotopes of cobalt, strontium, iodine, and cesium have been detected in liquid effluent, but well below limits set by the Atomic Energy Commission and low enough to meet radioactivity standards for drinking water. Typical nuclear power plant waste discharge contains from 1 to 10 picocuries[1] per liter. For comparison, domestic tap water contains 20 picocuries per liter, and river water from 10 to 100 picocuries per liter. In isolated cases, considerably more radiation has been released, usually after cleaning or maintenance operations.

Waste Heat

One inherent problem in the design of any nuclear power plant is a necessary limitation of the operating temperature, which reduces the efficiency of the process. In practical terms, this lowered efficiency means that for a nuclear electric generating plant, about two kilowatts of heat are rejected to the environment for every kilowatt of electricity produced. In a fossil-fuel plant, this heat loss amounts to 1.3 kilowatts for every useful kilowatt of electricity. The resulting thermal pollution

Gaseous diffusion is a vital process in the preparation of uranium for either military or civilian uses as the natural concentration of the fissionable isotope of uranium is so low. ^{235}U accounts for only 0.71% of all uranium atoms; only ^{235}U and not the plentiful (99.27%) ^{238}U can undergo fission.

Diffusion refers to the spontaneous spreading of a substance throughout a phase, such as the odor of mothballs becoming noticeable in the air of a closed room. Heavier gases diffuse more slowly than do lighter gases. (The exact ratio of their rates is determined by Graham's Law which states that the rate of diffusion is inversely proportional to the square root of the molecular weight.) Uranium hexafluoride (UF_6) is a gaseous compound of uranium. The percentage of UF_6 molecules containing ^{235}U is the same as the naturally occurring frequency of this isotope, 0.71%. The separation is based on the fact that the UF_6 in which the uranium atom is ^{238}U will move more slowly than the molecules containing ^{235}U. Thus, if UF_6 passes through a porous solid at low pressures, the gas mixture emerging will have a slightly higher percentage of the lighter gas than did the original mixture. This process, called enrichment, must be repeated thousands of times to bring about the required increase to 3.5 percent ^{235}U.

GASEOUS DIFFUSION STAGE

LOW PRESSURE

ENRICHED STREAM

HIGH PRESSURE

BARRIER

FEED STREAM

DEPLETED STREAM

LOW PRESSURE

(The United States Atomic Energy Commission)

---

[1]A picocurie is one trillionth of a curie, or 0.000001 microcurie.

(also referred to as thermal addition or thermal loading) is a major problem for all electric utilities, although other types of industries also contribute. (See Chapter 6 for more details on the effects of thermal pollution and the possible alternatives for utilizing or dispersing waste heat.)

Support Aspects of the Nuclear Industry

The nuclear reactor itself is only one part of the entire nuclear power industry. To correctly assess the environmental significance of nuclear power and its role in the total electric power production in the United States, it is necessary to look at the other components of the industry. Many steps are involved in the process of changing uranium ore into fuel suitable for use in a power reactor, and from that point on, fuel reprocessing and waste disposal become important considerations. A schematic diagram of the interlocking steps involved in the civilian industry, together with some comments, is presented in Figure 7.

Figure 7. Flowchart of the Nuclear Industry (Civilian Applications)

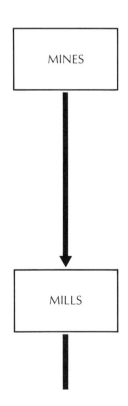

Comments
- Major areas in the United States producing uranium: western New Mexico, central Wyoming, Colorado-Utah border.
- Mined as "black oxide" (a mixture of uranium oxides with other minerals), uranium oxides account for 1.5 to 10 percent of the ore.
- Mines are mostly underground, some strip mining.
- Naturally occurring uranium atoms are only 0.71 percent ^{235}U, the isotope desired for fission.

Environmental significance
- Radioactive tailings.
- Exposure to radon "daughter" gas; must have adequate mine ventilation.
- Four fifths of all ^{238}U mined will eventually end up as discharged waste. ^{238}U is not fissionable, but is naturally radioactive.
- Use of irreplaceable natural resource.

Comments
- Purpose is to get the uranium oxide out of ore and concentrated.
- Do this by pulverizing and dissolving out uranium oxide; remove excess water, now "yellow cake" 70–90 percent U_3O_8.

Environmental significance
- Mechanical grinding of dry powder of uranium compound produces dust containing uranium, thorium.
- Adequate gas cleaning equipment must be used.

Uranium mining operations at Paguate Mine, Grants, New Mexico. *(The Anaconda Company)*

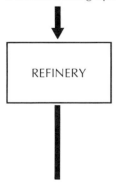

REFINERY

Comments
- Purified by dissolving U_3O_8 in nitric acid, changing it to uranium trioxide (UO_3) known as "orange oxide."
- UO_3 is converted to UO_2 and then to UF_4 (green salt) by reaction with hydrogen fluoride gas.
- Uranium metal may also be produced for nonpower uses.

Environmental significance
- Some radioactive liquid waste to be disposed of from chemical reactions.
- Also need control of airborne dust containing uranium, thorium.

San Onofre Nuclear Generating
Station, San Clemente, California.

Comments
- UF_4 is converted to UF_6 by reaction with fluorine gas.
- UF_6 is a solid at room temperature but changes to a gas at slightly elevated temperatures.
- Natural concentration of ^{235}U must be "enriched" to approximately 3.5% for usefulness as fuel.

Environmental significance
- Economic considerations help keep airborne discharge of uranium to a minimum.

Comments
- Changed to UO_2 (uranium dioxide) if to be used in boiling water and pressurized water reactors.
- Changed to uranium carbide if used in higher temperature systems such as sodium-graphite gas-cooled experimental reactors.
- Packed into pellets and placed in thin tubes made of stainless steel or zirconium steel.
- May be 6.75 million pellets in 28,000 tubes in a typical operating reactor.

Environmental significance
- Most costly step in preparation of fuel.
- Minimal losses.

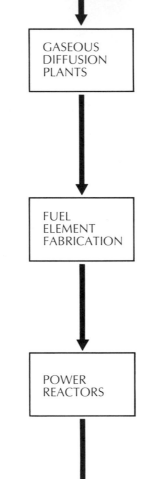

GASEOUS
DIFFUSION
PLANTS

FUEL
ELEMENT
FABRICATION

POWER
REACTORS

Palisades Nuclear Power Plant
on Lake Michigan, South Haven,
Michigan.

Note the difference in the external
appearance of the containment
structures. The Palisades plant is
the more recent design.

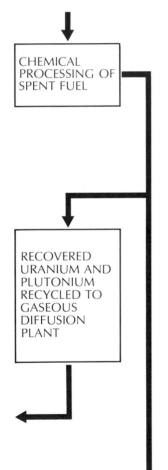

CHEMICAL
PROCESSING OF
SPENT FUEL

RECOVERED
URANIUM AND
PLUTONIUM
RECYCLED TO
GASEOUS
DIFFUSION
PLANT

Comments
- Fuel is stored under water in shielded area for several months to allow decrease in radioactivity.
- Fuel is dissolved and solution is processed to separate unfissioned uranium and plutonium from radioactive wastes.
- Numerous fission and activation products are separated into high-level and low-level wastes.
- Until 1966, only AEC owned and operated reprocessing plants (Hanford at Richland, Washington; Savannah River at Aiken, South Carolina; Idaho Falls, Idaho). Now two commercial facilities (Morris, Illinois and West Valley, New York) with more planned as number of power plants increases.

Environmental significance
- Greatest potential danger of environmental contamination at present (excluding a major reactor accident). It is estimated that the new commercial plant proposed for Barnwell, South Carolina, if operating at full capacity, could release 12 million curies of ^{85}Kr per year and 500,000 curies of ^3H from its stack.
- "High-level" wastes go to storage areas after separation, but "low-level" wastes are diluted and released to the environment.
- Gaseous releases include krypton-85 ($t_{1/2} - 10.8$ years), emitting beta and gamma radiation. Tritium, xenon-133, and iodine-131 also released from spent fuel and cladding. All of these except tritium could be trapped, but usually are not. Aerosols containing calcium-44, strontium-90, barium-140, and zirconium-95 also noted.
- Large volumes (up to 500,000 gallons/day) of low-level liquid wastes can be released from commercial fuel reprocessing plants. Most radioactivity comes from hard-to-separate tritium as HTO; ^{90}Sr, ^{144}Ce, ^{137}Cs, ^{131}I also reported.
- Larger reprocessing plants planned; these would discharge proportionally more airborne and waterborne waste.
- Sites should be selected with care to minimize risks associated with transportation and releases of radioisotopes. Geologic location should be considered, particularly if underground on-site storage is planned.

- At every step of the cycle there is danger of release of radioactivity due to the transportation process.

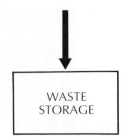

WASTE STORAGE

Comments
- Intensely radioactive waste solutions from extraction processes collected, reduced in volume, and stored underground in steel and concrete tanks, mainly at Hanford Plant in Richland, Washington (other storage areas: Oak Ridge, Tennessee; Savannah River, Aiken, South Carolina; and Idaho Falls, Idaho).
- Liquid wastes may boil for up to 3 years; then can be solidified into "salt cakes" for further storage. Hazardous for at least 600 years (based on 20 half-lives of ^{90}Sr).
- Intermediate and low-level liquid wastes can be injected into deep geologic basins in areas where water movement is slow.
- Salt mines might provide underground storage areas for solidified wastes. One proposed area was in Lyons, Kansas. Salt mines could provide a storage area without ground water flow (or salt would not be there as it is soluble) and with desirable properties of good heat conductivity, presence of access shafts, and the self-healing ability of the salt to slowly "flow" (rather like a soft candle) to repair and seal any fractures. Salt mines underlie 400,000 square miles in the United States, mainly in Kansas, Ohio, and Michigan.

Environmental significance
- Present underground storage sites are in "poor geologic locations" according to National Academy of Sciences.
- Leakage from tanks; of 149 tanks at Hanford, 11 have developed leaks from which at least 55,000 gallons of highly radioactive waste have escaped.
- Unknown geologic effects of pumping large amounts of liquid wastes into the earth; evidence in Denver, Colorado region indicates resulting earth movement.
- Possible contamination of ground water from either injection wells or storage tanks.
- Geologic, financial, and political problems have arisen to prevent salt mine disposal at the present. The structural integrity of the salt mines has been questioned. Transporation costs to place solidified wastes are very high. Attempts by the AEC to gloss over some safety aspects of mine usage have produced much local and statewide dissatisfaction in Kansas. Other alternatives particularly surface storage of solidified high-level wastes are now being studied.
- Present approach is to *manage* waste so that future generations can have the option of using improved technology for reuse or disposal of radioactive wastes. All solutions for getting rid of highly radioactive wastes are *storage* as there is no way to truly *dispose* of them. Successful solution of the storage problem is essential, particularly true if plutonium-based reactors become widespread. Plutonium wastes will be active for 480,000 years.

Proposed salt mine storage area, Lyons, Kansas. Solidified high-activity wastes would have been stored here. Recent AEC plans favor surface storage procedures. *(The United States Atomic Energy Commission)*

Large concrete-encased steel tanks under construction at the Savannah River nuclear facility. High-activity liquid wastes are concentrated and stored here. *(United States Atomic Energy Commission)*

Benefit versus Risk

With all of these environmental problems, should the nuclear power industry be allowed to continue? You will want to consider that question again after looking at fossil-fuel power plants in Chapter 5. If nuclear power is to be an important energy source in the United States, there is clearly the necessity of minimizing all exposure to ionizing radiation. This can largely be accomplished by strict application of safety regulations to *all* facets of the industry and not just to the reactor itself, from mining to storage wastes. This means both the expenditure of more money for control facilities and better monitoring by a truly independent agency prepared to back up violations with appropriate action. The public should be fully informed and allowed to participate in the essential question of risk versus benefit in evaluating further growth of nuclear power, acknowledging that there is, in fact, a risk and weighing the societal benefit. The Atomic Energy Commission does not gain any confidence by assuring us that the risk of damage from a nuclear power plant is far smaller than that incurred by driving an automobile. A citizen can choose not to drive but that same citizen has had up to now little direct choice over the amount of radiation he receives; an involuntary risk is never assumed as enthusiastically as a chosen one. The imminent growth in the amount of radioactivity discharged to the environment and stored as a future hazard requires us to proceed thoughtfully as any long-term buildup of radioactivity will have far-reaching effects on the future of man and his spaceship home.

Nuclear Alternatives of the Future: The Breeder

Even with the tremendous potential of fission reactors, some experts warn that since only 0.7 percent of naturally occurring uranium is the fissionable ^{235}U, supplies could be exhausted in 20 to 40 years. However, the essentially wasted ^{238}U is a very valuable "fertile" material for another type of reactor system, the breeder reactor. A fertile isotope is one that can be converted to fissionable material. Relatively abundant thorium can be converted to fissionable ^{233}U, but most research has been aimed at the conversion of ^{238}U into plutonium. In this case, the ^{238}U will absorb neutrons unused in the chain reactor to form a radioactive decay series leading to plutonium.

$$^{238}_{92}U + ^{1}_{0}n \longrightarrow ^{239}_{92}U \longrightarrow ^{0}_{-1}e + ^{239}_{93}Np \longrightarrow ^{239}_{94}Pu + ^{0}_{-1}e$$

$$\text{Neptunium} \qquad \text{Plutonium}$$

The plutonium formed has a half-life of 2.436×10^4 years and is fissionable. It is possible that by starting with fissionable plutonium surrounded by fertile ^{238}U in the fuel core of a nuclear reactor, the neutrons from fission will be producing more fissionable material than is actually consumed in the energy-producing process, thus "breeding" more fuel. The neutrons do not need to be moderated to cause this reaction to occur and therefore this is called a "fast" reactor. The cooling system is made from liquid sodium, an excellent material to transfer heat efficiently. Thus altogether, this type of reactor is known as the "light-metal-cooled-fast-breeder-reactor" (LMFBR).

Unfortunately, the technical problems involved in developing the LMFBR have been considerable. One of the most important has been the unusual irregular expansion and contraction behavior of plutonium metal with changes in temperature which would cause unacceptable changes in the dimensions of fuel rods to occur. Plutonium also has a rather low melting point (640°C) for this application, limiting the temperature that can be attained in the fuel element. The operating efficiency is expected to be close to that of a modern fossil-fuel plant. In addition, plutonium conducts heat poorly which again limits the design size of the fuel core. All of these drawbacks point to use of plutonium either in an alloy (metal mixture) or in a ceramic combination with carbon or nitrogen (a ceramic substance is a nonmetallic compound or even a mixture of compounds having a very high melting point). In addition, the sodium metal used for cooling is a difficult material to work with as it will burn in air and react with water to produce highly flammable hydrogen gas.

There are some special hazards involved with the use of plutonium. It is an alpha particle emitter; even though alpha particles cannot penetrate skin, the danger if plutonium enters the body by inhalation is very great. Once in the body, Pu is eliminated only very slowly (80 percent taken in will be there 50 years later) and up to 10 percent will deposit in the bones where it is known to damage the blood-forming bone marrow and produce leukemia or other diseases. Another hazard that must be faced is the possible diversion of plutonium to illegal military uses as one form of the "atomic bomb" is actually a plutonium fission device.

Early experience with the LMFBR has not been highly encouraging to this point. Many countries (France, United Kingdom, Germany, USSR) have constructed experimental breeder systems. The first breeder plant in the United States, Enrico Fermi Nuclear Power Plant near Detroit, Michigan, has produced only small amounts of electricity; both financially and technically it has not been a success since its start in 1963. An accident in 1966 forced a shutdown of the plant and only in 1969 did it begin to function again. In 1972 the plant was closed permanently. The core will be removed and turned over to the AEC for storage at an undisclosed location. Future economic success for breeder reactors seems to be dependent on a rapidly expanding need for power even if all the technical problems were overcome.

Future development of the LMFBR has been boosted by high-level interest. President Nixon stated that LMFBR development will be given first priority in his administration's energy policy. A $500 million joint government-industry project was announced in early 1972, leading to an operating breeder by 1980. The reactor will be within the Tennessee Valley Authority power system and will produce up to 500,000 kilowatts of electrical power.

Fusion Power

Man has successfully initiated fusion reactions but only in the case of a hydrogen bomb. The tremendous heat generated by this device is reflected in its common name—the thermonuclear bomb. The fusion bomb requires a fission-type atomic bomb as a fuse in order to produce a temperature high enough to start the reaction. This is an obviously unacceptable situation in power plants. Other technical problems have also appeared in trying to scale down the fusion reaction.

In order to successfully carry out controlled fusion, the nuclei must first be separated from their electrons so just the nuclei can collide and fuse. Extremely high temperatures can produce this "plasma," the name given to these separated atoms. The nuclei must also be accelerated so they can overcome their normal repulsion for each other. In addition, the plasma must be contained in a reasonable space and geometric configuration in order to achieve suitable densities of nuclei. This "confinement problem" is not easy to solve, considering the nature of the plasma. Magnetic fields have been employed to "hold" the plasma. Finally, the energy produced by controlled fusion must be in some usable form and not significantly diminished by radiation losses.

Current research into controlling the fusion process for application in the nuclear power industry is promising and shows the probability of such an application in the future. Despite $500 million dollars worth of research in twenty years, no prototype installations are yet under way. Recent experiments both by Russia and by the United States have demonstrated the feasibility of containing the plasma at temperatures of approximately 10,000,000°C or more for short periods of time, but even higher temperatures are needed for some types of fusion. It may be that new technological approaches altogether may be more successful than the older concept of magnetic field containment. The timetable for future development will depend to a large extent on the level of funding available. It has been estimated that a controlled fusion power plant is 50 years in the future if funding continues at the present rate, 25 years if funded at a planned accelerated rate, and only 10 years away if funded as a "national objective."

There are several different fusion reactions regarded as potentially useful for commercial reactors. All of the reactions given earlier (page 45) are under consideration. The deuterium-deuterium fusion has two possible outcomes occurring with equal probability.

$$\,^2_1\text{H} + \,^2_1\text{H} \longrightarrow \,^3_2\text{He} + \,^1_0\text{n} + \gamma$$

$$\,^2_1\text{H} + \,^2_1\text{H} \longrightarrow \,^3_1\text{H} + \,^1_1\text{H} + \gamma$$

Deuterium is naturally occurring (one atom of $\,^2_1\text{H}$ for every 6500 atoms of $\,^1_1\text{H}$ and therefore, isolation of deuterium from sea water would provide a relatively cheap and abundant supply. Another important reaction is the fusion of deuterium and tritium to produce helium and a neutron.

A particularly promising reaction involves the conversion of a proton and lithium-6 to helium nuclei of different weights.

$$_1^1H + {_3^6}Li \longrightarrow {_2^3}He + {_2^4}He + \gamma$$

This reaction consists entirely of charged particles since no neutrons are produced; this improves technical aspects of the plasma.

Ultimately it is hoped that high enough temperatures can be produced to allow direct energy conversion to electricity. Such a remarkable breakthrough would solve any thermal pollution problem. There are few biologically important waste products except tritium, and no possibility of a nuclear explosion or diversion of material into clandestine military purposes with fusion. The goal of controlled fusion is well worth pursuing for its promise of abundant and clean power.

Study Questions — Group A

1. a. In the equation showing Irene Joliot-Curie's transmutation of aluminum into phosphorus, how many protons are represented on each side? How many neutrons?
   b. In light of the generalizations we have drawn concerning neutron/proton ratios and nuclear stability, why is it particularly surprising that $_{15}^{30}P$ is not stable?

2. In what way is artificial radioactivity different from natural radioactivity? How is it similar?

3. $_{95}^{241}Am$ can be bombarded by an alpha particle. The resulting unstable nucleus emits a neutron and gamma rays. Write a nuclear equation for this reaction.

4. Write a nuclear equation showing the reaction when deuterium enters $_{26}^{56}Fe$. Two neutrons are emitted in this transmutation.

5. What element results when $_{29}^{63}Cu$ is bombarded with a deuteron, causing a proton to be emitted? Is this an example of a transmutation?

6. If $_{94}^{239}Pu$ is hit by an alpha particle, a neutron will be emitted from the nucleus. What isotope remains?

7. Given a nuclear equation, how could you recognize a fission reaction?

8. What elements are useful as starting materials for fission reactions?

9. Consider the nuclear reactions described in questions 3–6. Can any of these be useful in creating a nuclear chain reaction? Explain.

10. Which of the possible fission reactions of $_{92}^{235}U$ would theoretically lead to the most effective chain reaction?

11. Given a nuclear equation, how could you recognize a fusion reaction? What elements are useful as starting materials for fusion reactions?

12. The exact mass of deuterium is 2.01410 amu, of helium-3 is 3.01603 amu, and of a neutron is 1.00866 amu. Calculate the mass lost in a nuclear fusion of two deuterium atoms. Is the mass really "lost"?

13. It is thought that the fusion reaction of stars cooler than our own sun involves fusing two deuterons into an alpha particle. Write a nuclear equation for this type of energy-producing reaction.

14. Lithium-6 can fuse with deuterium to produce either two helium-4 nuclei or lithium-7 and a proton. Write two equations to illustrate the possibilities.

15. What is the difference between radiation units of intensity and units of dosage?

16. If electrons are removed from a neutral atom, will a positive or negative charge be created on the remaining ion? Why?

17. Why do two plasma nuclei tend to repel each other?

18. Explain why an alpha particle has more ionizing power than a proton.

19. What is measured by the factor R.B.E.?

20. In what case will radiation exposure measured in rads be equal numerically to the exposure as measured in rems?

21. Explain the principle of using a Geiger counter to detect radiation.

22. A 6000 mile jet airplane trip exposes you to approximately 4 millirems of radiation. What problem due to radiation could arise in carrying unexposed film on your flight?

23. How many hours of color TV viewing are radiologically equivalent to the dose received from one 6000 mile jet airplane trip? Even though these two exposures are numerically equivalent, what are the differences between the two types of exposures?

24. If krypton-85 were stored for 100 years, what fraction of its original activity would remain? (Half-life is 10.4 years; use 10 years as an approximation.)

25. What does a breeder reactor breed? How is this accomplished?

Study Questions – Group B

1. A 1971 study for the Environmental Protection Agency showed that the average natural radiation dose each American receives per year ranges from 100 millirems in Texas to 245 millirems in Wyoming and 250 millirems in Colorado. Why are the levels so high in these two states?

2. ^{235}U accounts for 0.71 percent and ^{238}U for 97.27 percent of all naturally occurring atoms of uranium. What makes up the rest? (A handy reference in this case would be the table of isotopes, *Handbook of Chemistry and Physics,* published by the Chemical Rubber Co.)

3. Another way to detect the presence of radioactivity is by means of an electroscope. What is an electroscope and how does it work?

4. Various devices are used to accelerate nuclear particles. The cyclotron was one of the earliest and most important of these machines. How does it accomplish its purpose?

5. Many of the radioisotopes produced artifically today have important uses in medicine, industry or agriculture. (Some of these same isotopes occur naturally as well.) If handled and used with the proper care due any radioactive material, their development must be included as a benefit of nuclear science. Find the use(s) for each of the following isotopes or report on others of interest to you.

$$^{60}_{27}Co \qquad ^{58}_{27}Co \qquad ^{137}_{55}Cs \qquad ^{74}_{33}As \qquad ^{64}_{29}Cu \qquad ^{51}_{24}Cr$$

$$^{131}_{53}I \qquad ^{136}_{53}I \qquad ^{67}_{31}Ga \qquad ^{14}_{6}C \qquad ^{32}_{15}P$$

6. Ions produced by radiation can serve as seeds for condensation in an atmosphere saturated with vapor. As radiation moves through the vapor, droplets form on the ions created. This produces a visible trail much like the contrail left by a jet as it crosses the sky at high altitudes. Although a powerful research tool, a simple "cloud chamber" can easily be constructed. Find directions for making a cloud chamber; if you are so inclined, make one and demonstrate its use to the class. Find some typical cloud chamber pictures in reference books to accompany your demonstration.

7. Space scientists have been puzzled by the light flashes seen by astronauts while in the total darkness of space. These pinpoint streaks of light were first reported by the astronauts of Apollo 11 and have been seen by all subsequent missions. It is now thought that helium ions and high energy neutrons are colliding with the atoms of the human eye, creating flashes of light. The retinal rods of the eye, not the optic nerve nor the brain, is the actual center of this phenomenon. Find out more about this newly discovered effect and how the information is helping to provide new understandings about the eye.

8. The impressive energy associated with nuclear fission has led to a variety of commercial and government projects other than the production of electric power. The Plowshare Program was the name for this group of projects. Find the purpose, development history, and current status for these projects:

a. Using nuclear explosives to dig a second Panama Canal

b. Project Gas Buggy

c. Project Rulison

d. Project Bronco

e. Project Sloop

f. Testing ABM (antiballistic missile) systems at the Amchitka Test Site, Aleutian Islands, Alaska (not part of Plowshare).

9. To find out more about fusion power and its role in fulfilling the energy needs of the United States, an excellent reference is:

Gough, William C., and Eastlund, Bernard J. "The Prospects of Fusion Power." *Scientific American* 224: 2 (1971): 50–64.

Many of the lesser known approaches to achieving fusion power are contained in this article:

Wood, Lowell and Nuckolls, John. "Fusion Power." *Environment* 14: 4 (1972): 29–33.

Read and prepare a short report on these two articles or other, even more recent material about fusion power.

10. At the end of Chapter 5, you will be asked to compare nuclear and fossil-fuel power plants. In preparation for that comparison, make an outline of what you consider to be the positive aspects and then the negative aspects of using this energy source.

11. The National Environmental Policy Act has proven to be quite unpopular with the Atomic Energy Commission. There have been several attempts to weaken the act by exempting, at least temporarily, nuclear power plants from the time-consuming requirement of writing environmental impact statements. Read and report on this continuing controversy.

12. "Social Institutions and Nuclear Energy" by Alvin M. Weinberg (*Science* 177 (July 7, 1972): 27–34) presents an interesting and thought-provoking review of the nuclear energy enterprise. The author discusses several potential problem areas but then speculates on the special demands that nuclear energy places on our human institutions. Read and report on this article.

Suggested Readings

"Understanding the Atom."

Series of approximately 50 booklets dealing with all aspects of nuclear science. An *Index* booklet is available as in *Nuclear Terms, a Brief Glossary*. Single copies (or entire sets for schools, libraries, or special groups) are available from

U.S. Atomic Energy Commission
P.O. Box 62
Oak Ridge, Tennessee 37830

The same address can be used by students and teachers needing other material on specific aspects of nuclear science. Be clear in stating your interests when you write.

Seaborg, Glenn T., and Corliss, William R. *Man and Atom. Building a New World through Nuclear Technology*. New York: E. P. Dutton, 1971.

A comprehensive look at the applications of nuclear science in agriculture, medicine, industry, even in space travel and forensic science. The role of the AEC and the relationship of our nuclear program with international cooperative efforts are explained. It would be hard to find an author with more experience in this field than Glenn Seaborg.

Curtis, Richard, and Hogan, Elizabeth. *Perils of the Peaceful Atom*. New York: Ballantine Books, Inc., 1969.

Stimulating criticism of the nuclear industry. Thoroughly documented book dealing with the hazards of nuclear power. Plea for reexamination of our program for nuclear power production.

Chapter 4
Molecules: Compounds and Reactions

Up to this point, we have been concerned mainly with the nucleus of the atom, since this structural feature is responsible for the reactions of radioactivity. Before beginning to study air pollution, water pollution, and the other topics yet to come, it will be necessary to extend our understanding of the chemical behavior of the atom.

A very fundamental question is why atoms combine to form molecules. We will look in more detail at the different theories regarding the distribution of electrons in the atom and how this affects the types of molecules formed. We will also be able to correlate position on the periodic table with electronic distribution and see how useful the table is in predicting the combination of elements.

As you continue through this book you will encounter several important classes of compounds. Some generalizations about the chemical nature of these compounds will be drawn in Part Two of this chapter. Part Three will deal with chemical reactions, both the reasons why they occur and the way they can be represented in equations.

You will want to consider this chapter in two ways: first, as necessary background for the material to come and second, as a reference chapter as you continue on through the book. Ideas first presented here will be picked up again as applicable in later chapters. General chemistry references to help you are listed in the bibliography at the end of this book. Additional references specific to chemical bonding and to environmental chemistry are found at the end of this chapter.

Part One: THE ARRANGEMENT OF ELECTRONS IN THE ATOM

In any neutral atom, the number of positively charged protons in the nucleus must be balanced by the same number of negatively charged electrons in the surrounding electron cloud. But no man has ever seen an individual atom, much less a tiny electron within that atom. Under such a handicap, is it possible to answer questions such as: Can the exact position of the electrons be located? What type of movement do the electrons have? Under what conditions will the electrons change position within the electron-cloud region or even leave it altogether? These are very difficult questions to answer and ultimately require us to start thinking about the electron in new ways.

The Importance of Models in Science

It is common, when faced with interpretation of some physical phenomena, for scientists to cast their ideas into a theoretical framework. Such a mental framework is called a scientific theory. A theory tries to organize, correlate, and explain some part of the physical universe. Sufficient evidence may be gathered in support of a theory; the concept may then be called a law. Laws tend to be rather specific statements while theories give underlying explanations for some observed set of facts. Theories may also be completely unrelated to observable phenomena but rather predict some future discovery.

Theories must at least be consistent with known facts and also accurate enough to be useful in prediction. Some theories also propose a physical model as a way to simplify our thinking. Often, as more information is discovered experimentally, scientific theories must be modified or changed entirely, and any physical model is changed accordingly.

The atomic theory is a classic example of a continually changing mental theory. From the early Greek ideas concerning the individual atomic units making up matter to the present sophisticated concepts of atomic structure, several different frameworks have been proposed and subsequently modified. We will look at two important models concerning the arrangement of electrons around the nucleus of an atom.

The Bohr Theory

Our present understanding of electrons in atoms essentially started with Niels Bohr (1885–1962), a Danish physicist who in 1912 made a series of very significant proposals concerning atomic structure. His ideas provided a reasonable explanation for many observed phenomena concerning the behavior of atoms and particularly of electrons associated with atoms. He drew an analogy between the movement of electrons around the nucleus and the movement of planets around the sun. This model envisioned rather fixed positions for the electrons in their "orbits" around the nucleus. Each orbit was considered to be at a specific energy level from the nucleus. If an electron absorbed energy, it might be "promoted" to a higher energy level further from the nucleus; giving up that extra energy would cause the electron to go back to its original lower energy level, emitting energy, commonly in the form of light. The model envisioned by Bohr for the simplest atom, hydrogen, can be diagrammed as shown in Figure 1.

Figure 1. Bohr's Concept of the Hydrogen Atom

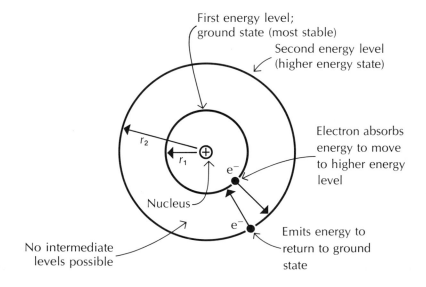

First energy level;
ground state (most stable)

Second energy level
(higher energy state)

Electron absorbs
energy to move
to higher energy
level

r_2

r_1

e^-

Nucleus

e^-

Emits energy to
return to ground
state

No intermediate
levels possible

The presence of specific energy levels was consistent with the fact that only certain wavelengths of light were observed in the spectrum of hydrogen gas. The spectrum is a pattern of light emitted from any atom when electrons are returning from excited states to ground states. (You see this same phenomenon when a neon light glows red; you are seeing light emitted by electrons in the neon as they return to ground state after being excited by an electrical discharge through the tube.) If the light is viewed through a prism or grating which separates the individual wavelengths of light, a characteristic pattern of lines corresponding to definite changes in energy levels will be seen. This pattern is so representative of a particular type of atom that line spectra can be used to identify atoms.

As important as the Bohr theory has been, it has been quantitatively successful only as applied to hydrogen or other one-electron species. Despite the introduction of several modifying assumptions, the Bohr model has never given satisfactory mathematical results for many-electron systems. Because it is relatively simple physically, the model has continued to be taught at many levels of chemistry, but more adequate theories have been developed.

What is Quantum Mechanics?

A newer point of view and one more successful in dealing with electronic structure can be traced back to 1924 when a French scientist, Louis de Broglie, suggested the startling idea that matter might also exhibit properties of waves. Traditionally matter and energy have been two completely separate things with totally different laws governing their properties, but the conceptual barriers between the two had already begun to fall. Developments in the late eighteen hundreds concerning the dual nature of light (having both wave and particulate natures) and Einstein's relationship of 1905 between mass and energy ($E = mc^2$) set the stage for de Broglie's assertion, quickly verified by experiment in 1927. Unless the particle is very small and moving very fast, the wavelike properties will not be observable. This is why the traditional laws of physics were successful in treating the macroscopic world of classical mechanics. (The wavelength associated with a large, slow-moving object such as a train is not detectable.) In the subatomic world of electrons, however, the new assumptions prove to be very important and form the basis for a new view of electrons in atoms.

In 1926, Edwin Schrodinger, an American scientist, proposed a set of equations that describe the properties of electrons by treating them as wave motions. The solutions of these equations produce "orbitals" or positions in space where the electron has a probability of being found. It is beyond the scope of this chapter to detail the mathematics involved with the equations, and in fact the advent of computers was a great aid to mathematicians in finding solutions for the Schrodinger equations. Despite their mathematical difficulty, the equations yield many interesting results. The solutions give probable arrangements of electrons within atoms and a set of quantum numbers.

The word quantum refers to the definite amount of energy liberated when an electron returns to a lower energy level from a higher level. This same amount of energy is absorbed when the electron moves up to a higher energy level. The principal quantum number roughly corresponds with the sequentially numbered energy levels of the Bohr theory. However, the quantum numbers arise from the equations themselves and are not arbitrarily assumed as they were in the Bohr theory. The quantum numbers determine energy, orientations, and interactions of electrons. The whole field of study is called quantum mechanics.

A Modern View of Electrons in Atoms

This highly mathematical theory can be interpreted in a visual model. By graphing one form of the equation, it is possible to obtain a "picture" of the space that the electrons could occupy. This space is what was meant by the term "electron cloud." It is a probability picture, much as though you took thousands of photographs of an electron in a hydrogen atom, for example, and then superimposed them. Usually to give the possible space in which you could find the electron some definable boundary, you choose to include 90 or 95 percent of the probable positions of the electron. These "pictures" are shown for the electron in the hydrogen atom in Figure 2.

Note that this picture of the electron associated with the hydrogen atom is quite different from the Bohr concept. Here the electron is not confined to one set distance from the nucleus but may be found in a large variety of locations both very close to and very far away from the nucleus. The darker shading corresponds to positions of higher probability of finding the electron. The general shape of this particular orbital, the 1s orbital, is still spherical as envisioned by Bohr, but instead of proposing a hollow ball, this model predicts that the electron could be within the boundary as well.

One interesting result of the Schrodinger interpretation of electronic distribution concerns atoms with several electrons. Some of the probable positions for additional electrons in the atom do not define a sphere but rather quite different shapes. Some of the nonspherical probability shapes are shown in Figure 3. Note that there are three different spatial orientations for p orbitals. Other than s and p orbitals, d and f orbitals also have been described. These orbitals are used by electrons in elements with atomic number greater than 20 (in the case of d) and 57 (in the case of

**Figure 2.
Probability Distribution for the Electron in the Hydrogen Atom; 1s Orbital**

Probability diagram
(two dimensions)

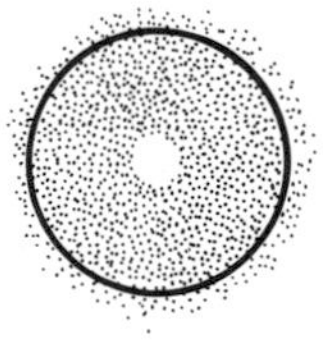

Boundary probability
diagram
(three dimensions;
includes 95 percent of
all positions)

Figure 3. Boundary Surfaces for Various Orbitals

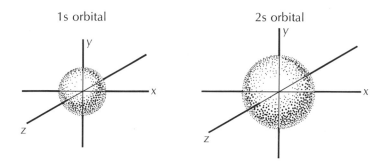

Principal quantum number 1   Principal quantum number 2

1s orbital   2s orbital

Three equal-energy 2p orbitals

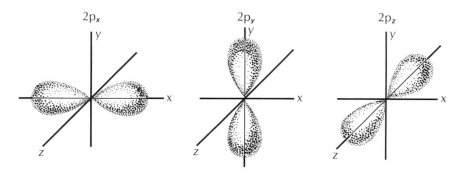

2p$_x$ 2p$_y$ 2p$_z$

f). There are five possible d orbitals and seven possible f orbitals. Hybrid orbitals are created when electrons from different orbitals relocate to achieve the maximum distance from each other.

Capacity of Orbitals

Each orbital can hold a maximum of two electrons. Therefore, for atoms containing many electrons, many possible orbitals will be used. Electrons will always be located in orbitals of lowest energy, for this is the most stable position. Combining these two pieces of information, consider the element boron. Since boron has five electrons, at least three orbitals must be used to contain the electrons. Placing them into the lowest energy orbitals available, two of the electrons would be found in a 1s orbital, two in a 2s orbital, and the last electron in any one of the

2p orbitals. This information can be conveyed compactly by means of this symbolism:

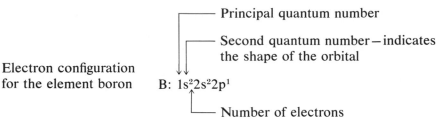

Electron configuration for the element boron

B: $1s^2 2s^2 2p^1$

Principal quantum number

Second quantum number — indicates the shape of the orbital

Number of electrons

The presence of a single electron in the 2p orbital gives rise to the possibility of the atom's combining with other atoms, for a full orbital is usually a condition of greater stability for the atom.

As another example of this symbolism, fluorine, with nine electrons, has electron configuration $1s^2\ 2s^2\ 2p_x^2\ 2p_y^2\ 2p_z^1$. It is common to combine all of the 2p orbitals, making the symbol $1s^2 2s^2 2p^5$. Note again that there is an unpaired electron available, creating the probability that the atom will combine with another atom.

The principal quantum number can be used to compute the maximum number of electrons to be found in all possible orbitals of that quantum number.

$$\text{Maximum capacity} = 2n^2 \text{ where } n = \text{principal quantum number}$$

For example, as we saw in Figure 3, the second main quantum level, 2, has orbitals designated 2s, $2p_x$, $2p_y$, $2p_z$. Since each orbital can hold two electrons, there are eight electrons as the maximum for the second quantum level. This same value can be easily computed by use of the formula above.

$$\text{Maximum capacity for the second level} = 2(2)^2 = 8$$

In the case of even higher levels, you would be unable to list all orbitals separately, but you can still compute the maximum number of electrons by means of this formula.

Remember that the relative energy determines the order of electrons occupying different orbitals. This means that the maximum number of electrons in a principal quantum number may not be reached until lower energy orbitals with a higher quantum number are occupied. This occurs particularly in the case of the heavier elements. For example, a 4s orbital is of lower energy than a 3d orbital, so the 4s orbital would be filled before the 3d orbital.

Electron Distribution and the Periodic Table

The orderly filling of electronic orbitals is the underlying reason for the form and order of the periodic table. We noted in Chapter 2 that elements with similar properties were arranged in groups or vertical columns of the periodic table. We can add to that observation by giving the basic reason for that similarity—a group of elements also has similar electron distribution. Refer to Figure 4 to verify this.

For example, each of the elements in the first vertical column (called Group IA or the alkali metal family) has an electron distribution ending with one unpaired electron in an s orbital. As you proceed down the family, the s orbital is in successively higher energy levels. This electronic similarity is responsible for the similarity in properties exhibited by this group.

The same type of trend is seen in the group of noble gases, Group VIII on the far right of the table. This family of elements is also known as

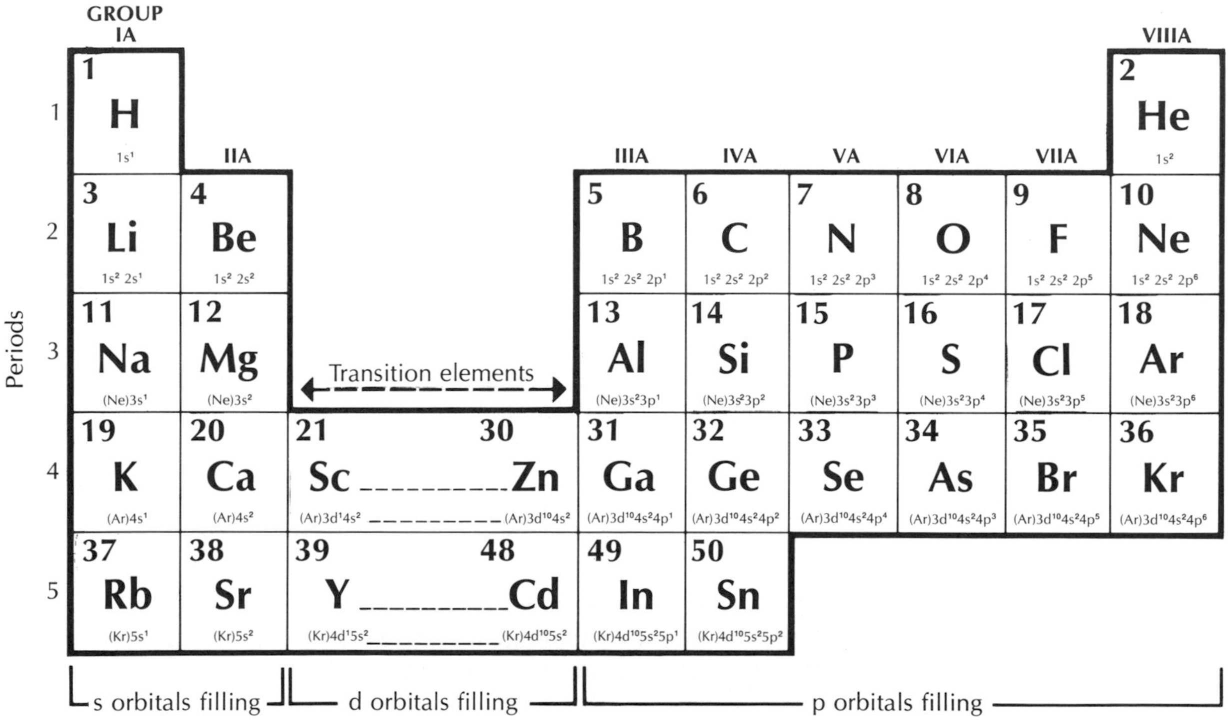

Figure 4. Correlation of Electron Distribution with Position on the Periodic Table of Elements

the inert gases. In each case, with the exception of helium which only has two electrons, the structure shows full s and p orbitals for the outermost energy level. This is a condition associated with particular chemical stability. Neon, for example, is almost completely nonreactive. Since this particular arrangement is so stable, the symbols of these elements are used as a shorthand in writing electronic configurations for other elements. For example, the structure of magnesium is shown as $[Ne]3s^2$ as a shorter way of writing $2s^22s^22p^63s^2$, since $[Ne]$ and $1s^22s^22p^6$ represent the same electron distribution.

There is also an orderly progression along each horizontal row or period of the table. We know the elements are in order of their atomic numbers. We also know the number of protons is equal to the number of electrons for the neutral atom, so the table is also arranged in order of increasing number of electrons. Each completed period corresponds to filling a set of s and p orbitals for that energy level. Again, we must except helium which only has two electrons. Therefore, it can only fill the 1s orbital.

The regular recurrence of properties as the atomic number increases, referred to as the Periodic Law, is thus caused by similarities and trends in electronic distribution. This arrangement of elements simplifies the study of chemistry, since families display similar properties and since properties in a period of elements will vary in a way consistent with their increasing electron population. The ways in which the periodic table can be used to predict types of chemical bonding will be discussed in the next section.

Part Two: ELEMENTS INTO COMPOUNDS

As was the case for elements, there is a special vocabulary connected with compounds. We know that atoms are the smallest units of an element to retain the essential properties of that element. When atoms join to form compounds, the smallest combined unit to retain all essential properties of the new compound is a molecule. An atom is represented by a symbol; a molecule by a formula. Thus the element neon is represented by the symbol Ne; the compound water by the formula H_2O. We have also defined the atomic weight and the gram-atomic weight for an element; one gram-atomic weight was referred to as a mole. If the atomic weights of each element in a compound are added together in the ratio given by the formula, we have the formula weight or molecular weight of the compound. Thus the formula weight of H_2O is $2(1.008) + 1(15.999) = 18.015$. This is approximately 18 so the weight of one gram-molecular weight or one mole of water is 18 grams. One mole of any compound contains Avogadro's number of molecules, 6.023×10^{23}.

Why Do Elements Join?

We have seen that the last family of the periodic table contains elements that are particularly nonreactive. In each case, their electronic structure consists of full s and p orbitals, which means eight electrons. There is a tendency for other atoms to enter into chemical reactions which result in an alteration of their electron distribution to resemble that of the noble gases, since this is a state of greater chemical stability. This tendency to achieve eight electrons is sometimes referred to as "the octet rule."

Ionic Bonding

One way that elements can achieve chemical stability through interaction is by means of ionic bonding. For example, chlorine is a member of the VIIA or halogen family, immediately to the left of the noble gas family on the periodic table. If a chlorine atom acquired one electron, it would have an electronic structure similar to stable argon. In fact, chlorine does so with the release of a rather large amount of energy (87.3 kcal/mole of atoms):

$$\text{Cl:}[\text{Ne}]3s^2 3p^5 \; + \; e^- \longrightarrow \text{Cl:}[\text{Ne}]3s^2 3p^6 \; + \; \text{energy released}$$

Neutral atom

17 protons
17 electrons

Charged ion

17 protons
18 electrons

Net charge: -1
(also referred to as chlorine's valence or oxidation state)

The magnitude of the energy released is an indication of the greater stability of the chloride ion relative to the chlorine atom.

The electron gained by chlorine must come from some other atom, and suitable donors can be found in Group I on the periodic table. Here there are atoms that could attain noble gas electronic structure if they lost an electron. Sodium, for example, has structure $[\text{Ne}]3s^1$ or $1s^2 2p^6 3s^1$. Losing the $3s^1$ electron would therefore result in the stable $[\text{Ne}]$ arrangement.

$$\text{Na:}[\text{Ne}]3s^1 \longrightarrow \text{Na:}[\text{Ne}] + e^-$$

Neutral atom

11 protons
11 electrons

Charged ion

11 protons
10 electrons

Net charge: $+1$
(valence, oxidation state)

Physical models are a useful reflection of the concepts developed to explain the bonding and structure of molecules. Several types of molecular model sets are in widespread use. These range in sophistication from styrofoam balls and toothpicks to carefully engineered (and correspondingly expensive) sets designed to accurately reflect many aspects of molecular structure. Here are examples of three types you may encounter, all used to represent the methane molecule, CH_4.

These models represent the number and type of atoms present in the methane molecule, as well as the hydrogen-carbon-hydrogen bond angles. Atoms other than carbon and hydrogen are color coded in all of the sets.

The simple ball-and-spring model is easily constructed and represents the basic structure. It does not give accurate information about the relative sizes of the atoms.

On the framework molecular model, the relative sizes of the atoms and their positions in the molecule are represented. The black stripes represent the centers of the hydrogen atoms; the center of the model is the center of the carbon atom. All internuclear distances can be constructed to scale, and bond angles are easily measured directly from the model. The use of different central "valence clusters" permits models with up to six bonds to be constructed, a feature lacking in other types of models shown. Construction of these models, however, does take time.

The relative sizes of the atoms are also shown by means of the space-filling model. The over-all effective shape of the molecule in three dimensions is best represented by this model, but you cannot conveniently measure bond angles. Placing this type of model on an overhead projector (or in the beam of an ordinary projector) will produce a useful molecular profile.

Examine and compare these three representations of the benzene molecule, C_6H_6, for the same types of features discussed for methane.

Models of the methane molecule

Ball-and-spring model

Framework molecular model

Space-filling model

Models of the benzene molecule

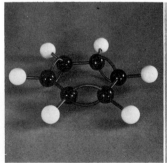 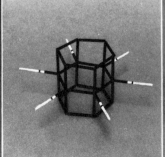 

In this step, energy is actually required to remove the electron from the sodium atom, since this must be done in opposition to the attraction of the positively charged nucleus for that electron. Once the positively charged sodium ion and the negatively charged chloride ion are formed, they are attracted by their opposite electrical charges and a regularly packed crystalline material results. This last step also releases energy. The over-all energy release is 98.2 kcal/mole for the entire process.

The result of the interaction between sodium and chlorine atoms has been a transfer of electrons. Charged ions have resulted, held together by the attractive force due to opposite charges, a type of electrostatic force. This type of chemical bond is called an ionic bond, sometimes also known as an electrostatic bond. Those elements most likely to form this bond are combinations involving Groups IA and IIA, metallic groups on the far left of the table with a tendency to lose one or two electrons, together with elements from nonmetallic Group VIA or VIIA with a tendency to gain one or two electrons to attain stable electronic structure.

Lewis Diagrams for Ionic Compounds

Another way of showing such an electron exchange is by means of an electron-dot representation, called a Lewis diagram. This system of electron accounting is named after the American scientist G. N. Lewis. Only the number of electrons in the outermost main energy level (highest principal quantum number) is shown. Lewis diagrams are not meant to be a physical picture of the atom in any way.

For the formation of sodium chloride, the electron-dot representation would be:

$$\text{Na}\cdot + :\ddot{\text{Cl}}: \longrightarrow \text{Na}^+ + \left[:\ddot{\text{Cl}}: \right]^-$$

Formula: NaCl

Other examples of ionic bonding represented in this way are:

$$\text{Mg}: + 2\left[:\ddot{\text{Cl}}: \right] \longrightarrow \text{Mg}^{+2} + 2\left[:\ddot{\text{Cl}}: \right]^-$$

Formula: $MgCl_2$

$$2\,\text{Na}\cdot + :\ddot{\text{S}}\cdot \longrightarrow 2\,\text{Na}^+ + \left[:\ddot{\text{S}}: \right]^{-2}$$

Formula: Na_2S

Figure 5. Covalent Bonding in the Cl₂ Molecule

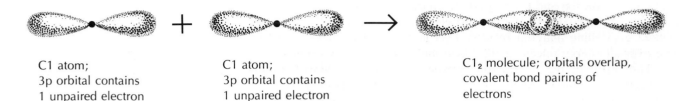

C1 atom;
3p orbital contains
1 unpaired electron

C1 atom;
3p orbital contains
1 unpaired electron

C1₂ molecule; orbitals overlap,
covalent bond pairing of
electrons

C1₂ molecule

Covalent Bonding

If the number of electrons to be transferred exceeds two, then it becomes less likely that the energy exchange will be favorable. It would take a large input of energy to remove three or more electrons from an atom. Elements of Groups III, IV, and V are therefore unlikely to display ionic bonding. Also, there are many combinations of atoms in which both elements would have the same tendency to gain or lose electrons. In these cases, the type of bonding that results involves the sharing of electrons between atoms, or covalent bonding.

For example, experiments show that chlorine gas is composed of molecular units of two atoms, Cl_2. Each atom has structure $[Ne]3s^23p^5$. The bonding between the chlorine atoms can be represented by an electron-dot diagram.

$$:\ddot{C}l: \ + \ :\ddot{C}l: \ \longrightarrow \ :\ddot{C}l:\ddot{C}l:$$

Chlorine
atom

Chlorine
atom

Chlorine
molecule

Formula: Cl_2

Each atom effectively has the stable eight electrons, since two electrons are shared between the two atoms. Often the dots representing shared electrons are replaced by a dash in a simplified Lewis structure; for chlorine, Cl—Cl. The unshared electrons are not usually shown.

A better idea of the molecule's bonding is obtained from looking at the orbital boundary diagrams for the electrons involved (see Figure 5). Each chlorine atom has one unpaired electron in one of the 3p orbitals. The overlapping of the orbitals results in the sharing of electrons. Remembering that the boundary diagrams are really probability pictures, there would now be a higher probability of finding the electrons between the two nuclei, and this constitutes the basis of the bond. The molecular orbital for Cl_2 would reflect that increased probability and the diagram could be represented as in the second part of Figure 5.

One other condition must be satisfied before electrons can be shared between two atoms. An electron can be rotating in one of two different directions around its own axis. Only if electrons with opposite spins form a pair will a stable covalent bond form. The whole reason for any chemical bond is achieving a lower energy or more stable state for the atoms involved. This condition is not met for a covalent bond if the electrons have the same spins. For example, consider the schematic energy diagram for the chlorine molecule in Figure 6. At large interatomic distances, there is no interaction between atoms. As the atoms approach each other, a variety of forces come into play. Each positively charged nucleus would have an attraction for the electrons of the other atom, but the electrons themselves tend to repel each other since their charges are alike. The over-all energy of the system falls as the two atoms approach only if the electrons that are to be shared have opposing spins. Their opposite spins create a magnetic field of attraction. The minimum energy corresponds to a stable internuclear distance for the chlorine molecule. If the atoms are pushed even closer, then internuclear repulsion will again increase the energy of the system.

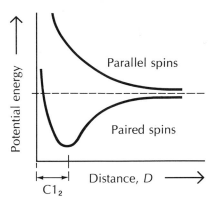

Figure 6. Energy and Electron Spin

Potential energy → (vertical axis)

Parallel spins

Paired spins

Distance, D →

Cl_2

Many other common elements exist in two-atom units; these are all referred to as diatomic molecules. In each of these, the electrons are shared equally between the two atoms, and the electrons have an equal probability of being associated with one nuclear center or the other. Such molecules are referred to as nonpolar. It is also possible for more than just one pair of electrons to be shared between two atoms as you can see in Table 1.

Covalent Polar Compounds

If atoms of two different elements join to form a covalent bond, then the electrons shared between them will be subject to unequal forces, depending on the relative ability of each atom to exert an attracting force. For example, in gaseous hydrogen chloride, HCl, the chlorine atom and the hydrogen atom share a pair of electrons, but the chlorine atom with its higher nuclear charge has a greater pull on the electron pair. This creates a polar bond; the shared pair of electrons has a greater probability of being closer to the chlorine atom than the hydrogen. This makes the chlorine end of the molecule more negatively charged than the hydrogen end, which has a slight deficiency of electrons or a partial positive charge.

In the case of hydrogen chloride, the molecule as a whole is also polar, since there is only one bond. In some molecules, polar bonds are

Table 1. Common Diatomic Covalent Molecules

Name	Formula	Electron-dot representation	Simplified Lewis structure
Hydrogen	H_2	H:H	H—H
Fluorine	F_2	:F̈:F̈:	F—F
Chlorine	Cl_2	:C̈l:C̈l:	Cl—Cl
Bromine	Br_2	:B̈r:B̈r:	Br—Br
Iodine	I_2	:Ï:Ï:	I—I
Oxygen	O_2	:Ö::Ö:	O=O
Nitrogen	N_2	:N⋮⋮N:	N≡N

Table 2. Common Covalent Molecules

Name	Formula	Electron-dot representation	Simplified Lewis structure	Polarity of molecule
Water	H_2O	H:Ö: Ḧ	H—O │ H	Polar
Methane	CH_4	H H:C̈:H Ḧ	H │ H—C—H │ H	Nonpolar
Carbon dioxide	CO_2	:Ö::C::Ö:	O=C=O	Nonpolar
Ethyl alcohol	C_2H_5OH	H H H:C̈:C̈:Ö:H H H	H H │ │ H—C—C—O—H │ │ H H	Polar
Ammonia	NH_3	H:N̈:H Ḧ	H—N—H │ H	Polar

arranged symmetrically, and therefore the molecule as a whole does not seem to be polar. The polarity of a covalently bonded compound is responsible for many of its properties. The electrons are not totally transferred in a polar covalent molecule; that happens only in the case of an ionic bond. The ionic bond, therefore, could be looked upon as the extreme case of a polar covalent bond. In fact, all degrees of polarity are known, depending on the relative attractive power of the atoms for electrons.

Polar covalent compounds play a particularly important role in biochemical reactions; most naturally occurring organic compounds are polar. Altogether, covalent bonding is a more important and widespread form of atoms joining together than is ionic bonding. Common examples of polar and nonpolar covalent molecules are given in Table 2.

Bond Angles for Covalent Molecules

Keep in mind that the Lewis structures shown in Table 2 do not necessarily give any information about the shapes of the molecules. It is more important to look at the orbitals involved in the bonding to draw any sound conclusions about molecular geometry. For example, the Lewis structure for the water molecule could be written H—O—H rather than H—O. The second representation is usually used to reflect the
$\quad\quad\;\;\;|$
$\quad\quad\;\;\;H$
fact that p orbitals are available for bonding the oxygen atom to the s orbitals of the hydrogen. Although normally p orbitals are at a 90° angle to each other, the actual bond angle in water is measured as 104.5°. This difference can be rationalized as being caused by the mutual repulsion of filled orbitals. The bond angle can also be explained using other types of hybrid orbitals not discussed here.

One type of hybrid orbital is of particular importance. The methane molecule, CH_4, illustrates this. Methane contains four identical carbon-to-hydrogen bonds. The electron-dot representation shows these bonds in two dimensions. The application of quantum mechanics to this molecule provides a predicted set of four equal orbitals that are directed in space from a central carbon atom towards the corners of an imaginary tetrahedron. Each orbital is 109° from the next. These four equal orbitals are called sp^3 hybrid orbitals. They are shown in Figure 7.

The symmetrical arrangement results in keeping the electron pairs as far apart as possible. This positioning avoids mutual repulsion and creates an exceedingly stable, nonpolar molecule. The tetrahedral shape is common to all molecules containing carbon in single bonds to other carbons or other types of atoms.

Figure 7. The Tetrahedral Carbon Atom: Methane

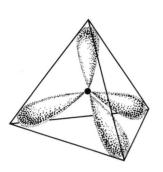

Four sp³ orbitals

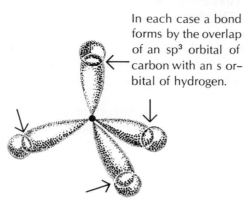

In each case a bond forms by the overlap of an sp³ orbital of carbon with an s orbital of hydrogen.

Methane; CH₄

Methane molecule as depicted with a ball-and-spring model.

Coexistence: Covalent and Ionic Together

Polar covalent bonds have been described as having properties somewhat intermediate to those of pure covalent or pure ionic types of bonding. But can both types of bonding coexist in the same compound? This happens quite commonly. Sodium sulfate, for example, is a compound in which the sodium ion is ionically attracted to covalently bonded groups of atoms carrying an electrical charge of negative two. Sodium sulfate, Na_2SO_4, consists of:

$$2\,Na^+ + \left[\begin{array}{c} :\ddot{O}: \\ :\ddot{O}:S:\ddot{O}: \\ :\ddot{O}: \end{array} \right]^{-2}$$

Table 3. Common Radical Ions

Name	Formula	Charge	Name	Formula	Charge
Acetate	$C_2H_3O_2$	−1	Cyanide	CN	−1
Ammonium	NH_4	+1	Hydroxyl	OH	−1
Carbonate	CO_3	−2	Nitrate	NO_3	−1
Chlorate	ClO_3	−1	Phosphate	PO_4	−3

The sulfate group may be referred to as a radical ion, meaning an electrically charged group of atoms that behaves like a single chemical unit. Because the atoms are bonded covalently within the radical, the group of atoms is not changed when it takes part in ionic reactions. Due to the electrical charge, radical ions are attracted to other atoms or radical ions of opposite charge. Other common radical ions are shown in Table 3.

Alternatives and Limitations

This brief discussion of ionic and covalent bonding does not come close to adequately describing all the possible ways in which atoms can join together, but it will give us a workable base from which to discuss the properties of many types of substances. You should keep in mind that other bonding types are possible. One is the metallic bond in which the electrons are less closely associated with some particular atom or set of atoms and instead are freer to move throughout the entire set of atoms. Macromolecular compounds such as quartz or diamond exhibit a special type of interlocking structure that is basically covalent in character.

Another fact of chemical life is that the "octet rule" (achieving eight electrons by filling s and all p orbitals) is not an infallible rule by any means. Some very common molecules form and are stable despite the fact that eight electrons are not either achieved or shared by the atoms involved. Nitric oxide, NO, is one such compound. There is no way that nitrogen, with five outer-level electrons, and oxygen, with six, can join to share or have eight electrons each. Even common oxygen gas presents a bonding problem for the structure given in Table 1 is disputed on the grounds that experimental evidence shows that there are unpaired electrons in the oxygen molecule. Some of these difficulties are overcome by treating bonding through alternate and more sophisticated models.

Properties and Bonding

A study of bonding is important, for it gives a great deal of information about properties of a given compound. Substances that are predominately ionic in bonding are good conductors of electricity if melted or if in solution; the ions present enable the current to pass. Many ionic substances are water soluble and generally are not soluble in nonpolar, covalent solvents such as carbon tetrachloride or benzene. Ionically bonded substances usually have relatively high melting points; commonly, they melt below 1000°C although some melt at temperatures up to 2000°C. The main forces holding ionic substance together are electrostatic attractions. Many substances classed as inorganic materials, such as table salt, are ionic in bonding character and have properties typical of this class of compounds.

Molecular models can help to illustrate another important feature of carbon chemistry. Compounds containing the same number and types of atoms but differing with respect to their atomic arrangement or orientation in space are termed isomers. A few minutes of work with the models will reveal that for the compound $C_2H_2Cl_2$, there are three ways in which to join the atoms.

1   **2**   **3**

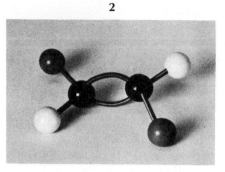

The fact that compounds 2 and 3 are actually different reflects the effectiveness of the carbon-to-carbon double bond in preventing free rotation of the two parts of the molecule along this axis. In single bonds, such rotation is possible. To check your understanding of isomers, how many are there for the compound butane, C_4H_{10}? How many isomers are there for the compound butene, C_4H_8?

Why is the existence of isomers important? Subtle changes in structural arrangement or spatial orientation can mean important changes in physical properties, as illustrated by these representative figures.

	1	2	3
Density (20°C)	1.22 g/ml	1.26 g/ml	1.28 g/ml
Melting point	−122°C	−50°C	−80°C
Boiling point	32°C	48°C	60°C

Chemical properties and biological activity are also different for isomers. This slight structural variation may make the difference between an effective or a useless pesticide, a powerful or a weak drug, a useful food material or one that cannot be metabolized. Thus knowing a compound's formula does not tell the whole story—the structural arrangement must also be determined. Often, models can be of great use in helping to visualize a very complicated molecule.

Far more compounds have predominately covalent character, and such substances can generally be expected to have much lower melting points. Since ions are not present, they are nonconductors of electricity. (If the bond has some ionic character it may be a slight conductor of electricity.) Regular crystalline structure is not as common in the absence of strong electrostatic forces. These molecules generally are not water soluble, but are soluble in benzene or other nonpolar solvents. Forces between molecules become relatively important, particularly for polar covalent molecules.

As the science of chemistry developed, two broad types of materials were seen: *inorganic,* or those substances derived from minerals and rocks, and *organic,* or those substances which were a part of living or once-living material. There was thought to be a "vital force" associated with the formation of organic materials and therefore although organic materials had been chemically changed to produce inorganic substances (by burning, for example) the reverse process was deemed impossible. This inability to produce organic materials was closely tied in with the philosophy of the times, and the nature of the "vital force" was widely discussed.

In 1828, Friedrich Wohler came forth with some surprising evidence to contradict the uniqueness of organic substances. He converted an inorganic salt into a product recognized as being organic in nature; we can represent the reaction in modern form by means of this equation.

$$(NH_4)^+(OCN)^- \xrightarrow{\text{heat}}
\begin{array}{c}
\quad\quad H \\
\quad\quad | \\
H-N \\
\quad\quad\quad \diagdown \\
\quad\quad\quad\quad C=O \\
\quad\quad\quad \diagup \\
H-N \\
\quad\quad | \\
\quad\quad H
\end{array}$$

Ammonium cyanate   Urea
(inorganic—   (organic—
mineral origin)   living origin)

This discovery led to the eventual realization that the laws of chemistry are not uniquely different for inorganic and organic materials. Nevertheless, the term "organic" survived and now specifically means the chemistry of carbon compounds. This includes not just compounds of living organisms, but a wide array of carbon-containing molecules such as fabrics, plastics, paper, soaps and detergents, insecticides, and drugs. By convention, certain carbon compounds such as carbon monoxide, carbon dioxide, and carbonate salts are placed in the study of inorganic chemistry.

Organic Chemistry

The fact that covalent molecules are more widespread can be accounted for in large part by the great number of covalently bonded carbon compounds that occur in nature. Carbon, with four electrons in the second main energy level, forms four covalent bonds and in particular, has the ability to join with other carbon atoms over and over again to create long chains and ring structures. This one element, known to be part of approximately two million different compounds, is so important that an entire branch of chemistry deals with just carbon compounds; *organic chemistry*. Some important types of organic compounds are shown in Table 4. You will meet many of these types in chapters to come, at which point their significant properties will be discussed.

Table 4. Important Classes of Organic Compounds

Name	Generic formula	Structural arrangement (two dimensions)	Examples
Hydrocarbons • Paraffin or alkane series (saturated)	C_nH_{2n+2}	$^aR—C—H$ (with H above and H below central C)	Methane $H—C—H$ (with H above and H below)
• Olefins or alkene series (unsaturated)	C_nH_{2n}	$R—C{=}C—R$ (with H above each C)	Ethene (ethylene) $H—C{=}C—H$ (with H above each C)
• Acetylenes or alkyne series (unsaturated)	C_nH_{2n-2}	$R—C{\equiv}C—R$	Ethyne (acetylene) $H—C{\equiv}C—H$
Alcohol	$R—OH$	$R—C—O—H$ (with H above and H below the C)	Ethyl alcohol $H—C—C—O—H$ (with H above and below each C)

^{a}R— is used to represent the rest of a hydrocarbon chain. This may be simply one hydrogen atom or a very long chain such as $C_{12}H_{25}$—, the dodecyl group. In some cases R may represent a ring structure such as a phenyl group, C_6H_5—. A ring structure (with double bonds) is referred to as an aromatic group and the chain as an alkyl group.

Table 4. (continued)

Acid

• Carboxylic acid	$R-COOH$	$R-C{\Large\langle}^O_{O-H}$	Acetic acid (ethanoic acid)	acetic acid structure
• Amino acid	$R-CHNH_2-COOH$	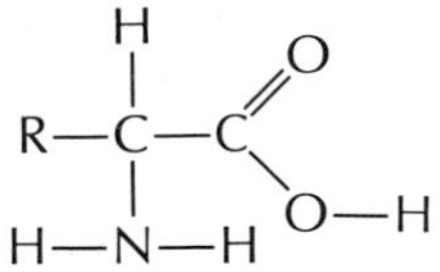 amino acid structure	Glycine	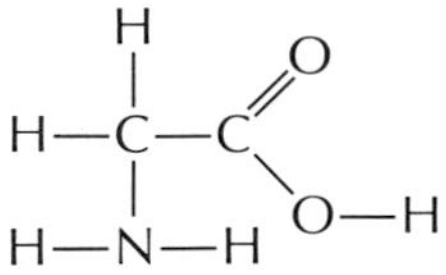 glycine structure
Ester	$R-COOR'$	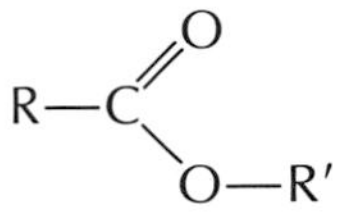 ester structure	Methyl acetate	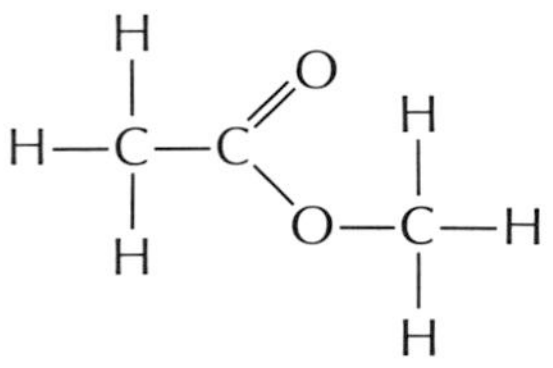 methyl acetate structure
Aldehyde	$R-COH$	$R-\overset{O}{\overset{\|}{C}}-H$	Formaldehyde (methanal)	$H-\overset{O}{\overset{\|}{C}}-H$
Ketone	$R-COR'$	$R-\overset{O}{\overset{\|}{C}}-R'$	Methyl ethyl ketone	methyl ethyl ketone structure
Amine	$R-NH_2$	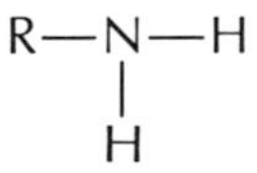 $R-\overset{}{\underset{H}{N}}-H$	Methyl amine	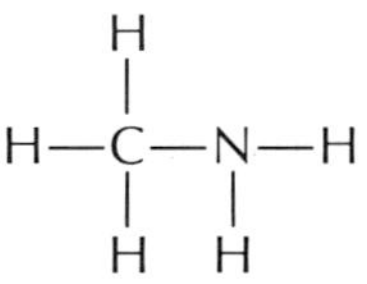 methyl amine structure
Amide	$R-CONH_2$	$R-\overset{O}{\overset{\|}{C}}-\overset{}{\underset{H}{N}}-H$	Acetamide	acetamide structure
Halides	$R-X$	$R-\overset{}{\underset{H}{\overset{H}{C}}}-X$	Methylchloride	$H-\overset{H}{\underset{H}{C}}-Cl$

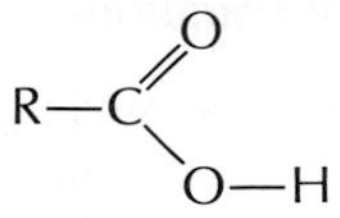

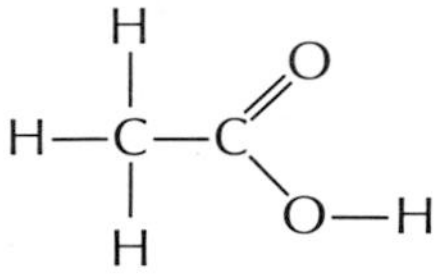

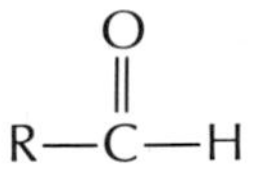

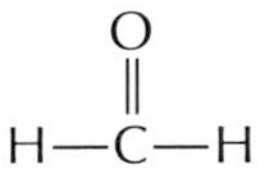

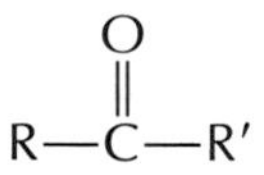

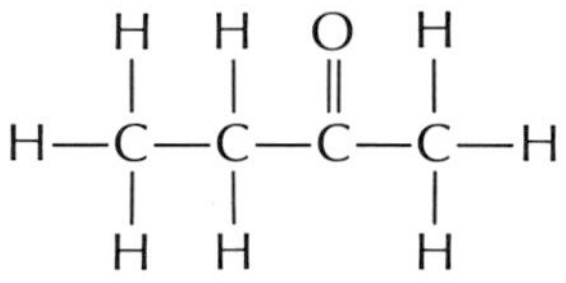

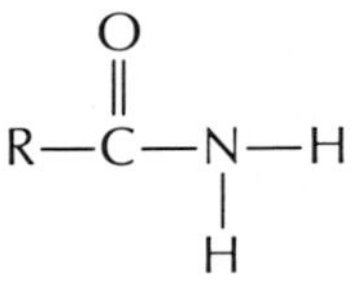

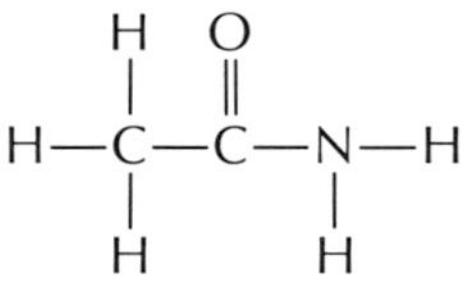

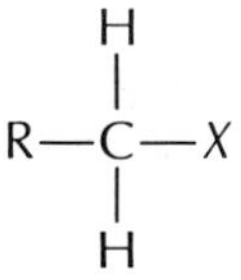

$X =$ F, Cl, Br, I

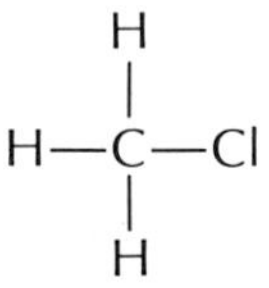

Part Three: CHEMICAL REACTIONS

Chemical Equations

Just as a nuclear equation is a shorthand representation of a nuclear change, a chemical equation gives a condensed expression of a chemical change. The conventions and interpretation of an equation may be illustrated by means of this synthesis reaction which describes the burning of sulfur, an environmental problem of air pollution.

Word equation: sulfur + oxygen $\longrightarrow$ sulfur dioxide

Chemical equation: S + O_2 $\longrightarrow$ SO_2

Oxygen, a   Correct formula for
diatomic gas   sulfur dioxide gas

Since each side of the equation has the same number of atoms for each element, this equation is said to be balanced. The law of conservation of mass requires that all mass be accounted for in a chemical reaction. Sulfur and oxygen are said to be the reactants; sulfur dioxide, the product.

There is a great deal of information packed into that small set of symbols, such as:

$$1 \text{ atom} + 1 \text{ molecule} \longrightarrow 1 \text{ molecule}$$

Or, using Avogadro's Principle (6.023×10^{23} particles/mole; one mole = one gram-atomic or one gram-molecular weight).

1 gram-atomic weight of sulfur	+	1 gram-molecular weight of oxygen gas	$\longrightarrow$	1 gram-molecular weight of sulfur dioxide
1 mole	+	1 mole	$\longrightarrow$	1 mole
32 g	+	$2 \cdot (16 \text{ g})$	$\longrightarrow$	$64 \text{ g}[32 + 2(16)]$

This mathematical relationship can be used in this case to compute the weight of sulfur dioxide gas produced if coal containing a certain percentage sulfur is burned.

Balancing Equations

When nitrogen burns, the main product is nitric oxide, NO. Both nitrogen and oxygen are diatomic gases, so the skeleton equation would be:

$$N_2 + O_2 \longrightarrow NO \qquad \text{(unbalanced)}$$

Although the molecular formulas are correct, this equation does not have equal numbers of atoms for each element on the left and right side. To balance this equation, a "2" would have to be placed before the product NO molecule on the right side of the equations, to show that two molecules of NO are produced.

$$N_2 + O_2 \longrightarrow 2 \ NO \qquad \text{(balanced)}$$

This illustrates the general order in which you proceed. First write correct formulas for all reactants and products. Then place proper coefficients to achieve mass balance.

When a hydrocarbon burns completely, the products are water and carbon dioxide. The chemical reaction for burning propane can be represented by this equation.

$$C_3H_8 + 5 \ O_2 \longrightarrow 4 \ H_2O + 3 \ CO_2 \qquad \text{(balanced)}$$

From the equation it can be seen that 5 moles of oxygen (or $5 \cdot 32$ grams $= 160$ g) are needed to completely burn 1 mole of propane, for a ratio of 160 g O_2/44.0 g propane. It similarly is possible to calculate the relative weights of water and carbon dioxide produced.

Reaction Mechanisms

All of the equations thus far have illustrated reactions involving covalently bonded molecules. As a class, such reactions have a tendency to occur rather slowly, since the breaking of bonds followed by the formation of new bonds must occur for the reaction to be completed. The equations do not give any information about the actual mechanism of the reaction. Particularly in reactions involving hydrocarbons, the formation of "free radicals" may be the most important step in the reaction. A free radical is a molecular fragment that has an unpaired electron.[1] Since unpaired electrons are prime candidates for the formation of chemical bonds, free radicals are particularly reactive species. For example, one of the key reactions in photochemical smog formation involves the reaction of atomic oxygen, itself a free radical, with a hydrocarbon to form another free radical.

$$[O] + C_xH_y \longrightarrow C_xH_yO\cdot$$

This species in turn can react with either free oxygen or with another hydrocarbon to produce more products that are associated with smog. Free radical mechanisms are also important in polymerization, the forming of large molecules by joining together many small molecules (see Chapter 9).

---

[1]Do not confuse free radicals (which have an unpaired electron) with radical ions (which have an over-all ionic charge).

Reaction Rates

Just as the equation does not give any information as to the mechanism of the reaction, it also does not indicate the rate of the reaction. In fact, it is possible to write balanced equations for reactions that will never occur. In general, a reaction will occur if the potential energy of the products is lower than the potential energy of the reactants. However, it still may be necessary to add energy to a system to cause such a reaction to take place at a reasonable rate. As potentially reacting molecules approach each other, molecular collisions must occur with sufficient energy to cause the bonds to break, a step that precedes the formation of new bonds. Those molecules that have sufficient energy are said to be "activated." The amount of the activation energy varies greatly from reaction to reaction and helps determine if a reaction will ever occur at a reasonable rate. This concept is shown graphically in Figure 8 with A and B as reactants, C and D as products.

Catalysts

The dotted reaction path (Case II) shown in Figure 8 indicates one possible way of reducing the necessary activation energy for a reaction, thereby increasing the probability that colliding molecules will have enough energy to react and bring about a faster reaction. This is by means of a catalyst, a substance that changes the rate of a reaction but is not consumed itself in the reaction. Most useful catalysts increase the

Figure 8. Potential Energy Changes During a Reaction; Two Cases

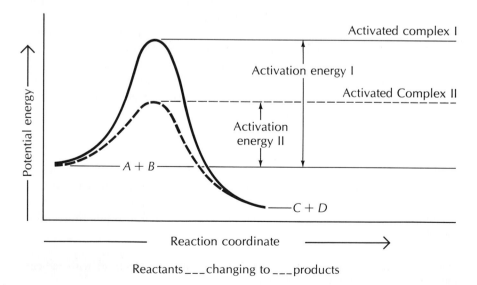

speed of a reaction. Usually the specific concentration and type of catalyst is determined by experiment. In many cases the exact method of action is unclear. However, a wide background of experience has provided chemists with many practical catalysts used in industrial processes, and nature has provided many biological catalysts in the form of enzymes.

For example, platinum metal is a widely used catalyst, particularly if the process involves hydrogen. Platinum will speed the union of hydrogen with oxygen and also increase the addition of hydrogen to unsaturated fats (those containing double or triple bonds between carbons) to form saturated fats (all single bonds between carbons, therefore containing the maximum number of hydrogen atoms). Pepsin is a natural enzyme in gastric juice that accelerates the otherwise very slow conversion of starch in our food to sugar, a useful energy producer for our bodies. In some cases the catalyst's effect has been a surprise to scientists, such as the rather recent discovery that natural enzymes in our waterways were converting metallic mercury into the much more harmful methyl mercury form.

Reactions of Ionic Compounds

Ionic reactions show significant differences from those chemical changes involving covalent bonds. Generally ionic reactions occur instantaneously or at least much more rapidly than the typical organic reaction. This is due to the fact that many ionic reactions take place in solutions where the ions are free to move and react. For example, alum, chemically aluminum sulfate, is often added to water in order to cause coagulation. This process involves the formation of a rather gelatinous precipitate due to the reaction of the alum with either the natural alkalinity of the water or with added lime. The precipitate helps to carry down finely divided suspended solid materials. This reaction can be represented by the equation:

$$Al_2(SO_4)_3 \ + \ 3\ Ca(OH)_2 \longrightarrow 2\ Al(OH)_3\downarrow \ + \ 3\ CaSO_4$$

| Alum: aluminum sulfate | Lime: calcium hydroxide | Aluminum hydroxide, the precipitate ($\downarrow$ indicates a precipitate) | Calcium sulfate |

Since the reactants are ionic in nature, the equation could also be written to emphasize this by including just those ions that actually produce the product.

$$Al^{+3} + 3\ OH^{-1} \longrightarrow Al(OH)_3\downarrow$$

Since the product is insoluble, it removes ions from solution, providing the reason for the completion of the reaction. Other means of removing ions from solution include the formation of gases that escape or the formation of covalently bonded products such as water.

Equilibrium Reactions

Not all reactions proceed completely to form products, for in many cases the reactants themselves have an appreciable tendency to break down back to the original reactants. In such a case, the reaction is called reversible, and both the forward reaction and the reverse reactions occur simultaneously. For example, two molecules of nitrogen dioxide undergo a conversion to dinitrogen tetroxide as shown in this equation:

$$2\ NO_2 \quad \xrightleftharpoons[\text{supply heat}]{\text{remove heat}} \quad N_2O_4$$

Red-brown gas   Yellow
(responsible   liquid
for color in
smog layers)

When the rate of the forward reaction equals the rate of the reverse reaction, no further change in concentration of either substance is observed and chemical equilibrium has been established.

In this particular equilibrium, an increase in temperature increases the reverse reaction, producing more NO_2, since the reverse reaction is the change that uses heat. This is an example of altering the equilibrium by applying a stress on the system; in this case the stress is temperature. Changes in concentration or pressure may also shift the established equilibrium. If the conditions of a system in equilibrium are changed, processes will occur in the system to counterbalance that change so that the stress is relieved and a new equilibrium established. Some equilibrium systems respond to stress rather quickly and rapidly establish a new set of equilibrium conditions. However, the more complicated the original equilibrium, the longer it may take for a new equilibrium to be established. In addition, competing reactions may prevent the products from reestablishing equilibrium by removing the compounds through alternate reactions. We shall see the importance of this mechanism in the formation of photochemical smog, discussed in the next chapter.

Study Questions – Group A

1. In what ways can the Bohr theory of atomic structure be compared with the solar system? In what ways are the Bohr theory and the solar system different?

2. Is an "orbit" of the Bohr theory the same as an "orbital" of the quantum mechanical model of atomic structure? Explain.

3. What is a "quantum"?

4. What elements make up the IVA family? What similarity in electronic distribution do these elements share?

5. What elements make up the VIA family? What similarity in electronic distribution do these elements share?

6. What is the maximum number of electrons associated with all orbitals of the second quantum level? Is this the same as the number of elements in the second period of the periodic table? Why or why not?

7. What is the maximum number of electrons associated with all orbitals of the fourth quantum level? Is this the same as the number of elements in the fourth period? Why or why not?

8. Why are there only two elements in the first period while the next two periods have eight elements each?

9. Which atom would you predict would have the larger volume — fluorine or chlorine? Why?

10. What similarity in electronic distribution is shared by the members of the noble gas family?

11. Explain why the formula of sodium chloride is NaCl but the formula for magnesium chloride is $MgCl_2$.

12. Predict the formula if:
   a. aluminum joins with chlorine.   c. magnesium joins with sulfur.
   b. potassium joins with bromine.   d. sodium joins with oxygen.

13. Predict the formula if:
   a. sodium joins with the sulfate radical.
   b. magnesium joins with the chlorate radical.
   c. potassium joins with the phosphate radical.
   d. hydrogen joins with the nitrate radical.

14. Find the gram-formula weights for:
   a. calcium hydroxide, $Ca(OH)_2$.
   b. sulfuric acid, H_2SO_4.
   c. carbon monoxide, CO.
   d. acetic acid, $HC_2H_3O_2$.
   e. aluminum sulfate, $Al_2(SO_4)_3$.
   f. phosphoric acid, H_3PO_4.

15. What is the weight of one mole of ethylene? (see Table 4) What is the weight of one molecule?

16. What are the main differences between ionic and covalent bonding? Give an example of a compound held together by each type.

17. Most compounds containing nitrates and phosphates are ionic. How does this help to account for their widespread distribution in water systems such as rivers?

18. Carbon (four electrons in the outermost energy level) can join with oxygen (six electrons in the outermost energy level) to form either CO, carbon monoxide, or CO_2, carbon dioxide. Both of these compounds are covalently bonded. Write Lewis diagrams for each of these oxides.

19. Compare the number of molecules in a mole of CO with the number of molecules in a mole of CO_2. Also compare the number of atoms present in a mole of each compound.

20. Draw a Lewis diagram for methyl amine, CH_3NH_2 (see Table 4 for the structural formula). Check to be sure that each atom other than hydrogen has a share in eight electrons. How many electrons should each hydrogen share?

21. Draw a Lewis diagram for formaldehyde; for acetic acid.

22. If two moles of ethane (C_2H_6) combine with five moles of oxygen gas (O_2), one possible set of products is four moles of carbon monoxide (CO) and six moles of water (H_2O). Write a chemical equation showing all of this information.

23. Each of the following chemical equations has correct formulas for both reactants and products. Balance them (if needed) by placing the proper coefficients in front of the formulas.
    a. $H_2 + Cl_2 \longrightarrow HCl$
    b. $CaO + H_2O \longrightarrow Ca(OH)_2$
    c. $SO_2 + O_2 \longrightarrow SO_3$
    d. $NaOH + H_2SO_4 \longrightarrow Na_2SO_4 + H_2O$
    e. $NH_3 + O_2 \longrightarrow NO + H_2O$
    f. $C_2H_6 + O_2 \longrightarrow CO_2 + H_2O$

24. For predicting if a reaction will take place in the laboratory, why is it necessary to know more than just the potential energy of the products compared to the potential energy of the reactants?

25. If a reversible chemical reaction has reached equilibrium, the concentrations of both reactants and products are not changing. Does this mean that no chemical reaction is taking place?

Study Questions — Group B

1. The tendency of an element to enter into chemical reactions is governed by its ability to gain, lose, or share electrons. One way to measure the relative reactivity is by use of a scale of electronegativity.

Electronegativity measures the relative tendency of an atom to attract an electron. These numbers were first developed by Linus Pauling. Values for the first eighteen elements are shown in Figure 9.

Figure 9.

H						
2.1						

Li	Be
1.0	1.5

Na	Mg
0.9	1.2

B	C	N	O	F	Ne
2.0	2.5	3.0	3.5	4.0	0.0

Al	Si	P	S	Cl	Ar
1.5	1.8	2.1	2.5	3.0	0.0

He
0.0

a. Why does fluorine have the highest value for electronegativity of all the elements?

b. Why does sodium have a low value?

c. Why does the noble gas family have zero electronegativity?

d. Explain the trend from sodium to chlorine.

e. Would you expect potassium to have an electronegativity higher or lower than that of sodium? Offer a possible explanation for potassium's relative value.

2. The true character of a bond can be expressed as its percent ionic character. This can be calculated by use of the electronegativity values. The difference between the electronegativity of the two bonding elements is correlated with the percent ionic character by means of Table 5.

Difference in electronegativity	0.1	0.2	0.3	0.4	0.5	0.6	0.7	0.8	0.9	1.0	1.1	1.2	1.3	1.4	1.5	1.6	1.7	1.8	1.9	2.0	2.1	2.2	2.3	2.4	2.5	2.6	2.7	2.8	2.9	3.0	3.1	3.2
Percent ionic character %	0.5	1	2	4	6	9	12	15	19	22	26	30	34	39	43	47	51	55	59	63	67	70	74	76	79	82	84	86	88	89	91	92

Find the percent ionic character for a bond between:

a. carbon and hydrogen.

b. sodium and chlorine.

c. chlorine and fluorine.

d. nitrogen and hydrogen.

e. sulfur and oxygen.

3. New artificial elements with atomic numbers greater than 104 are being researched by both the United States and the Soviet Union (see page 43). Elements up to atomic number 168 have been theorized, and this gives rise to the question of their proper placement

in the periodic table of elements. Much as Mendeleev originally predicted properties of "missing" elements, scientists are predicting the characteristics of these yet-to-be-discovered synthetic elements. An interesting article concerning this work is "From Mendeleev to Mendelevium and Beyond," by Glenn Seaborg, *Chemistry* 43: 1 (1970): 6–9. On page 27 of that same issue, you can find a spiral form of the periodic table. Read and report on these predicted super-heavy elements and where they will fit into each form of the periodic table.

4. It would be very helpful to your understanding of organic molecules to obtain model sets and to construct and sketch some of the compounds given in Table 4. What information does the model give you that the table cannot? If different types of model sets are available, what are the virtues and drawbacks of each? (If formal kits are not available, styrofoam balls and toothpicks can be useful too; consult your instructor for correct bond angles.)

5. In June of 1962, Neil Bartlett of the University of British Columbia shocked the scientific world by preparing xenon tetrafluoride, the first true compound of an inert gas. This feat was rapidly followed by other preparations and has caused some reevaluation in bonding theories (and increased interest in using the name noble gas family rather than inert gases!). If you are interested in reading more about this and reporting to the class, you might start with:

Mellor, D. P., "The Noble Gases and Their Compounds," *Chemistry* 41: 10 (1968): 16.

For even more information (although some of this will be rather technical) try:

Hyman, Herbert H., *Noble-Gas Compounds*. University of Chicago Press, 1963.

Suggested Readings

Sebera, Donald K., *Electronic Structure and Chemical Bonding*. New York: Blaisdell, 1964.

This paperback introduces the reader to many different models connected with atomic structure. In addition to the clearly written discussions of electron distribution and types of bonding, consideration is also given to topics not discussed in this chapter. It is an excellent supplementary source of information.

Cleaning Our Environment, The Chemical Basis for Action. The American Chemical Society, 1969.

A Supplement to Cleaning Our Environment, The Chemical Basis for Action. American Chemical Society, 1971.

These books are a report by the Subcommittee on Environmental Improvement of the American Chemical Society. Now that you have been introduced to the vocabulary of chemistry, these references should be invaluable as you move through the rest of your study of environmental chemistry. These references give recommendations for action following study of the air environment, the water environment, solid wastes, and pesticides in the environment.

Chapter 5
Chemistry of the Air Environment

None of us can afford to ignore the quality of our air, as we depend on its purity for life itself. Despite that, man has continued to treat our limited airspace as a never-ending receptacle for a growing amount of solid, liquid, and gaseous materials. In additon to just the sheer amount of pollution added to the air, the pollutants are reactants in chemical reactions which are taking place in our atmosphere. The end result is felt in increasing medical, aesthetic, and economic effects. Acid rainfall, global climatic effects, lead particles in mid-ocean, and a host of other known or suspected problems are the legacy of our neglect in keeping our atmosphere clean.

First we will look at what we would normally expect to find in our atmosphere and then at the substances introduced by man which alter the expected composition. Sources of emissions will be discussed in Part Two, including the major role played by combustion processes. The chemical properties, expected effects, and means of control for the major pollutants will form Part Three, leading to a discussion of the reactions of photochemical smog formation in Part Four. In Part Five, the role of the automobile in causing air pollution will be the focus, together with a look at possible modifications and alternatives to the internal combustion engine.

Part One: WHAT'S UP THERE?

The air around us is constantly in a state of change as solids, liquids, and gases are added, mixed, reacted, dispersed, absorbed, and in some cases accumulated in our thin slice of life-supporting atmosphere. Altogether our earth is surrounded by a layer of mixed gases which extends out as far as 62,000 miles if solar particles trapped by our earth's magnetic field are included. Since about 90 percent of the total weight of the atmosphere is trapped within roughly 10 miles of the earth's surface, this region, called the troposphere, concerns us most. The name troposphere is derived from the Greek "tropos" meaning turning, and the action of winds in this region keeps the system in constant motion. Even the extent of the troposphere itself is changing: its height is approximately five miles at the poles and eleven miles at the equator, and the heights are subject to seasonal change.

Composition of Our Atmosphere

In order to discuss the pollution of our troposphere, it is necessary to consider the mix of gases normally present. Table 1 lists the major components in order of their natural concentrations in the atmosphere.

Another normal component of air is water vapor. Its concentration varies greatly, averaging from 1 to 3 percent. Other gases may sometimes be added locally to the atmosphere as the result of natural processes, particularly by volcanic eruptions that emit hydrochloric and hydrofluoric acids as well as large quantities of the oxides of sulfur. Volcanic eruptions may add a great deal of dust and other particulate

Table 1. Composition of Clean, Dry Air near Sea Level

Component	Content		Component	Content	
	% by volume	ppm[a]		% by volume	ppm
Nitrogen	78.09	780,900	Hydrogen	.00005	0.5
Oxygen	20.94	209,400	Methane	.00015	1.5
Argon	.93	9,300	Nitrogen dioxide	.0000001	0.001
Carbon dioxide	.0318	318	Ozone	.000002	0.02
Neon	.0018	18	Sulfur dioxide	.00000002	0.0002
Helium	.00052	5.2	Carbon monoxide	.00001	0.1
Krypton	.0001	1	Ammonia	.000001	0.01
Xenon	.000008	0.08			
Nitrous oxide	.000025	0.25			

[a]ppm = parts per million.

One common type of unit used in reporting the concentration of a gas in air is ppm (parts per million). The conversion from percent by volume to ppm is quite easily accomplished by taking note of the fact that percentages are parts per hundred. Therefore, taking neon as an example from Table 1,

$$.0018\% \text{ means } \frac{.0018}{100}$$

To find parts per million, a suitable unit for any gas present in relatively small amounts, a proportion can be set up.

$$\frac{.0018}{100} = \frac{x}{1,000,000}$$

$$x = \frac{.0018 \times 1,000,000}{100} = 18 \text{ ppm}$$

This is equivalent to taking the original percent composition and multiplying by 10,000 (10^4) which means moving the decimal four places to the right.

matter to the earth's atmosphere, even having a global effect. The dust from the 1883 eruption of Krakatoa (an Indonesian volcanic island) remained in the atmosphere for over a year and increased sunset colors all over the world.

Types of Pollutants

How does man alter the composition of the air? Some of the possible types of pollutants are given in Table 2. We shall discuss these materials, their sources, and their effects.

Table 2. Classification of Air Pollutants

Major classes	Subclasses	Typical members of the subclasses
Inorganic gases	Oxides of nitrogen	Nitric oxide, nitrogen dioxide
	Oxides of sulfur	Sulfur dioxide, sulfur trioxide
	Oxides of carbon	Carbon monoxide, carbon dioxide[a]
	Other inorganics	Hydrogen sulfide, hydrogen fluoride, ammonia, chlorine
Organic gases	Hydrocarbons	Methane, butane, octane, benzene acetylene, ethylene, butadiene
	Aldehydes and ketones	Formaldehyde, acetone
	Other organics	Chlorinated hydrocarbons, benzo–[a]–pyrene, alcohols, organic acids
Particulates[b]	Solid particulates	Fume, dust, smoke; ash, carbon, lead, asbestos
	Liquid particulates	Mist, spray; oil, grease, acids

[a]Some sources would not consider CO_2 as a pollutant as it is a natural component of the atmosphere and takes part in no significant chemical reactions. However, it is not natural to have it present in ever-increasing concentrations; this point will be discussed in Part Three.
[b]Solid or liquid particulates of specific size suspended in the air may also be called aerosols. This classification has rather indefinite limits, generally given as being between 0.1 and 100 microns (1 micron = 10^{-4} cm or 10^{-6} m; this is one millionth of a meter. The abbreviation for a micron is μ). The particulates responsible for reducing visibility, as occurs in smog formation, are generally between 0.01 and 2 microns in size.

Figure 1. Nationwide Emissions and their Sources

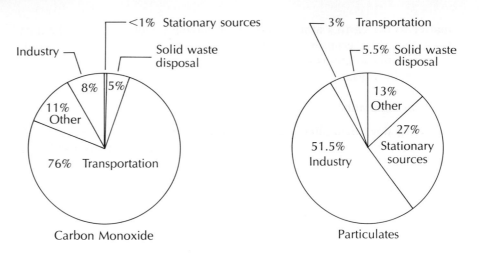

Carbon Monoxide

- <1% Stationary sources
- Solid waste disposal
- Industry
- 8%
- 5%
- 11% Other
- 76% Transportation

Particulates

- 3% Transportation
- 5.5% Solid waste disposal
- 13% Other
- 27% Stationary sources
- 51.5% Industry

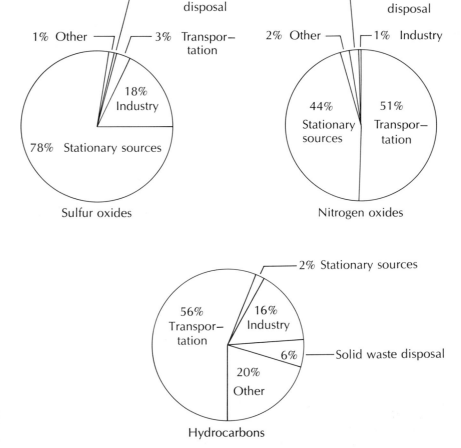

Sulfur oxides

- <1% Solid waste disposal
- 1% Other
- 3% Transportation
- 18% Industry
- 78% Stationary sources

Nitrogen oxides

- 2% Solid waste disposal
- 2% Other
- 1% Industry
- 44% Stationary sources
- 51% Transportation

Hydrocarbons

- 2% Stationary sources
- 56% Transportation
- 16% Industry
- 6% Solid waste disposal
- 20% Other

Automated monitoring equipment is used to check continuously the air quality at this site in East St. Louis, Illinois. Current conditions are evaluated and a broad data base for future reference is gathered.

Part Two: WHERE'S IT ALL COMING FROM?

From the large variety of possible substances shown in Table 2, it is possible to identify five major pollutants. The top five, in terms of tonnage emitted per year are: (1) carbon monoxide, (2) sulfur oxides, (3) hydrocarbons, (4) particulates, and (5) nitrogen oxides. The sources of these pollutants are given in Table 3. Figure 1 presents the same data graphically.

As can be seen from the preceding table and figure, many of the most widespread forms of air pollutants result from man's use of burning processes to produce the energy needed to manipulate the environment to his advantage. These chemical processes by which energy is released are variously referred to as oxidation, combustion, or burning, all similar processes but not exactly identical from a chemical viewpoint.

Chemical Oxidation

Oxygen unites chemically with many substances. This union defines oxidation in the simplest sense of the word. Many times this oxidation takes place so slowly that no noticeable heat or light is given off, for

The open burning of trash has been a commonly accepted procedure in the past. The low temperature tends to encourage incomplete combustion and produces great quantities of smoke and unpleasant odors. *(Michael D. Erikson)*

Table 3. Estimated Nationwide Emissions, 1970
(in millions of tons per year)

Source	Carbon monoxide	Particulates	Sulfur oxides	Hydro- carbons	Nitrogen oxides	Total
Transportation	111.0	0.7	1.0	19.5	11.7	143.9
Fuel combustion in stationary sources[a]	0.8	6.8	26.5	0.6	10.0	44.7
Industrial processes	11.4	13.1	6.0	5.5	0.2	36.2
Solid waste disposal	7.2	1.4	0.1	2.0	0.4	11.1
Miscellaneous[b]	16.8	3.4	0.3	7.1	0.4	28.0
Total	147.2	25.4	33.9	34.7	22.7	263.9

Source: Environmental Quality, The third annual report of the Council on
　　　　 Environmental Quality, August 1972, p. 6.

[a]Primarily power plants.
[b]Primarily forest fires, agricultural burning, coal waste fires.

example in the slow rusting of an iron object left unprotected from the air and rain.[1]

$$4 \text{ Fe} + 3 \text{ O}_2 + x \text{ H}_2\text{O} \longrightarrow 2 \text{ Fe}_2\text{O}_3 \cdot x \text{ H}_2\text{O}$$

Sometimes visible light is produced, as in the case of magnesium present in flash cubes.

$$2 \text{ Mg} + \text{O}_2 \longrightarrow 2 \text{ MgO} + \text{light}$$

In each of the reactions the oxygen has changed from O_2, a free element with oxidation state of zero, to an oxide with oxygen in an oxidation state of -2, meaning each atom has gained 2 electrons in the chemical change. Magnesium has, for example, gone from the free element, oxidation state of zero, to the magnesium ion with an oxidation state of $+2$, meaning it has lost 2 electrons per atom.

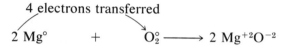

$$2 \text{ Mg}^{\circ} \quad + \quad \text{O}_2^{\circ} \longrightarrow 2 \text{ Mg}^{+2}\text{O}^{-2}$$

Mg has *lost* electrons but gained numerically in oxidation number; it is said to be oxidized. It also has caused the reduction of O_2 so Mg is also referred to as the reducing agent.

O_2 has *gained* electrons but lost numerically in oxidation number; it is said to be reduced. O_2 has caused the oxidation of the Mg and so O_2 is the oxidizing agent.

In summary:

$$2 \text{ Mg} \quad + \quad \text{O}_2 \quad \longrightarrow 2 \text{ MgO}$$

Substance oxidized and reducing agent	Substance reduced and oxidizing agent

It should be clear now that oxidation and reduction take place together. If the focus of attention is on the substance losing electrons, then the over-all process may be referred to as oxidation. Oxidation can now be more specifically defined as a process that causes an atom to increase in oxidation number due to the removal of electrons.

---

[1]Rust usually consists of a ratio of 2 moles of Fe_2O_3 to 3 moles of water, although the amount of water can vary; this is indicated by the x in the equation. The raised dot between Fe_2O_3 and H_2O indicates this product is a hydrate. The water is either mechanically held within the crystalline Fe_2O_3 or is loosely associated with part of the Fe_2O_3 but it is not tightly bound. Many common inorganic substances exist as hydrates. The blue color of copper sulfate is due to the hydrate $CuSO_4 \cdot 5 \text{ H}_2\text{O}$; heating drives off the water and leaves white $CuSO_4$.

Another example of this same concept is provided by the oxidation of sulfur.

$$\overset{\overset{\displaystyle \text{4 Electrons}}{\frown}}{S} \quad + \quad O_2 \quad \longrightarrow \quad SO_2$$

Substance oxidized
and reducing agent

Substance reduced
and oxidizing agent

The resulting sulfur dioxide can be further oxidized to sulfur trioxide, in which case the sulfur dioxide is the substance oxidized and the reducing agent, $SO_2 + [O] \longrightarrow SO_3$. Oxygen, ozone, or other oxidizing agents can carry out this conversion that is important in some smog mechanisms as shall be seen in Part Four.

Oxidation of Organic Compounds

The concept of oxidation extends to organic molecules as well. In this case oxygen combines with various hydrocarbons; although the concept of oxidation number is not easily applied to organic molecules, the basic principle is still the same. The oxidizing agent enters the reaction to gain electrons or at least to gain a share in those electrons from the substance oxidized. This explains why the oxidizing agent usually joins an organic molecule at a region of high electron density, such as at the double bond of a hydrocarbon.

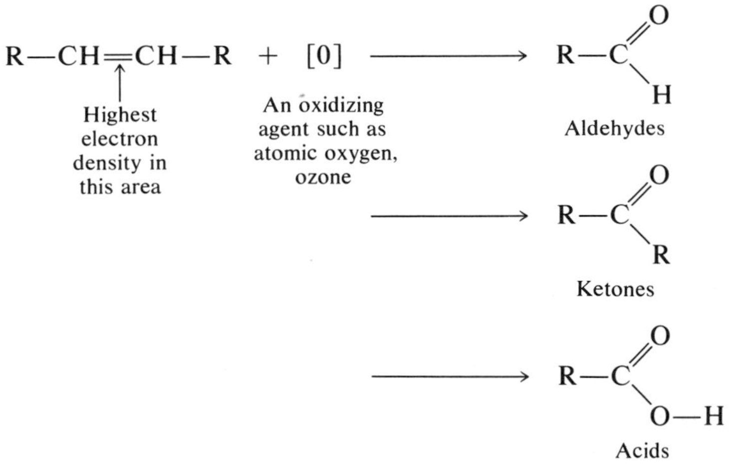

$$R-CH=CH-R \; + \; [0] \; \longrightarrow \; R-C{\overset{\displaystyle O}{\diagdown_H}}$$

Highest electron density in this area

An oxidizing agent such as atomic oxygen, ozone

Aldehydes

$$\longrightarrow \; R-C{\overset{\displaystyle O}{\diagdown_R}}$$

Ketones

$$\longrightarrow \; R-C{\overset{\displaystyle O}{\diagdown_{O-H}}}$$

Acids

Note that aldehydes, ketones, and acids are common pollutants of the atmosphere as shown in Table 2.

"Oxidant" is a general term used to describe oxidizing agents. It includes not only the expected molecules such as O_2, O_3 and [O] (atomic oxygen), but also includes organic molecules capable of gaining electrons such as the peroxide radical[2] ($R—O\cdot$) as well as such inorganic substances as Cl_2 which have a high tendency to attract electrons to themselves. In Part Four we will see that measuring oxidants is a good way to monitor air pollution.

Energy from Oxidation

The most useful form of oxidation is rapid oxidation in which the fuel is oxidized quickly in order to liberate heat. This process is referred to as combustion or burning. It is carried out in power plants where coal, natural gas, or fuel oil may be burned and the heat used to create steam used in generating electricity. The same process is carried out in the internal combustion engine where the petroleum product gasoline is burned, causing hot gaseous products that expand, giving mechanical energy to the pistons. The basic source of the heat energy is the capacity of these carbon-containing fuels to form stable chemical bonds with oxygen, releasing energy.

Carbon combines with excess oxygen to produce CO_2, carbon dioxide. If only limited amounts of oxygen are present or the combustion temperature is low, carbon monoxide is produced. Energy is released in the formation of stable carbon-to-oxygen bonds.

$$C + O_2 \longrightarrow CO_2 + 94 \text{ kcal of heat per mole}$$
$$\text{of } CO_2 \text{ produced at}$$
$$\text{standard conditions}$$

The actual heat value of a fuel depends on the percentage of carbon present in the fuel, as can be seen from examining the heat content of various coals given in Table 4.

Energy from Hydrocarbons

Many fuels do not contain elemental carbon but rather chemically combined carbon. Particularly important are those fuels containing hydrocarbons, which, as the name implies, are compounds containing hydrogen and carbon. An amazing variety of different combinations of these two elements are found in petroleum and its byproducts.

If a hydrocarbon is burned, the products will include water as well as carbon dioxide. For the general case:

$$C_xH_y + O_2 \longrightarrow CO_2 + H_2O + \text{heat energy}$$

---

[2]An organic peroxide has general structure $R—O—O—R'$ and is unstable, breaking apart into two free radicals ($R—O\cdot$ and $R'—O\cdot$). Each has an unpaired electron; they are very reactive species.

Table 4. Composition and Heat Values for Different Types of Coals

	Lignite (brown coal)	Bituminous (soft coal)	Anthracite (hard coal)
% Carbon (by weight)	60–70%	75–90%	85–93%
% Hydrogen (by weight)	6	4–6	2–4
Volatile matter	20–28	14–26	3–5
Water	6–20	2–12	2–7
Ash	7–10	4–8	5–10
Heat value (kcal/g of coal)	3.6	7.2	7.4

Fuel combustion to create electric power is another major source of air pollution. This fossil-fueled power plant is on Monterey Bay at Moss Point, California.

Figure 2. Fractional Distillation of Petroleum

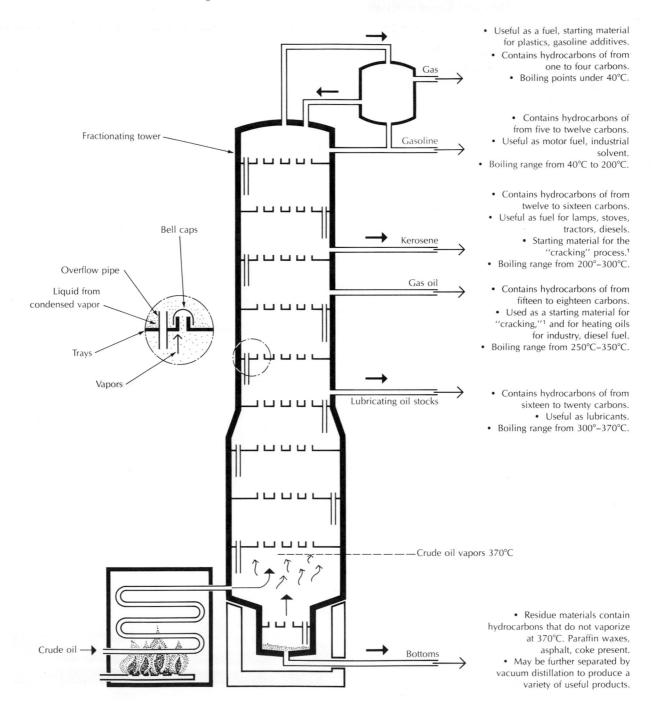

Useful as a fuel, starting material for plastics, gasoline additives.
- Contains hydrocarbons of from one to four carbons.
- Boiling points under 40°C.

- Contains hydrocarbons of from five to twelve carbons.
- Useful as motor fuel, industrial solvent.
- Boiling range from 40°C to 200°C.

- Contains hydrocarbons of from twelve to sixteen carbons.
- Useful as fuel for lamps, stoves, tractors, diesels.
- Starting material for the "cracking" process.[1]
- Boiling range from 200°–300°C.

- Contains hydrocarbons of from fifteen to eighteen carbons.
- Used as a starting material for "cracking,"[1] and for heating oils for industry, diesel fuel.
- Boiling range from 250°C–350°C.

- Contains hydrocarbons of from sixteen to twenty carbons.
- Useful as lubricants.
- Boiling range from 300°–370°C.

- Residue materials contain hydrocarbons that do not vaporize at 370°C. Paraffin waxes, asphalt, coke present.
- May be further separated by vacuum distillation to produce a variety of useful products.

Again, if limited oxygen or low combustion temperatures are used, carbon monoxide or even free carbon may be a part of the resulting gases. Unburned hydrocarbons may also be released to the atmosphere in any burning process. Here the heat energy produced by the total reaction can be thought of as the difference between the energy given off by the stable products and the energy necessary to decompose the hydrocarbon. Some energy is required in each case to start the reaction. The energy may be supplied from a match or from a set of spark plugs, but the return in energy for combustion reactions is well worth the initial energy investment. (Of course, for an equal weight of fuel, the energy derived from combustion does not come close to the amount released in a nuclear reaction.) Sample heats of combustion for various hydrocarbons are given in Table 5.

Hydrocarbons from Petroleum

The tremendous mixture of hydrocarbons found in petroleum presents an interesting chemical challenge, for it is necessary to separate the components so that they may be useful in different applications. Fortunately, the hydrocarbon components differ widely in their boiling points. This property is used in separating them by means of fractional distillation. This process is illustrated in Figure 2.

The crude petroleum oil mixture is heated to 700°F as it enters the fractionating tower. This causes a large percentage of the material to

Table 5. Heats of Combustion for Various Hydrocarbons
(all heats measured at standard conditions)

Comments	Name	Formula	kcal/mole	kcal/gram
Gaseous hydrocarbons Natural gas is mainly methane and ethane. "Bottled" gas is usually liquefied propane and butane.	Methane	CH_4	210.8	13.2
	Ethane	C_2H_6	368.4	12.3
	Propane	C_3H_8	526.3	12.0
	Butane	C_4H_{10}	683.4	11.8
	Pentane	C_5H_{12}	838.3	11.6
	Acetylene	C_2H_2	312.0	12.0
Liquid hydrocarbons Gasoline for automobiles usually contains hydrocarbons from C_6 to C_{10}.	Benzene	C_6H_6	782.3	10.0
	Hexane	C_6H_{14}	989.8	11.5
	Octane	C_8H_{18}	1302.7	11.4
	Isooctane	C_8H_{18}	1303.9	11.4
	Decane	$C_{10}H_{22}$	1610.2	10.3

vaporize, and the vapors rise in the tower. The heavier fractions with higher boiling points soon condense on distillation trays and are removed. The lighter materials of lower boiling point remain as vapors until they reach the higher and cooler trays, where they are withdrawn. Any un-condensed gaseous material is trapped and recycled into the top fraction from the tower. Some materials never vaporize and form tarry residues on the bottom of the tower; this is a rich source of trace organic materials useful for medical and other purposes. The end result has been to separate the mixture into several usable fractions.

The process of fractional distillation finds many applications in chemistry; for example, pure oxygen can be produced by the fractional distillation of liquefied air since the major components of air have quite different boiling points. Simple distillation is important in removing the salt from seawater.

In a cracking process, the heavier low-grade fractions are converted into gasolines by the use of catalysts. The heavy fractions are heated and pressure applied in the absence of air but in the presence of a catalyst such as alumina, nickel, rhenium, sulfuric acid, platinum, or palladium. This succeeds in breaking apart oils into the lighter, higher-value products more useful as fuels. Standard Oil's Isomax unit shown here can crack 60,000 barrels of heavy gas oils per day. *(Standard Oil Company of California)*

Since coal and petroleum are the fossilized remains of plants and animals, they are referred to as *fossil fuels*. Our present coal and petroleum deposits are thought to have had their origins 250–300 million years ago when large areas were covered with lush plant growth and ancient seas covered a larger percentage of the land masses. Large quantities of tree leaves, roots, twigs, and ferns present in swampy regions were covered by sediments and subjected to increasing temperature and pressure across millions of years; this resulted in a conversion from spongy, partially decomposed organic masses to peat and lignite to bituminous and finally hard, or an anthracite coal. Since the origin of coal was originally plant life, carbon is the main ingredient but small amounts of other substances are also present, including water, nitrogen and oxygen compounds, inorganic minerals and, most bothersome in terms of current environmental impact, sulfur. Petroleum also has this sulfur content, having been formed in a similar manner. The difference is that since petroleum deposits are found only in beds of ancient seas, it is generally accepted that the primary materials here were microscopic marine plant life which settled together with clay and sand. Time and pressure caused the material to form the complex mixture of hydrocarbons that make up petroleum. The petroleum may be trapped with a pocket of natural gas above it in an identifiable geologic structure. Since the natural gas does not have the sulfur content of either petroleum or coal, it is a preferred fuel.

Part Three: WHAT'S IT LIKE?

In Part Two we saw that the processes of complete and incomplete combustion account for a large share of the pollutants we put in our airspace. Some of these products are relatively harmless, at least in the short run. Other products pose a direct threat to all who breathe them in large enough concentrations. In this section the chemical properties and effects of the pollutants will be discussed, starting with the most prevalent pollutants in terms of tons emitted.

Oxides of Carbon

There are two common oxides of carbon; these are carbon monoxide and carbon dioxide. Their properties are compared in Table 6.

Carbon Monoxide. The simplest oxide of carbon, carbon monoxide, is generated in urban areas mainly by the automobile. Transportation may account for over 90 percent by weight of all carbon monoxide in the air in large cities, especially if little heavy industry is present. The remaining carbon monoxide in urban areas is produced by industries, power plants, and from solid waste disposal. On a global scale, the great majority (80 percent) of the carbon monoxide in the atmosphere comes from oxidation of the methane emitted by decaying organic matter. Hydroxyl radicals (OH^-) accomplish this natural oxidation process. Natural sources of carbon monoxide also include releases from the oceans which contain the dissolved gas.

Hydroxyl radicals also serve to oxidize CO to CO_2, serving as a mechanism for removal of CO from the troposphere. Biological action in soils may also be an important factor in removing carbon monoxide. Direct oxidation to CO_2 by oxygen is not a significant removal mechanism except possibly in the stratosphere.

Health Effects of CO. Carbon monoxide has a unique mechanism of action, which differs from other common air pollutants. Unlike most gaseous pollutants, which irritate the respiratory tract, CO passes through the lungs directly into the blood stream. The toxic effects are caused by the affinity of the hemoglobin in the blood for the CO molecule. The normal function of the hemoglobin is to carry oxygen from the lungs to

Table 6. Properties of the Oxides of Carbon

Formula	Name	Melting point	Boiling point	Physical properties	Comments	Relevance to air pollution
CO	Carbon monoxide	−199°C	−191.5°C	• Colorless • Odorless • Density = 1.25 g/l as a gas	• Important industrial reducing agent	• Formed by incomplete combustion • Poisonous gas
CO_2	Carbon dioxide		−78.5°C[a]	• Colorless, • Odorless • d = 1.98 g/l as a gas • d = 1.56 g/ml as a solid (dry ice)	• Somewhat soluble in water − 1.45 g/l at 25°C	• Formed by complete combustion • Possible climatic effects

[a]This is the temperature at which carbon dioxide changes directly from the solid state to a gaseous state at normal atmospheric pressures. This type of change in state is known as sublimation.

body tissue. CO binds very strongly to the hemoglobin and therefore prevents the hemoglobin from carrying O_2, its normal function. Carbon monoxide is not known to have any effect on plants.

The symptoms of CO poisoning given in Figure 3 are primarily symptoms of oxygen deprivation; in addition, the person may have a flushed appearance. Hemoglobin rapidly regains its ability to carry oxygen if the person gets to fresh air and has artificial respiration if needed. Carbon monoxide poisoning is therefore reversible in all but the most serious cases. If the victim has been deprived of enough oxygen, he may

Figure 3. Effects of Carbon Monoxide on Humans

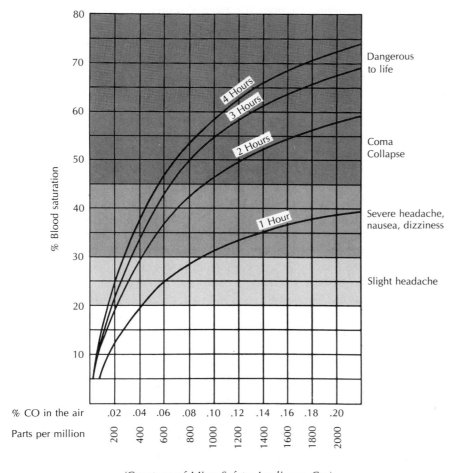

(Courtesy of Mine Safety Appliance Co.)

take on a blue appearance; there is usually permanent damage at this point. Since the heart and brain are most sensitive to oxygen deprivation, they show the most serious effects of carbon monoxide poisoning. (Current research indicates that chances of recovering from a coronary are less favored if any hemoglobin—CO bonds exist.) Note in Figure 3 that the extent of the physiological effect depends on the length of the exposure as well as in the concentration of CO in the air. Those factors, along with depth of respiration, general physical condition, and total body weight, help determine the actual percent blood saturation with CO.[3]

Five to thirty ppm CO in the atmosphere is usually suggested as a reasonable limit for continuous exposure for the general population, although higher concentrations can be tolerated for short periods of time without apparent adverse effects. The new federal standards are 9.0 ppm for an eight-hour average, 35 ppm for a one-hour time period. Despite those limits, 25 ppm for twelve hours has been observed in Los Angeles, and it is felt that it may be impossible to reach the standard unless new and stringent rules are enacted to limit the use of the internal combustion engine. The 1968 model cars are required to put out no more than 1.5 percent CO (15,000 ppm); recommended limits for 1975, as put forth by the California Air Resources Board, suggest 0.55 percent or 5,500 ppm as the limit. Comparing those concentrations with Figure 3, it is easy to understand how congested traffic can lead to a headache in more ways than one.

Carbon Dioxide. Carbon dioxide is formed by oxidation and combustion processes, both natural and man-caused. CO_2 is also produced from the conversion of CO due to hydroxyl radicals, as noted earlier. Unlike carbon monoxide, carbon dioxide is not itself toxic. Therefore, from our present perspective, it seems to rank as one of the least important pollutants. From a long-term viewpoint, CO_2 could turn out to be quite significant. Carbon dioxide is a necessary component for the life cycles of plants (and therefore is essential to animals) as it is used in this photosynthesis reaction.

$$CO_2(gas) + H_2O \xrightarrow{\text{sunlight}} \text{carbohydrates} + O_2(gas)$$

The CO_2 utilized in this process, as well as the CO_2 released as a by-product of respiration in man are both important parts of the over-all carbon-carbon dioxide cycle (see Figure 4).

---

[3]Cigarette smoke contains 200 to 400 ppm CO. It has been estimated that 5 to 15 percent of a smoker's hemoglobin is bound with CO when smoking. Even this magnitude of oxygen deprivation is thought by some researchers to affect the person's time and visual perception.

Figure 4. Carbon-Carbon Dioxide Cycle

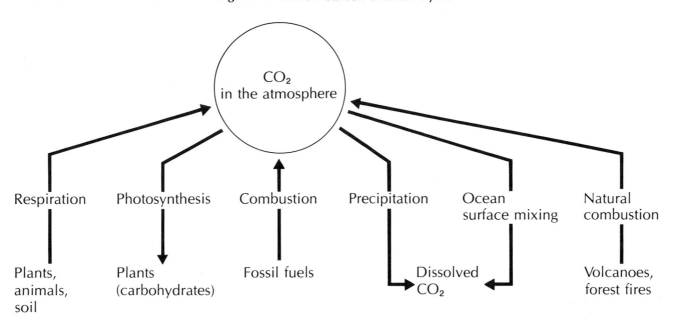

The balance between atmospheric and dissolved CO_2 is typical of many natural cycles; an equilibrium is established that depends on the concentration present as well as the time available for mixing. For example, the dissolved CO_2 reacts with H_2O to form carbonic acid, H_2CO_3.[4] Carbonic acid is a weak acid—that is, it only partially ionizes. This interlocking set of reactions can be shown in this way:

$$CO_2 + H_2O \rightleftharpoons H_2CO_3 \rightleftharpoons H^+ + HCO_3^- \rightleftharpoons 2H^+ + CO_3^{-2}$$

These reactions are all reversible; the extent and direction of the reaction depend on local conditions. If there were a local atmospheric depletion of CO_2, the oceans could release some CO_2 to reestablish the concentration in the air; in turn, such a release would change the concentration of H_2CO_3 in the water, setting off a chain of compensating reactions for the other chemical species involved in the equilibrium. Adding atmospheric CO_2 should increase H_2CO_3 and therefore HCO_3^- and CO_3^{-2} concentrations. However, the time factor becomes important here. As we noted earlier, with changes in conditions, changes in equilibrium do occur, but they do not happen instantaneously. Particularly if reactions

---

[4] In general, any oxide of a nonmetal that dissolves in water to form an acid such that the oxide and acid both contain the element (carbon in this case) in the same oxidation state is said to be an acid anhydride.

in deep waters are involved, the time for assimilation of excess CO_2 may be very long indeed, on the order of thousands of years. This entire scheme is not well understood at the present time.

Environmental Effects of CO_2. It has been estimated that the huge amount of carbon dioxide now released into the atmosphere each year due to combustion of fossil fuels would amount to an increase of 2.3 ppm per year if no removal mechanisms were at work. Since the total increases actually observed account for approximately one third that amount, it must be assumed that the rest of the CO_2 has been taken up by the oceans or has increased plant growth. One example of the increasing carbon dioxide content of the atmosphere is shown in Figure 5. It is estimated that the concentration of CO_2 will reach 375 ppm by the turn of the century as compared with 310 ppm in 1950 and 292 ppm in 1860.

The increase in CO_2 atmospheric content has far-reaching implications as to whether or not a system can reestablish a new equilibrium concentration over a long period of time. This point may be purely academic, for the increase is of immediate concern due to the "greenhouse effect." The glass roof of a greenhouse allows shortwave light energy to pass through to the inside but does not allow heat energy to escape to the outside, which keeps the internal temperature higher than the external temperature. You probably have noted this phenomena if you return to your closed car on a warm day—your window glass has the same ability to trap heat. Carbon dioxide in our atmosphere has a similar effect—the CO_2 molecules absorb heat energy and prevent its

Figure 5. Increase in Carbon Dioxide Content

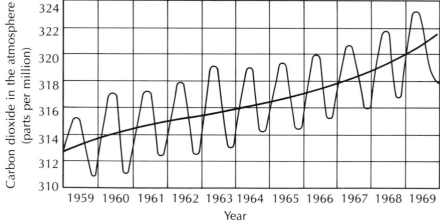

Both seasonal variations and the long-term trend in the carbon dioxide content of the atmosphere are shown. Data were taken at the Mauna Loa Observatory, Hawaii. *(From "The Carbon Cycle" by Bert Bolin. Copyright © September 1970 by Scientific American, Inc. All rights reserved.)*

passage into space from the lower atmosphere. The result of increasing carbon dioxide content could therefore be an increase in the earth's mean temperature with far-reaching effects on ocean levels due to melting of ice caps. In addition, there would be changes in every natural cycle dependent upon temperature. A less drastic and opposing result could be increased evaporation of the oceans, which would lead to more clouds and cooling of the atmosphere due to increased reflection of the sun's rays.

From 1880 to 1940, the average temperature of the world rose by 0.5°C. The carbon dioxide content rose approximately 11 percent during that same time period. However, since 1940, despite increasing carbon dioxide, the temperature has been declining slowly, now down about 0.3°C altogether. This reverse trend can be attributed to the increased clouds as noted above or to increased particulate matter which scatters incoming sunlight. Is this a case of two environmental wrongs accidentally producing an environmental right? The fluctuations in temperature may also be due to some natural cycle that we do not understand well enough to predict.

Oxides of Sulfur

Sulfur, in its many forms, has long been recognized as an important contributor to air pollution. This is particularly true in industrialized

Table 7. Properties of the Oxides of Sulfur

Name	Formula	Oxidation state of sulfur	Boiling point	Comments	Relevance to air pollution
Sulfur dioxide	SO_2	+4	−10°C	• Colorless gas, suffocating odor • Density = 2.93 g/l • Solubility in water = 22.8 g/100 ml • Combines with water to form sulfurous acid, H_2SO_3	• First product of combustion; accounts for 95% of man's emissions of sulfur to the atmosphere • Changes slowly to SO_3 • If dissolved, oxidizes slowly to SO_4^{-2}
Sulfur trioxide	SO_3	+6	44.8°C	• Soluble in cold and hot water • Combines with water to form sulfuric acid, H_2SO_4	• Sulfuric acid may be present as an aerosol in air; reacts to form sulfate aerosols

areas, for man has overwhelmed the considerable ability of nature to put sulfur compounds into the atmosphere. Again, the principal man-made compounds of sulfur are the oxides resulting from burning fossil fuels. The properties of the two oxides, SO_2 and SO_3, are given in Table 7.

Oxidation of Sulfur: Two Steps. When any fuel containing sulfur burns, the original product is SO_2, sulfur dioxide. Slowly, if no catalyst is present, the SO_2 is converted to SO_3.

$$S + O_2 \longrightarrow SO_2$$

$$SO_2 + [O] \longrightarrow SO_3$$

The mechanism by which the SO_2 is converted to SO_3 depends on the surrounding atmosphere. The conversion may be due to oxygen, ozone, or the presence of a hydrocarbon free radical. Some researchers feel the transition is due to the presence of NO, according to this series of reactions.

$$NO + O_2 \longrightarrow [NO_3] \quad \begin{cases} + SO_2 \longrightarrow SO_3 + NO_2 & \text{(predominates at low concentrations of NO)} \\ + NO \longrightarrow 2\,NO_2 & \text{(predominates at high concentrations of NO)} \end{cases}$$

If this reaction scheme is shown to be a major conversion, the presence of sulfur dioxide will be one cause of increasing NO_2 concentrations, an important compound in smog formation.

The conversion of SO_2 to SO_3 apparently can be catalyzed also by materials present in fly ash, such as the oxides of iron and manganese. In the commercial production of sulfuric acid, vanadium pentoxide, V_2O_5, is used for changing SO_2 to SO_3. The SO_3 is then converted to sulfuric acid by simply dissolving it in water.

Other Sulfur Compounds in the Environment. In addition to the oxide forms, sulfur is often found in the atmosphere as H_2S (hydrogen sulfide) and in the mercaptan form, for example, methyl mercaptan, CH_3SH. These compounds are added both naturally and by man's activities. Even very small amounts of the sulfides or mercaptans are offensive for their odors; H_2S is the agent responsible for the odor of rotten eggs and butyl mercaptan (C_4H_9SH) is a component of skunk secretion. Pentyl mercaptan ($C_5H_{11}SH$) is added in small quantities to natural gas so that the odor of leaking gas might be more easily detected. These compounds and the oxide forms are part of a complex cycle similar to the carbon-carbon oxides system shown earlier. The distribution of sulfur in our environment is shown in Figure 6.

Figure 6. The Sulfur-Sulfur Oxides Cycle

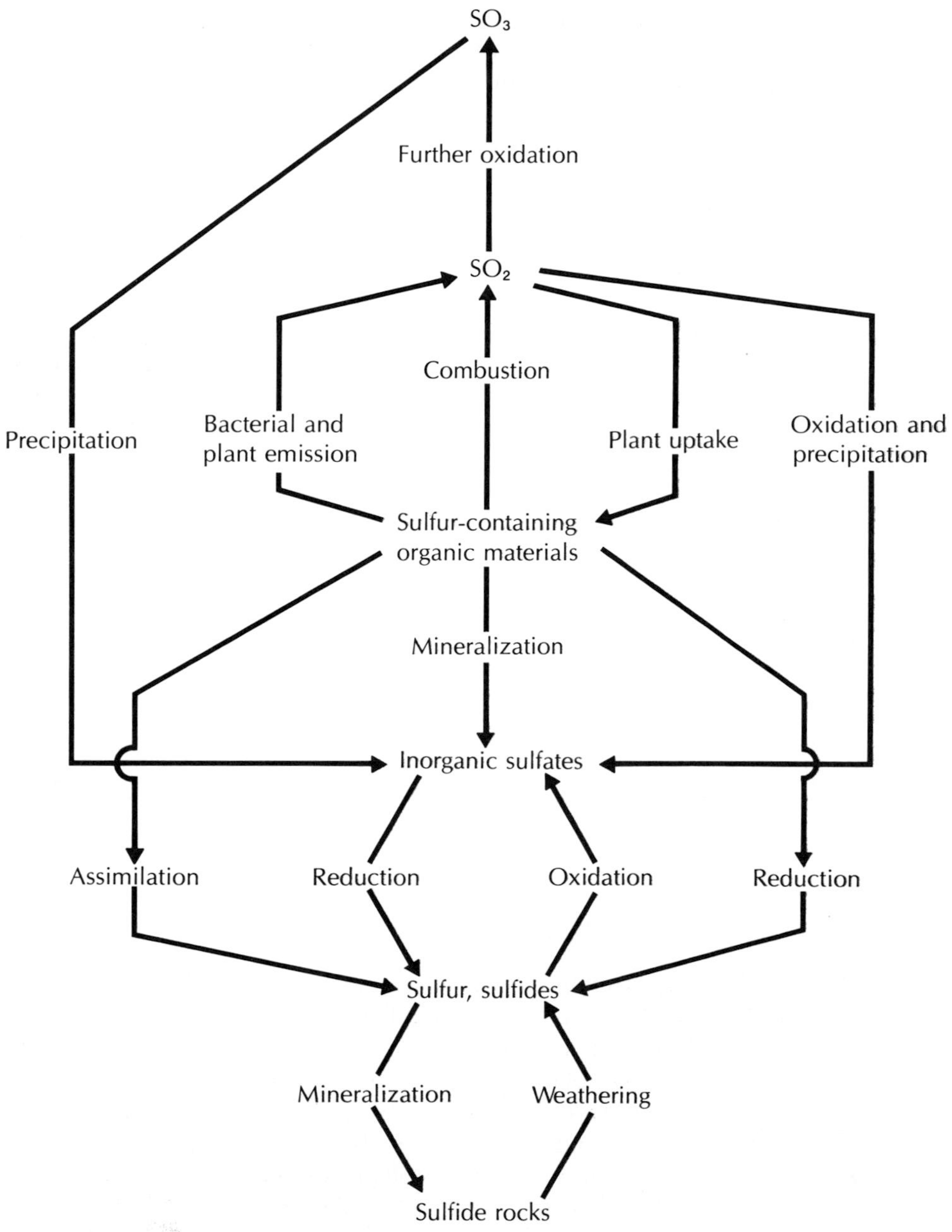

Environmental Effects of Sulfur Oxides. Sulfur oxides in the atmosphere have far-reaching effects on vegetation, materials, and man. The damage caused by sulfur dioxide on vegetation is well documented and shows up in many areas of the country. Leaves of affected plants show a splotchy bleaching pattern; in some plants the spots take on a reddish-brown color. Apple and pear trees are particularly susceptible and show damage even after a six-hour exposure at 0.5 ppm. Ponderosa pine, alfalfa, and barley are also sensitive species.

In some cases, the damage is due to the fact that in the atmosphere, SO_2 dissolves to form H_2SO_3 (sulfurous acid) while SO_3 dissolves to form an aerosol haze of H_2SO_4 (sulfuric acid). These suspended acids will wash down during the first rain. The use of sulfur-containing fuels may therefore lead to some rather unpleasant effects due to the acidity of the rain.

Rain would be expected to be slightly acid (5.7) due to water's reaction with CO_2 to form the weak acid H_2CO_3. However, measurements in Europe showed a change in rain's acidity from a pH of 5.0 in 1958 to a pH of 4.0 in 1966. At the same time, similar changes in pH occurred in lakes and rivers, and the evidence strongly suggests the oxides of sulfur to be a cause. Similar studies in this country found pH readings of 3 to 5 in most rain samples and positive identification of both sulfuric and nitric acids.

The pH scale is a set of values defined in order to measure the acidity or alkalinity of a solution. (The letters literally represent the French expression "pouvoir hydrogene" or hydrogen power; power is used here in its mathematical meaning of exponent.) The scale is based on the concentrations of hydrogen ion in pure water at 25°C.

$$\text{concentration } H^+ = 1.0 \times 10^{-7} \text{ moles/liter}$$

$$pH = -\log [H^+] = -\log [1.0 \times 10^{-7}]$$

$$pH = 7$$

Seven is therefore taken as the value for neutrality; any solution containing more hydrogen ions per liter than water will be an acid and will have a pH lower than 7; any solution containing fewer hydrogen ions will have a higher pH than 7 and thus the higher numbers represent the alkaline (excess of hydroxide ions, OH^-) part of the scale.

Controlling pH is important in many chemical preparations, industrial procedures, and biological systems. Blood, for example, normally has a pH of between 7.4 to 7.5; if the pH falls below this range of values, a condition known as acidosis results and treatment must restore the normal pH values. Soils range in pH from 3 to 9 but crops usually will grow only in soil with pH between 6 and 7. Other common pH values are:

Gastric juices	pH = 2
Lemon juice	2.3
Vinegar	2.8
Carbonated water	3
Tomatoes	4.0–4.5
Urine	5–7
Plant tissue	5.2
Milk	6.5–7.0
Seawater	8.5–10.0

This acid precipitation can corrode metals, attack nylons and other fabrics, and can have even more severe effects on plant life. Corroding rainfall can also cause severe deterioration of structural materials, a problem that has become severe in some areas as building facades and statues corrode away. Limestone and marble, both forms of calcium carbonate, are particularly susceptible. The following reaction is one that occurs.

$$CaCO_3 + H_2SO_4 \longrightarrow H_2O + CO_2 \uparrow + CaSO_4$$

Many priceless works of art and architecture have suffered more damage in the last 20 years than in the previous 200 years as the result of increased sulfur dioxide content in the atmosphere. Many large Italian cities have been particularly bothered by this aspect of air pollution but it is not just a European problem. The marble in the Lincoln Memorial in Washington D.C. is deteriorating due to acid attack; one official compared the Memorial in the rain to a giant Alka-Seltzer tablet.

Respiratory Effects. Sulfur dioxide's effect on man is the result of irritation by the gas itself and the products formed in the atmosphere. More than 95 percent of inhaled high concentrations of SO_2 is absorbed in the upper part of the respiratory system; this percentage falls to 50 percent at low concentrations such as 0.1 ppm. The SO_2 acts as an irritant and is known to increase symptoms for patients with bronchitis, emphysema, and other lung diseases. The established relationship between concentrations of SO_2 and respiratory symptoms has caused the World Health Organization to rate sulfur dioxide as the most dangerous pollutant.

Part of the danger of sulfur dioxide stems from the changes it undergoes in the atmosphere. Since it can end up as sulfuric acid aerosol, the final product may be particulate matter such as $(NH_4)_2SO_4$, ammonium sulfate which can result in the air from a reaction between sulfuric acid and ammonia. These particles can be carried deep into the lungs and lodge there, causing even more severe health problems. This is an example of a synergistic effect; the total effect of the two causes (in this case sulfur dioxide and particulates) is greater than the effect that would be caused by each factor separately. Since many sources produce both types of pollutants, the synergism is a particularly worrisome problem. Many of the recorded severe air pollutions episodes (intervals of limited duration when levels of air pollutants were very high due to lack of air circulation) involved the presence of both sulfur oxides and particles. During the 1952 London episode SO_2 levels were recorded at 1.34 ppm maximum and particulates at 4.5 mg/m³. It was estimated that 4000 human deaths occurred as a result of the polluted air which remained stagnant for five days. Most of the deaths were in the very old or very young age groups.

Federal standards for sulfur oxides are 0.14 ppm for twenty-four hours and 0.03 ppm annually. California standards for sulfur oxides are presently 0.04 ppm for a twenty-four hour average and 0.50 ppm for a one-hour average. Concentrations of 0.12 ppm for twenty-four hours and 0.80 ppm for one hour have been recorded in Los Angeles. Exceeding the standard for SO_x is a common occurrence in many cities; strict control of the sulfur content of fuels will be vital to lowering the threat to life and property.

Reducing Emissions from Fuel Combustion. Since such a large part of the sulfur oxides in the atmosphere results from the combustion of fuels, much attention has been focused on finding and using low sulfur fuels. "Low sulfur fuels" usually implies a sulfur content of less than 1 percent; natural gas with no sulfur content and fuel oil with an average sulfur content of 0.76 percent are most desirable from this standpoint but are increasingly difficult to obtain in sufficient quantities. Residual fuel oil, or those fractions left behind when the components with lower boiling points are removed, tends to concentrate the sulfur content and therefore averages above 1 percent. This is still well below the usual sulfur content in coals. Supplies of low sulfur coal are substantial but geographically difficult to obtain. For domestic coal, the sulfur content can be in the 6 to 8 percent range; 20 to 60 percent of the sulfur in that coal is in the form of iron pyrite, FeS_2, a form that is relatively easy to remove by physical means. Pulverizing and washing coal, including deep washing procedures, results in coal of less than 2 percent sulfur. Other methods have been tried, but for the immediate future, methods of controlling SO_2 in the stack gas will continue to be important if coal is burned.

The limestone-dolomite process has received considerable attention in this country as a promising means of removing sulfur oxides from stack gas. The pulverized carbonate mineral is heated in the boiler, a process which drives off carbon dioxide and forms the corresponding oxide. Sulfur oxides react with the mineral oxide to form solid particles of sulfites or sulfates which are then removed along with other particulate matter. The over-all reaction is

$$2\ CaCO_3 + 2\ SO_2 + O_2 \longrightarrow 2\ CaSO_4 + 2\ CO_2.$$

An alternative is to combine the process with a conventional wet scrubber which will dissolve unreacted sulfur oxides and complete their reaction with the calcium or magnesium oxides. This combination of processes has succeeded in removing up to 95 percent of sulfur dioxide in a pilot-scale system. Figure 7 shows the over-all process.

Figure 7. The Limestone-Dolomite Wet Process

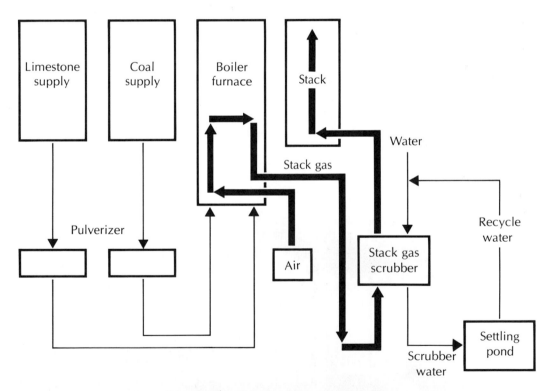

Source: Cleaning Our Environment, p. 69.

Other promising methods for removing sulfur oxides from stack gases include catalytic conversion to SO_3, followed by absorption into water to give sulfuric acid, and adsorption by spheres of Al_2O_3 and Na_2O, followed by reduction to give free sulfur. In each case, a marketable commodity would be produced as a byproduct of the antipollution measure. Hopefully this economic incentive would make fighting SO_x pollution profitable.

Hydrocarbons

Nature puts about 85 percent of all hydrocarbons into the air on a global basis, but man-made sources nevertheless account for the largest amount in urban areas. Forests and vegetation emit various hydrocarbons in their normal biological processes; bacterial decomposition of organic matter produces principally methane gas. Man enters the hydrocarbon picture by incinerating, by allowing industrial solvents to evaporate, and by carrying out incomplete combustion of coal, oil, and wood. The largest source of airborne hydrocarbons, however, is the entire cycle consisting of processing and using petroleum.

Particularly significant, for the amount of hydrocarbons emitted in each step, is the production and use of gasoline. Not only do hydrocarbons come out the tailpipe as partially or totally unoxidized materials, but losses also occur by evaporation from the fuel tank and carburetor. Previously hydrocarbons from crankcase "blowby" were a problem, but since 1968, these emissions have been totally eliminated by employing a positive crankcase ventilation (PCV) system which recycles hydrocarbons back to the engine intake.

Environmental Effects of Hydrocarbons. The wide variety of hydrocarbons emitted makes it difficult to generalize about their effects. Reactive hydrocarbons play an important role in smog formation (Part Four). Certain of the hydrocarbons have been implicated in health problems, such as the evidence that links benzo–[a]–pyrene with cancer. Other aromatic hydrocarbons are similarly suspect, and their use as gasoline additives has been questioned. We will return to the use of hydrocarbons again in Part Five where octane ratings and gasoline additives will be discussed. Since standards for hydrocarbons are usually covered by total oxidant standards, they will be given in Part Four after the reactions of photochemical smog have been discussed.

The air quality in the vicinity of an industrial process can be severely deteriorated by the presence of some types of industry. Here for example are a pulp and paper operation in Canton, North Carolina; a carbon black plant in Odessa, Texas; a copper smelter in Miami, Arizona; and a chemical producer near Wilmington, Delaware. Photos are labeled clockwise from top left.

Particulates

Particulate matter is an enormously complex category of solids and liquids found in our airspace. Natural emissions occur as dry soil is blown by the wind, pollen is airborne, or volcanic eruptions occur. Man-made particulate pollution comes from industrial operations involving grinding and spraying, fly ash produced in combustion processes, and once again from the automobile.

Reducing Particulate Emissions. Control of industrial particulate pollution was one of the first areas to receive technical attention due to the obvious visible nature of the pollutants. Therefore, many processes

Table 8. Particulate Control Devices

Type of device	Force or mechanism responsible for separation	Minimum particle size (microns) for 90% efficiency	Comments
Settling chamber	Gravity	~50	•Low installation and maintenance costs
Cyclone collector	Centrifugal; impact separation	>5–25	•Gas is given a spiraling motion by directing it through a series of baffles; centrifugal force spins particles to outside of gas stream; particles hit sides, fall to bottom.
Scrubber	Impact separation; direct interception; centrifugal in some models	<1 for Venturi-type scrubber; 5 for most; 25 for simple spray tower	•Provides finely divided water droplets in which particulates can be absorbed or simply knocked out of the main gas flow; Venturi model also spins to provide centrifugal force.
Filter	Impact separation; direct interception; diffusion or electro-static in some models	<1–10 (as low as 0.01 for cellulose acetate membrane filters)	•Fabric directly intercepts particulates. •Can use cotton, wool, orlon, silicon-coated cloth, polyesters. •Operating temperatures help to determine choice of fabric.
Electrostatic precipitator	Electrostatic	<1–10	•Smoke passes through a strong electric field; particles given an electrical charge; then attracted to collecting surfaces of opposite charge. Dust is then removed mechanically from the surface.

exist today for removing particulate matter. The characteristics of the particles to be removed, including their size and density, have to be considered along with the nature and operational characteristics of the carrier gas in order to pick the best process for any application. Other process and economic decisions enter into the final choice. Some of the available types of equipment are given in Table 8. Of course, a combination of devices may prove to be the best answer for cleaning stack gas. For example, a settling chamber may be used as a precleaner before using more efficient cleaning devices.

New work in removing particulates includes the use of sonic waves to cause the material to form larger particles which settle. Ideally, particulates are removed by altering the process so that no solids or liquid aerosols are produced, but clearly that is not always desirable or economical. In some cases, the main emphasis for particulate removal is not the resulting improvement in air quality but rather the economic value of materials present in the fly ash. Of course, there is no reason why the two goals of air pollution control and economic gain cannot be pursued simultaneously.

Metallic Particulates in the Atmosphere. Of all types of particulates in our air, the presence of trace metals known to be toxic may constitute the greatest health hazard. Metals account for only 0.01 to 3.0 percent of all particulate air pollution, but their significance may be far greater due to accumulation and possible synergistic effects in human tissue. In addition, inhalation of metals often has been shown to produce a greater effect than receiving the same doses by way of the food we eat or the water we drink, so it is particularly important to evaluate the sources of airborne metals.

Of all the toxic metals found in the atmosphere, the one present in largest concentration is lead. Since most atmospheric lead comes from burning gasoline where it is present as the additive tetraethyl lead, a consideration of its properties will be deferred to Part Five. The other metals forming part of the atmospheric pollution problem come from the burning of fossil fuels, industrial processes, or the incineration of products containing those metals.

Toxic and Widespread Metals. At the present time four metals are considered to represent known and widespread hazards to human health: lead, cadmium, nickel, and mercury. Cadmium, for example, is implicated in causing cardiovascular disease and hypertension. In addition, it interferes with proper zinc and copper metabolism. Most of the airborne cadmium results from the disposal and incineration of cadmium-containing products, including such things as rubber tires and some types of plastic containers. Cadmium also enters the air as a byproduct from the refining of other metals, principally zinc. In fact, concentrations of zinc and cadmium show a correlation in several urban and nonurban areas tested. (Zinc is not considered to be toxic itself; it is essential to human health.) The range of concentrations for cadmium is from 0.004 $\mu g/m^3$ to 0.026 $\mu g/m^3$. Much of the released cadmium could be prevented from entering the atmosphere and recycled if efficient systems were employed in metal processing operations as well as in municipal incinerators.

Nickel concentrations range widely, in some cases showing as much as a hundredfold difference in the same area. Over-all, concentrations range from 0.0006 to 0.012 $\mu g/m^3$. The nickel is thought to be present as nickel carbonyl, NiCO, which is formed when finely divided nickel is emitted into an atmosphere containing carbon monoxide. These conditions are met in the combustion of coal, diesel fuel, and residual oils, as well as in nickel refineries and in industrial processes such as the manufacture of stainless steel. NiCO is also formed in tobacco smoke. Future sources may include the automobile if nickel is used with greater frequency as a gasoline additive. Nickel carbonyl has been shown to cause changes in the air pockets of the lungs, resulting in respiratory symptoms and lung cancer in both men and animals. Nickel does not seem to be accumulated in the human lung.

Airborne mercury is only a small part of the over-all mercury problem, but some does enter the air; elemental mercury is quite easily vaporized. Coal and petroleum both contain small amounts of mercury which probably vaporize. The concentration ranges from 0.003 to 0.009 $\mu g/m^3$ in the air, all well below the suggested limit of 50 $\mu g/m^3$. The more serious aspect of mercury pollution lies in the ability of mercury to form alkyl compounds; this possibility will be discussed in connection with water pollution. The alkyl compounds are highly toxic but the inorganic compounds of mercury are rapidly excreted by the body and little accumulation occurs. Inhalation of mercury vapor should be avoided as should direct skin contact.

Problem Metals in the Future? Of other metals in the air, four more are known to be toxic but seem to present no danger at their present concentrations. Beryllium exposure is a very serious occupational problem, causing chronic systemic poisoning, respiratory ailments, and increased lung cancer. Beryllium is used in alloys as a hardening agent and thus may be released to the atmosphere in small concentrations during reprocessing of scrap metal. At present, the airborne concentration is only around 0.00013 $\mu g/m^3$, but new uses of this metal, such as an additive in rocket fuel and proposed uses in the nuclear power industry, will increase the amount of beryllium already added to our atmosphere from the combustion of coal and from industrial uses.

Tin, like mercury, is most toxic in the alkyl form and thus is more of a water pollution than air pollution problem. Alkyl tin enters tissue of nerve and brain cells, and accumulates in several organs. Present airborne concentrations of elemental tin are in the 0.0002 to 0.0018 $\mu g/m^3$ range. Bismuth and antimony have also been found in air samples, but present levels are low and the extent of the hazard uncertain, although some evidence exists to classify these materials as toxic.

Several low-toxicity metals have been detected in air samples, including aluminum, titanium, barium, strontium, zirconium, niobium, and vanadium. Some of these metals are the result of fuel oil burning; for some, their source in the air is unknown. Some trace metals are judged essential to the life and health of man, and of these chromium, manganese, iron, cobalt, copper, and zinc are found in the air. It is doubtful that the metals are helpful nutritionally when inhaled, so their presence in the air is not necessary. Additionally, all metals can become toxic in large enough doses.

Asbestos—Mineral Menace. One final type of particulate matter that is of increasing concern is asbestos. Asbestos is a broad term used for a number of fibrous minerals. The minerals are a complicated mixture of the oxides of silicon, magnesium, iron, aluminum, calcium, and sodium, together with a small amount of water. Inhalation of large amounts of asbestos dust produces symptoms similar to those caused by beryllium; it may be the size of these particles, rather than their chemical composition, that is responsible for observed health effects. Construction workers and home do-it-yourself fans have always been subject to possible asbestos poisoning, but a report from the Environmental Protection Agency indicates that current asbestos concentrations in urban areas are approaching the levels encountered by workers in the industry. Studies of insulation workers from 1943–71 have shown increased incidence of lung and gastrointestinal cancers. Other than from construction, asbestos in the atmosphere comes from the automobile, for almost all asbestos (97 to 99 percent) used in brake linings is eventually converted into airborne particles.

Oxides of Nitrogen

The oxides of nitrogen, generally referred to as NO_x, are generated mainly by the automobile and the electric power industry. Unlike carbon and sulfur, in this case the element oxidized is not found in the fuel itself but rather comes from the air which these sophisticated combustion processes use. For this reason, nitrogen oxides are sometimes ironically referred to as the "status symbol" pollutants, characteristic of a developed country. Nitrogen is able to form a dizzying array of covalently bonded compounds with oxygen. The gaseous oxides and their properties are summarized in Table 9.

Table 9. Properties of Oxides of Nitrogen

Formula	Oxidation state of N	Melting point °C	Boiling point °C	Relative weight[a] g	Color	Comments	Relevance to air pollution
N_2O nitrous oxide	+1	−90.8°	−88.5°	16.0	Colorless	• Moderately soluble at room temp. • Used as a carrier gas in aerosol containers • Laughing gas	• 0.25 ppm normal concentration in air • Relatively inert • Not a product of combustion
NO nitric oxide	+2	−163.6°	−151.7°	32.0	Colorless (g) Blue (l or s)	• Paramagnetic (unpaired electron in electron structure)	• Trace constituent of air • Main product of combustion of nitrogen • Oxidized to NO_2 slowly by O_2 • Oxidized to NO_2 more rapidly by O_3
N_2O_3 dinitrogen trioxide	+3	−103°	3.5°	48.0	Brown (g) Blue (l)	• Unstable at or above room temp. • Reacts with H_2O to form HNO_2, nitrous acid[b]	—
NO_2 nitrogen dioxide	+4	−11.2°	21.2°	64.0	Brown (g) Yellow (l) White (s)	• $2\ NO_2 \rightleftharpoons N_2O_4$ Brown Colorless • Color deepens as temp is raised (at 135°C, 99% NO_2, 1% N_2O_4)	• 0.001 ppm—normal conc. in air • Forms from NO by oxidation • Strong absorber of ultraviolet light; "trigger" for photochemical reactions that produce smog • May be catalytically decomposed to N_2 and O_2; possible method of control
N_2O_5 dinitrogen pentoxide	+5	sublimes at 32.4°		90.0	Colorless (g) White (s)	• Decomposes at room T • Reacts with H_2O to form HNO_3, nitric acid[b]	—

Note: Some chemical and spectroscopic evidence exists for NO_3 and N_2O_6 compounds but they have not been isolated in pure form yet.

[a] Weight of oxygen that combines with 28.0 g of nitrogen.

[b] Neither of these anhydrides are common products of combustion so acidity of precipitation must be mainly due to oxides of sulfur rather than nitrogen.

This series of nitrogen oxides illustrates the law of multiple proportions which states that if you compare the weights of an element (oxygen for example) that joins with a fixed weight of another element (nitrogen for example), then the weights of the variable element will be in a ratio of small whole numbers to each other. In this case, using 28 grams of nitrogen as a convenient fixed weight, the weights of oxygen are 16, 32, 48, 64 and 90 grams respectively and the ratio is 1:2:3:4:5. Ratios such as these are strong evidence for the existence of atoms, the smallest unit or basic building block for that element that has all the characteristics of the element.

Transport of Nitrogen in the Environment. Man's production of oxides of nitrogen fits into the larger scheme of nitrogen transport and equilibrium called the nitrogen cycle. Although nitrogen is essential to life, it cannot be directly assimilated by plants; it must be converted into usable form. *Nitrogen fixation* is a term used to describe the conversion of N_2 into its compounds, largely nitrates (NO_3^-) and ammonia (NH_3). One mechanism for converting atmospheric nitrogen into oxides is combustion; industrial fixation and lightning also play a role. The most important fixation processes, however, are biological. Bacteria found on the root nodules of peas, clover, and beans convert nitrogen to compounds. Free-living nitrogen fixers such as blue-green algae are also important biological agents. The over-all cycle is shown in Figure 8.

Notice that going from N_2 to NO_3^- is an oxidation process, as nitrogen's oxidation number changes from 0 to $+5$. Once the NO_3^- has formed it may be assimilated directly and thereby changed into various organic nitrogen compounds such as amino acids, or urea, or it could be acted on by denitrifying bacteria changing the NO_3^- to NO_2^-, or NH_3, or back to N_2, all reduction processes.

The conversion of atmospheric nitrogen to ammonia, commonly the first step in biological conversion to nitrates, is an example of a reaction with a high energy of activation. Altogether 147 kilocalories of energy must be put into the reaction in order to split molecular nitrogen and molecular hydrogen into separate atoms so they can form ammonia. The equation for the reaction is:

$$N_2 + 3\ H_2 \longrightarrow 2\ NH_3$$

Ordinarily this large an input of energy would cause the reaction not to occur but this reaction is catalyzed by enzymes in nitrogen -fixing organisms, thus lowering the required activation energy.

Figure 8. The Nitrogen Cycle

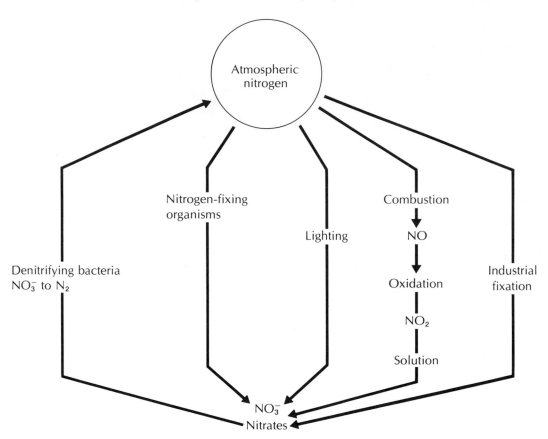

Environmental Effects of NO$_x$. Even though the most significant environmental effect of NO$_x$ emission is the role NO$_2$ plays in smog formation, other economic, aesthetic, and medical problems are associated with the oxides of nitrogen. Although less widely publicized than the deterioration of metals and materials caused by sulfur oxides and ozone, nitrogen dioxide and nitric oxide are known to cause fading in acetate, cotton, and rayon fibers; exposure to concentrations in the range 0.6 ppm to 2 ppm over a two-to-three-month period causes fading. (These concentrations are typical of those found in gas dryers.) Yellowing of white fabrics has also been shown to occur in the presence of NO$_x$. Both the discoloration and fading reaction require conditions of high humidity. Similarly, if water vapor is present, there is a correlation between high NO_x levels and stress-corrosion failures of nickel-brass wire springs used on telephone relays. The airborne nitrates resulting from NO_x at concentrations as low as .05 ppm have been shown to aggravate this corrosion.

Many kinds of plants show acute leaf injury when exposed to very high NO_x concentrations, such as 25 ppm. Such a concentration might be expected only in the vicinity of a specific industrial source, such as a nitric acid chemical factory. The threshold for injury (defined as level that injures 5 percent of leaf area) is as low as 4 to 8 ppm for one hour, but the extent of injury depends greatly on the type and age of the plant as well as the duration of exposure. For long-term damage, a concentration of NO_2 of 0.25 ppm for eight months has been shown to increase leaf-drop and reduce yields of navel oranges. Research on lower levels of NO_x is continuing; experimentally, the brown margins and black spots on leaves caused by NO_x are hard to distinguish from similar problems caused by SO_2. Both very young and mature leaves are more resistant to NO_2 than are the rapidly expanding leaves; damage in this stage of growth can provide help in identifying NO_2 as the cause.

The effects of NO_x to man are not a serious problem at present levels. Nitric oxide is not an irritant, and its main toxic potential results from its oxidation to NO_2. However, NO will attach to hemoglobin and thus in large concentrations could have oxygen-deprivation effects similar to those of carbon monoxide. Research on this point is only starting. Nitrogen dioxide is an irritant to eyes and the respiratory tract. Experimentation with animals indicates many pathological changes connected with lung function as well as increased susceptibility to infection. Emphysema has been induced in laboratory animals following long-term exposures to 10 to 25 ppm NO_2. Humans appear to have a threshold of about 0.12 ppm for detection of the chlorine-like odor of NO_2, and therefore high concentrations can be easily detected.

The federal standards for NO_x (excluding N_2O which occurs naturally at 0.25 ppm) are 0.05 ppm for one year and 0.13 ppm for twenty-four hours. Current California standards are set at 0.25 ppm for one hour; concentrations as high as 0.70 ppm for one hour have been recorded in the Los Angeles area.

Control of NO_x Emissions. Recent aerial monitoring of air pollution in the Los Angeles area found smog clouds at the 2000-foot level containing NO_x ranging up to 6 ppm—many times exceeding the California and federal standards. Ground monitoring systems clearly do not do a sufficient job in presenting the entire air pollution story; this new information may lead to considerable reevaluation of control strategies.

One recurrent problem in trying to control NO_x is that some of the factors that tend to reduce other types of pollution cause an increase in

What a contrast between San Diego as seen on a clear day and as somewhat visible on a smoggy day! A similar set of pictures could probably be taken in any city of the world. The same factors are present in all cities; only the relative contributions vary in importance. The number of automobiles, types of industry present, and the methods used to generate power are all pertinent data needed to evaluate the smog potential of an area. It is equally important to know how well each of these air polluters has succeeded in minimizing emissions. The local geography and climate can greatly influence the likelihood of waking up to a clear, beautiful day or instead, being reminded by smarting eyes, a faintly brown color, and perhaps a hint of pungent odor that all is not right with our air. Do we have a choice?

Some of the effects of air pollution are well documented but as of yet, the total impact of this sometimes invisible attack has not been recognized by the public. Is it possible to ignore our own health, plant damage, and the many economic effects due to early deterioration of materials? Is the mere sight of filthy air enough incentive to attempt to clean it up? Is it even possible?

Many experts have insisted that the only way the Federal Air Quality Standards will be met is by some drastic changes in everyday life. Surely these would include a lessening dependence on the private automobile and a change in the pattern of increasing power consumption. Economic measures ranging from the individual (increased gasoline tax, mandatory automotive emission devices, periodic vehicle inspection) to the federal level (increased funds for supporting research on alternate power resources, development of rapid transit) may be necessary steps. Taxing polluters is another idea frequently mentioned. Whatever path is taken, there are many hard choices to be made if the quality of our air is to improve.

NO_x production. For example, in an automobile engine, increasing temperature or making the fuel-oxygen mix more oxygen-rich will encourage complete combustion and therefore decrease the hydrocarbons and carbon monoxide produced. These same factors, however, will increase the NO formed. This can be seen from the equilibrium implied by the equation:

$$N_2 + O_2 \xrightleftharpoons[\text{low temperature}]{\text{high temperature}} 2\,NO$$

Nitrogen requires a rather large amount of energy to cause it to react—160 kcal/mole must be supplied to N_2 to break the molecule into two nitrogen atoms for combustion. High temperatures supply this necessary activation energy. The NO, once produced, usually does not have sufficient time to reestablish equilibrium with N_2 and O_2; rather it is oxidized to NO_2 first. Recycling the exhaust back into the engine, which will cool the cylinder temperature and change the fuel-air mix, and divided catalytic converters are two plans being experimentally tried as methods to control NO_x emissions from the automobile. In a divided catalytic converter, one part oxidizes hydrocarbons and carbon monoxide to carbon dioxide and water vapor; the other part reduces nitric oxide to nitrogen and oxygen.

Stationary sources such as power plants are working with the same general problem. Both alteration of burner design and experimentation with different fuel-air mixes have produced some success in lowering NO_x. Using copper as a catalyst to reduce the nitrogen oxides back to free N_2 and O_2 has been accomplished on a laboratory scale.

Part Four: WHAT'S IT DOING UP THERE?

The total effect in terms of health, aesthetics, and dollar damage of all the pollutants added to the air is greater than the simple sum of each gaseous, liquid, or solid pollutant. The troposphere serves locally as a giant reaction vessel in which a complex series of chemical reactions take place aided by the energy from sunlight. This chemical interaction of hydrocarbons, oxides of nitrogen, and oxygen in the presence of the sun's ultraviolet light produces photochemical smog, or simply smog as the word has come to be used. Originally "smog" was a contraction of the words smoke and fog, coined by a British physician around 1905 and applied to the particular type of atmospheric mix found in London. That type of "smog" was mainly particulates and sulfur oxides; photochemical smog contains a wider variety of pollutants and produces new products as the result of the reaction catalyzed by the sunlight.

The Reactions of Photochemical Smog: The Trigger

The starting mechanism for photochemical smog (referred to as smog hereafter) is the absorption of energy by NO_2. This causes the nitrogen dioxide to decompose into nitric oxide and atomic oxygen.

$$NO_2 + \text{ultraviolet light} \longrightarrow NO + [O] \qquad (1)$$
$$\text{atomic}$$
$$\text{oxygen}$$

Atomic oxygen is an extremely reactive species, as might be predicted by noting that it now has only six electrons in its outermost main energy level. The atomic oxygen will now enter into two possible reactions.

$$[O] + O_2 \longrightarrow O_3 \qquad (2)$$
$$[O] + C_xH_y \longrightarrow C_xH_yO \cdot \qquad (3)$$

The first of these combinations produces the extremely reactive oxidizing agent ozone, O_3. Ozone may be naturally present in small amounts due to lightning discharges. During smog episodes, ozone concentrations build up to dangerous levels, because one mechanism for removing ozone is partially eliminated. Normally ozone is removed in this way:

$$O_3 + NO \longrightarrow NO_2 + O_2 \qquad (4)$$

Therefore, normally a cyclic process occurs—from NO_2 to NO and back to NO_2. In smog the cycle is short-circuited by the fact that NO is removed by reaction with hydrocarbons (see equation 8) before it can react with the ozone.

Environmental Effects of Ozone

Ozone is a vigorous oxidizing agent and is thought to be the primary agent causing smog damage to vegetation. Upper surfaces of many types of leaves show discoloration patterns, often including bleached spotty areas. Some crops, particularly tomatoes, tobacco, and some beans, are sensitive at levels as low as 0.05 ppm. Ponderosa pine in the San Bernardino Mountains, southeast of Los Angeles, are showing pronounced effects from ozone damage as the result of their continued exposure to smog drifting from the city. Other damaging effects of ozone are also attributed to its oxidizing abilities, notably the shortened life of rubber and textiles due to cracking and fading. Ozone is an irritant gas to humans, producing eye, nose, and throat symptoms as well as alteration of normal lung function. Studies of track athletes correlate high ozone levels with poorer performance. Preliminary studies with animals indicate decreased life expectancy with higher concentrations of ozone.

Tobacco leaves are particularly susceptible to ozone damage. The healthy leaf in the upper right-hand corner does not show the bleached areas caused by ozone in the atmosphere. *(Courtesy, University of California, Riverside, Statewide Air Pollution Research Center)*

Reactive Hydrocarbons

If hydrocarbons are present, particularly reactive hydrocarbons such as alkenes ($R-CH=CH_2$, for example), then the conditions for producing smog are complete. As shown in equation 3, atomic oxygen will react to produce an oxidized free radical form of the hydrocarbon. Oxygen will act in a similar manner to produce a still more reactive species.

$$O_2 + C_xH_yO \cdot \longrightarrow C_xH_yO_3 \cdot \qquad \text{(acyl peroxy radical)} \qquad (5)$$

The presence of an unpaired electron makes the free radical very reactive. An astounding variety of products result from the production of the free radicals with their ability to join to themselves over and over. (This process is called polymerization and will be discussed with reference to plastics.) Some reactions are termination reactions, forming products with another hydrocarbon molecule.

$$C_xH_yO_3 \cdot + C_{x'}H_{y'} \longrightarrow \text{aldehydes} \quad \overset{\displaystyle O}{\overset{\displaystyle \|}{R-C-H}}$$

$$\text{and} \qquad \overset{\displaystyle O}{\overset{\displaystyle \|}{}} \qquad (6)$$

$$\text{ketones} \quad R-C-R'$$

Therefore aldehydes and ketones accumulate in smog. The acyl peroxy radical can combine with NO_2 to form a set of compounds known as PANs or peroxy acyl nitrates, another type of end-product of smog.

$$C_xH_yO_3 \cdot + NO_2 \longrightarrow C_xH_yO_3NO_2 \qquad (7)$$

$$\text{(Structure } R-\overset{\displaystyle O}{\overset{\displaystyle \|}{C}}-O-O-NO_2)$$

Ethylene, $CH_2=CH_2$, in the atmosphere caused this damage to delicate orchids. Reactive hydrocarbons are capable of severe damage to plants. *(Courtesy, University of California, Riverside, Statewide Air Pollution Research Center)*

The PANs are extremely irritating compounds and create the same types of symptoms that result from ozone exposure. The plant damage from PANs usually appears as a silvery or bronzed coloration on the lower leaf surface. Some vegetable crops and citrus fruits are quite sensitive to this pollutant, effects being observed at 0.2 ppm. For all oxidant smog gases together, including ozone and PANs as the principal components, the federal standard is 0.06 ppm for one hour. Most urban areas regularly exceed these standards and actually attaining prescribed low levels of oxidants may be impossible without drastic change in the pattern of life in our cities.

The acyl peroxy radical may be acted upon by either NO or O_2 to produce another oxidized hydrocarbon radical, as well as more O_3 and NO_2.

$$C_xH_yO_3 \cdot + NO \longrightarrow C_xH_yO_2 \cdot + NO_2 \qquad (8)$$

$$C_xH_yO_3 \cdot + O_2 \longrightarrow C_xH_yO_2 \cdot + O_3 \qquad (9)$$

This product can give one atom of oxygen to NO and therefore generate even more NO_2, as shown in equation 10.

$$C_xH_yO_2 \cdot + NO \longrightarrow NO_2 + C_xH_yO \cdot \qquad (10)$$

The peroxy radicals may also give oxygen to sulfur dioxide, accelerating its oxidation to SO_3 and therefore to sulfuric acid upon contact with water vapor, forming an aerosol responsible for haze.

$$SO_2 + [O] \longrightarrow SO_3 \qquad (11)$$

$$SO_3 + H_2O \longrightarrow H_2SO_4 \qquad (12)$$

Put It All Together: It Smells Smog

This is a formidable set of reactions and yet necessary to understand the complexity of the smog formation. The twelve reactions given are by no means the only important chemical changes that occur but are chosen to illustrate the general reaction scheme. Other reactions that undoubtedly contribute to the over-all process have been omitted, for example the chemical interactions of the hydroxide and water molecules. To summarize the information presented, Figure 9 shows the relationships involved between different reactive species. The numbers refer to equations 1 through 12.

Figure 9 indicates the reactants and products of smog formation and therefore gives suggestions for both control and measurement. If some of the necessary ingredients for smog formation are missing,

PANs have caused the silvery appearance on the underside of the bean leaf on the top. A healthy leaf appears on the bottom for comparison. (*Courtesy, University of California, Riverside, Statewide Air Pollution Research Center*)

Figure 9. The Photochemistry of Smog

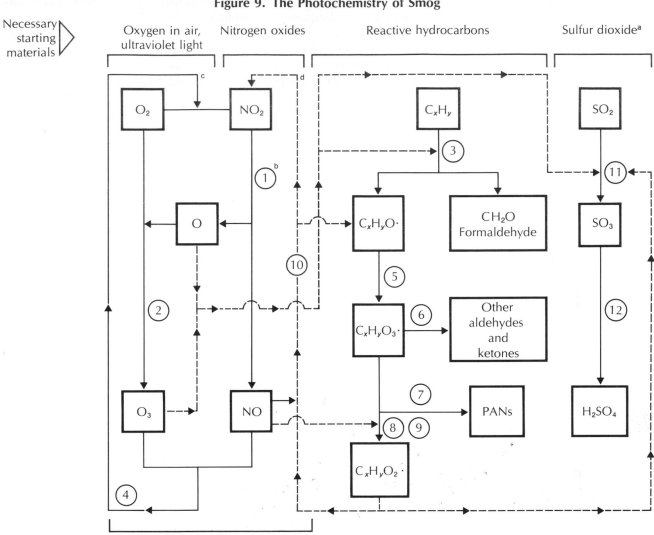

This system would be perfectly in balance
if there were no interference from
hydrocarbons.

ᵃSO₂ does not have to be present to have photochemical smog. Notice that the SO₂–H₂SO₄ conversion reacts in only one place with the rest of the cycle.

ᵇNumbers refer to the equations given previously.

ᶜ _____ means a reaction path within a cycle   ᵈ_ _ _ _ _ _ _ _ _ _ means a reaction path between cycles.

the cycles of reaction cannot occur. Removal of excess NO_x and hydrocarbons would eliminate the problem to a large extent. Note that carbon monoxide does not appear at all in the chain of smog-producing reactions. On the other end of the reaction cycle, the concentrations of ozone and PAN compounds can be used as an indication of the extent of smog levels as these oxidizing materials are formed and build up in the atmosphere as products of smog.

Total oxidant levels can be measured by means of the color change that occurs when the colorless iodide ion is changed to free iodine, I_2.

$$2I^- \longrightarrow I_2 + 2e^-$$

Iodine is a silver-grey solid or appears blue if adsorbed on starch.

In this reaction, the iodide ion gains in oxidation number ($^-1$ to zero) and loses electrons. It has therefore been oxidized by the various oxidizing agents present in smog.

This test may give misleading results if there are high levels of SO_2 in the air, for sulfur dioxide is a reducing agent and may reverse the above reaction, giving deceptively low oxidant values.

A newer and more reliable method to measure oxidants works on the principle of chemiluminescence. When ozone (and other oxidants) react with hydrocarbons such as ethylene, $CH_2{=}CH_2$, the reaction releases energy in the form of light as the result of the new chemical bonds forming. By measuring the light intensity under specified conditions, the concentration of the oxidants can be determined.

The Smog Potential of Stagnant Air

The chemical processes of smog formation are often aided by the weather and topographic conditions present at the site. If air is not able to circulate freely, pollutants have a better chance to concentrate and react rather than disperse. Blocking mountains and hills can serve as a barrier to free circulation with resulting smog buildup. Under some conditions, mountains can also act as a ventilating system. The sun warms air at the base of the mountains, causing the air to rise, taking smog with it over the mountains.

Another important factor in determining the ability of air to circulate freely is the temperature profile of that air column. The normal state of affairs in the troposphere is that air becomes cooler as you ascend. Many conditions can act to cause a reversal or an inversion in this normal pattern of temperature change. For example, very often in the early morning there is a temporary inversion of temperatures near the ground due to

In southern California, smog from urban areas has been blown up into the mountain areas and has damaged vegetation. Particularly hard hit have been the pines in the Lake Arrowhead region.

different cooling rates for the land and the air. The air directly above the land is cooler than the higher air; pollutants will be held down near their sources, unable to rise. This phenomenon will usually disappear as the morning sun warms the atmosphere.

A high-level inversion layer is potentially more of a problem. It can be formed, for example, from stable warmer air in a high-pressure system, trapping cooler air beneath it and preventing dispersal of the smog-filled layer. Contaminants will not penetrate through the warmer air boundary (since at this point they are cooler and hence denser than the air above them). Often they can be seen moving horizontally at the interface of the cooler and warmer layers. The situation is made worse by the fact that the layer above the inversion boundary is warm and dry and therefore allows sunlight to penetrate, increasing the smog sequence of reactions. If the inversion remains in position for several days, severe restrictions must be placed on all emissions to try to prevent pollution levels from reaching values dangerous to health. Such episodes as the August 1969 smog buildup over St. Louis and surrounding areas are flirtations with true disaster. If the inversion had not broken there when it did, heavy loss of life could have resulted.

Inversion layer, Medford, Oregon.

Burning chips and bark from lumbering operations in Medford, Oregon, place a plume of smoke into the otherwise clean, early morning air. Besides the obvious particulate matter, the smoke will contain water vapor, CO_2, CO, sulfur oxides, and a wide variety of organic compounds. Although there may be other inversion layers at higher altitudes, they are not visible if there is no confined pollution.

The normal condition is that the temperature drops as altitude increases. However, in an inversion layer the temperature increases with altitude. The layer of warmer air keeps the smoke from rising any farther. The pollution is held close to the ground. As the day progresses, the sun will warm the air above the ground and dissipate the nighttime inversion layer.

If an inversion layer does not break quickly, such as can happen if stagnant air accumulates in an area, the trapped pollutants may reach dangerous concentrations. There may be some geographical feature such as a low range of blocking mountains that prevents the air from circulating freely. The entire trapped layer accumulates the pollutants added to it, and as they react to form photochemical smog, the layer constitutes a giant chemical reaction vessel. This view of the city of El Cajon, east of San Diego, California, shows such an inversion layer with its buildup of trapped pollutants.

Inversion layer, El Cajon, California.

The role of temperature inversions in providing an optimum environment for the reactions of photochemical smog is just beginning to be investigated in detail. The idea of a single inversion is generally an oversimplification; as many as sixteen different alternating temperature layers have been detected in the atmosphere over Los Angeles. Several schemes have been offered to artificially break up inversion layers but none has yet been shown to work on a large scale.

Part Five: THE AUTOMOBILE IS KILLING US

The motor vehicle is the single most important source of air pollution in the United States. The internal combustion engine accounts for 60 to 90 percent by weight of all air pollutants, the percentage being largest in urban areas with little heavy industry. Thus in Los Angeles, with a great concentration of cars and few polluting industries, the automobile is responsible for a greater share of airborne pollution than it is in Cleveland. In all areas, however, the automobile has changed from a symbol of technological achievement to technological menace. The public is showing an increased awareness that air pollution must be reduced for medical, economic, social, and political reasons; the major contributor is a logical point to focus the attack.

The Automobile as a Polluter

Automobiles are guilty of several types of emissions: crankcase ventilation emissions (which are now controlled), evaporative losses from the carburetor and fuel tanks, and vapor hydrocarbon losses which occur during tank filling. The major problem with the internal combustion engine is that it is also an external exhaust engine resulting in the addition of undesirable products to our air. Given the need to reduce emissions, the next question is, "To what extent is it possible to reduce motor vehicle emissions?" To answer this question, a study was carried

What are the sources of air pollution? More than half of the total tonnage comes from transportation such as automobiles, trucks, and airplanes.

out in 1967 by the United States Department of Commerce to try to identify the levels of emissions that seemed technologically feasible. (The report is known as the Morse Report.) A similar industry report tried to answer the same question. A summary of goals that have been set by government agencies as well as by the two technological surveys are listed in Table 10 along with estimated precontrol emissions for comparison.

The unit that is now generally in use for measuring automotive emissions is grams per mile, derived from knowing the mass of a pollutant emitted in relationship to the number of miles driven. This method of reporting gives more information than simply reporting parts per million. Although a compact car and a huge gas-eating super special might have the same concentration of carbon monoxide, the volume of exhaust per mile would be greater for the larger car, a

Table 10. Automotive Emissions Standards and Goals

(all concentrations given in grams/mile)

	Hydrocarbons	Carbon monoxide	NO_x
Estimated level prior to controls	11.0	80.0	4.0
California Pure Air Act, standard for: 1966	3.4	34.0	—
1971	2.2	23.0	4.0
1972	1.5	23.0	3.0
1974	1.5	23.0	1.3
California Low Emission Act, standard for 1975	0.5	11.0	0.75
Federal Standards for: 1970	4.1	34.0	4.0
1975	0.41	3.4	3.0
1976	0.41	3.4	0.4
Morse Report, goals for 1975	0.6	12.0	1.0
Interindustry Emission Council, goals for 1975(?)	0.82	7.1	0.68

Source: Technical Advisors Committee, California Air Resources Board.

fact that would be reflected in the grams/mile figure. A constant volume sampler is now used to take measurements of the total volume exhaust while simultaneously measuring concentration of pollutants. These values are then used to compute grams/mile. The grams/mile concentration does not include emissions other than those from the tailpipe and therefore evaporation and crankcase hydrocarbon losses should be added in separately to get a total picture.

How is it possible to reduce emissions? The main approach so far has been by means of technological advances in fuel preparation, completeness of combustion, and exhaust devices. Before considering some of the engine improvements, let's start closer to home. For the consumer, the quest for cleaner air can start at the gas station as he chooses the type of gasoline necessary for proper functioning of his well-tuned automobile. Given the fact that you own a particular car at this point in time, how do you choose the proper gasoline? The first point to consider is the octane rating necessary for your engine's proper functioning.

Your Automobile–Choosing Gasoline by Octane Rating

When gasoline is burned in an internal combustion engine, the heat of combustion is transformed into mechanical energy. If the fuel and air mix is held at a high compression in the firing chamber, a more efficient burning is possible. However, the theoretical increase in efficiency may be offset by an increased tendency to have pre-ignition of the compressed fuel, resulting in loss of power, wasted fuel, and a vibration known as "knocking." As automobiles were built with higher compression ratios, better fuels were developed to cope with the tendency to pre-ignite. In order to have a way of rating fuels, a standard one-cylinder test engine was set up and reference hydrocarbon fuels picked. Pure isooctane which burns rather smoothly, was assigned an octane number of 100; normal (straight-chain) heptane causes bad knocking and was given an octane number of 0. The structures of these compounds are shown in Figure 10.

Isooctane
"Octane number" = 100

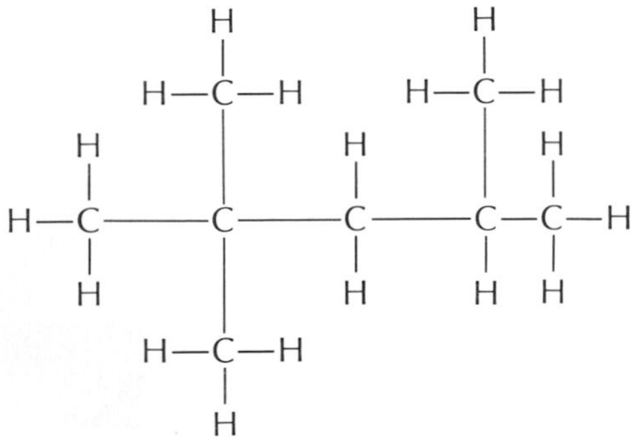

Figure 10.
Isooctane and Normal Heptane

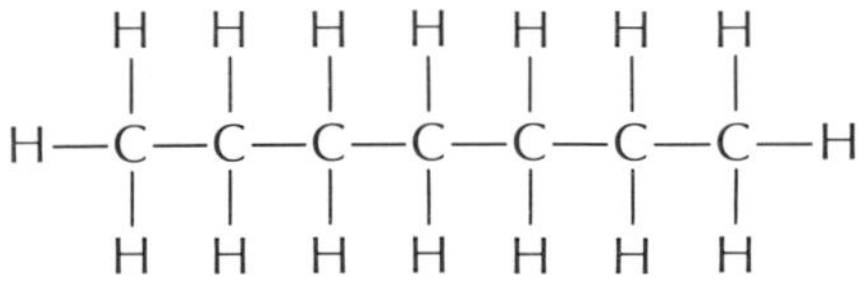

n-heptane
"Octane number" = 0

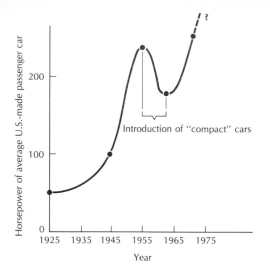

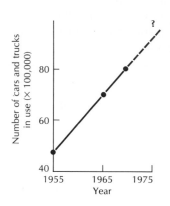

Transportation in the United States in 1970 accounted for 111.0 million tons of CO, 0.7 million tons of particulate matter (lead, asbestos, rubber), 1.0 million tons of SO_x, and 19.5 million tons of NO_x. Other pollutants are hydrocarbons and noise. If alternate power sources are utilized for transportation, how many of these pollutants would be eliminated?

The growing number of automobiles generate more and more pollutants. The other pertinent factor is the changing technology associated with manufacturing automobiles. Particularly in the period since 1946, low-power, low-compression engines have been replaced by high-power, high-compression engines. This in turn means that the engines require higher octane gasolines, for which tetraethyl lead was introduced. Higher operating temperatures also mean increased NO_x emissions.

Smog machine

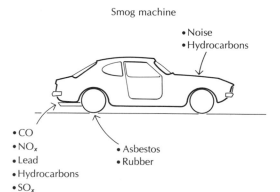

CO_2 and H_2O will also be produced as products of the complete combustion of gasoline. Are these compounds considered pollutants too?

**Table 11. Octane Rating Necessary
for Your Engine**

Compression ratio	Octane rating required for knock-free operation
5:1	73
6:1	81
7:1	87
8:1	91
9:1	95
10:1	98
11:1	100
12:1	102

Mixtures of these two fuels give knocking properties intermediate to the two extremes, and therefore any new fuel is tested by comparing its knocking properties under specified conditions with mixtures of n-heptane and isooctane. The octane number is determined by the percentage of isooctane in the heptane-isooctane mix that gives the same knocking properties as the fuel being tested. So, for example, if a fuel tested has the same knocking properties as a 10 percent heptane and 90 percent isooctane mix, the octane number would be assigned as 90. Some fuels containing more highly branched hydrocarbons or aromatic compounds may be given an octane number greater than 100 if they burn more smoothly than isooctane itself.

You can find the compression ratio for your car in your owner's manual; this determines the octane rating necessary for gasoline giving knock-free performance in your car as shown in Table 11. (This table holds for standard internal combustion engines and not for the new rotary engines. Despite a 9.4 to 1 compression ratio, they can recommend a low octane, nonleaded gasoline due to the difference in engine design).

Most gasoline companies do not list the octane rating of their gasolines on the pump, but this information may be required by law in the near future. In the meantime, such information is available by writing to the companies or in various references. As a general rule, 94 octane is considered "regular" and 100 as "premium."

Lead—A Dangerous Additive

One of the best ways to raise the octane number of a gasoline is by adding small amounts of lead in the form $Pb(C_2H_4)_4$, tetraethyl lead. (This is the origin of the expression "ethyl" to mean premium or high-octane gasoline.) Exactly why this addition works in improving performance is not clear, but the addition of less than 3 grams per gallon can improve octane rating by 10 units. Along with the lead compound, ethylene dibromide or dichloride ($C_2H_2Br_2$ or $C_2H_2Cl_2$) are added as scavengers. These compounds will decompose, producing the corresponding bromine or chlorine which in turn will react with the lead, forming a gaseous compound and therefore removing the lead from inside the engine.

In 1968, 260,000 tons of lead were used in manufacturing gasoline additives in the United States, and it is estimated that over 75 to 90 percent of the lead goes out the tailpipe. The increasing concentrations of toxic lead in airborne particulate matter has become of great concern, particularly in urban atmospheres. Increases in concentrations of airborne lead are well documented for several cities; Los Angeles had a startling 56 percent average increase in the 1960s, as compared to an 18 percent increase in Philadelphia and a 17 percent increase in Cincinnati for the same time period.

Lead in the air is potentially far more dangerous than lead that accumulates to the same level in water or soil, as there is more direct absorption by the body in the case of the inhaled material. Still, lead-based paints present a hazard if they are consumed, and studies will be continued to see if concentrations of lead in edible plants and animal food products are changing. Once in the body, lead accumulates and low-level doses can cause such symptoms as anemia, headaches, sterility, miscarriage, or the birth of brain-damaged babies, even though adult symptoms are not clinically noticeable. Brain damage, known as lead encephalopathy, manifests itself in convulsions, coma, blindness, mental retardation, or death in the case of larger doses.

In recognition of these threats the California Air Resources Board has set a standard for lead of 1.5 $\mu g/m^3$ for a thirty-day average; this value is regularly exceeded in many cities today, placing the public and also such special groups as auto mechanics and street policemen in particular danger. The EPA has not set a standard for airborne lead.

In response to public demand, gasolines are now available with a wide variety of lead content. To determine if your present car can use a no- or low-lead gasoline, it is only necessary to find the octane rating needed for your car and then pick a no- or low-lead gasoline that achieves that rating. Not all the gasolines are alike by any means, and not all varieties are available in every community. It is estimated that 50 percent or more of all cars on the road today could use at least a low-lead if not a no-lead gasoline. The EPA has proposed a two-step reduction of lead in gasoline. By mid-1974, all large service stations will have to provide at least one pump of 91 or higher octane gasoline containing no more than 0.05 grams of lead per gallon. By 1977, no gasoline can be sold containing more than 1.25 grams of lead per gallon.

What Happens if We "Get the Lead Out"?

As with many environmental issues, a new problem may be created in attempting to solve an existing one, for some gasolines contain other potentially harmful additives as substitutes for the lead removed. Manganese can also be used as an antiknock additive but would be a dangerous material in the atmosphere as the metal causes nerve damage in humans. Aromatic hydrocarbons, particularly with six to nine total carbons, are often used in gasoline blends due to their high octane ratings. Benzene, C_6H_6, has an octane number of 106; toluene's rating is 118 to 120 depending on the purity. The compounds are fairly reactive, however, and it seems that their increased use could have a serious effect on the reactions involved in photochemical smog formation. Another possible replacement for lead that would increase octane rating would be the alkylates, saturated hydrocarbons composed of from two to five carbon atoms. Cyclopentane (a ring of five carbons and ten hydrogens) has an octane rating of 101, for example. Since the saturated hydrocarbons are less reactive as a group than unsaturated, the alkylates would be less likely to participate in smog reactions. Octane ratings can also be increased during the refining process by encouraging the formation of more branched hydrocarbons such as isooctane, since they will burn smoothly. Usually aluminum chloride and sulfuric acid are the catalysts used to help bring about increased branching.

A problem can be created in older cars by using low or nonleaded gasoline; the lead in the gasoline also acts as a necessary lubricant and sealer for the valves. This drawback can be minimized in the older cars by the use of small amounts of phosphrous-containing additives (again, total effect unknown) or by alternating tanks of nonleaded and leaded gasolines. Cars designed for 1975 and later will be engineered with this in mind and valves will be permanently coated to prevent valve problems. Early studies have indicated that even older cars attain greater economy of operation with lower emissions on low or nonleaded gasolines of sufficient octane rating.

Catalytic Control Devices and Lead

Despite the lack of complete information, development of no- and low-lead gasolines will continue to be given some priority, for the presence of lead in post-1975 model cars would seriously hamper the effectiveness of units such as catalytic and thermal converters that are proposed to control other exhaust pollutants. Oxidizing the fuel more completely will help to eliminate carbon monoxide and hydrocarbons; this can be accomplished in an automobile by altering the fuel-air ratio, using a recycling exhaust system, changing spark timing, or providing catalytic converters using metals and metallic oxides as the effective agents. Remember that most methods that improve combustion will lower hydrocarbon and carbon monoxide output, but will increase NO_x emissions since more N_2 will be joined with O_2 unless special provisions are made to eliminate the NO_x. Catalytic systems to convert the nitrogen oxides back to N_2 and O_2 are being developed but the lead must be removed from gasoline to avoid "poisoning" the catalyst by coating on its exposed faces and therefore reducing the surface area's effectiveness.

Prospects for the Future: Alterations

Most attempts so far to minimize emissions from automobiles have centered around improvements on the internal combustion engine, ICE. This has been a logical approach since so much money and technological expertise have been invested in this type of engine. Impressive gains have been made using some of the strategies mentioned so far—catalysts, changes in fuel-air ratio, and recycling exhaust systems. A newly developed "stratified-charge" engine, designed by the Ford Motor Company, has produced emissions low enough to meet 1976 federal standards. Tests are continuing on this modified internal combustion engine to see if its durability also meets the expected levels. It appears to be promising but, according to Ford engineers, could not be ready for the assembly line before 1979.

The Wankel or rotary combustion engine is now available from Japanese automobile manufacturers. Mazda cars with the rotary engine have been introduced successfully into eastern and California markets, with plans to sell the car throughout the United States. Several American automotive firms have licensing agreements with German producers that could result in their marketing the Wankel. This engine, of simple design (see Figure 11) and convenient size and weight, is also a low-noise engine and has the potential for being helpful in reducing emissions. Tests of the engine by itself have shown rather high levels of unburned hydrocarbons and carbon monoxide but low concentrations of the oxides of nitrogen. If the engine is combined with exhaust reactors, which are most effective for hydrocarbons and carbon monoxide, the over-all reduction in emissions is very significant. Many engineers are also enthusiastic about the Wankel's potential for powering a car that is safer to operate and has increased passenger space. Both of these aspects are possible due to the smaller engine size and weight.

Alternatives to the ICE

There are several other types of power plants which are possible alternatives to the internal combustion engine. One of the oldest engine concepts is the steam engine, which shows promise of producing very low levels of exhaust emissions. Earlier problems of steam explosions

Figure 11. The Wankel Engine

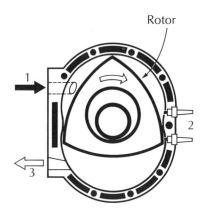

Rotor

1. Fuel Intake
2. Compression and ignition
3. Expansion and exhaust

Table 12. Emissions from Alternative Power Plants and Fuels (grams/mile)

	H_xC_y	CO	NO_x
Steam car	0.2–0.7	1.0–4.0	0.15–0.4
Gas turbine	0.5–1.2	3.0–7.0	1.3–5.2
Wankel engine	1.0–1.9	5.4–10.3	0.8–1.4
Natural gas fuel	1.5	6.0	1.5
Ford, stratified charge engine	0.41	3.4	0.4
1971 federal standard (for comparison)	2.2	23.0	4.0

Source: Technical Advisors Committee, California Air Resources Board; Environmental Protection Agency.

have been eliminated by advanced designs, but the engine's large size and weight, poor economy, and long startup time are problems. More tests are necessary here. Application for trucks and buses may prove to be better than for the private automobile.

Gas turbines, on the other hand, have been tested extensively and have many favorable characteristics, including low noise, low fuel consumption, a variety of possible fuels, and acceptable range of emissions for carbon monoxide and hydrocarbons. Emissions of NO_x have been harder to control. This problem, along with higher costs, has dampened some of the optimism but some still feel that the gas turbine engine could be ready for initial mass production in 1978.

A summary of emissions data for these alterations and alternatives is presented in Table 12. Some types of engines have not had large-scale testing as yet, and that is reflected by the lack of a range of values. Continual modification and improvement in engine design or operation also greatly affects these values, so you can expect to see lower values in the near future. Data are also given for a liquefied natural gas fuel system, which has been shown to effectively reduce emissions over a long-range series of tests. The use of clean-burning natural gas for other combustion purposes may limit the development of this application, since not enough would be left for cars.

A Zero Pollution Automobile?

Electric automobiles are those using batteries or fuel cells. The great attraction of batteries and fuel cells is that they are able to convert chemical energy directly into electrical energy. The efficiency of such devices is very high, as little energy is wasted in the form of heat. Some observers feel electric automobiles are a decade away from competition with the internal combustion engine cars, although if the demand for speed were reduced, their performance could be more favorably compared. At present their range in miles is limited. If the recharging of the car's batteries must be accomplished by using electric power, and if that is provided by burning fossil fuels, a simple trade-off has been brought about in the source of the pollution. Zero pollution might be the measurement at the tailpipe, but electric power production at the generating station would still present environmental problems. The goal of a zero-pollution car is still unobtainable.

Is Technology Enough?

All methods of controlling automotive emissions by technological means will probably provide only temporary relief if no other measures are taken; it is predicted that the increase in total number of automobiles on the road will cause a rise in pollution levels after 1985 even if all presently conceived control devices are fully operational. Another point to remember is that all proposed methods of reducing emissions will continue to produce carbon dioxide and water vapor as products and therefore the "pollutionless" engine cannot exist if based on standard hydrocarbon combustion principles. All control efforts are based on minimizing the levels of pollution.

For the long range too, purely technical solutions are not the entire answer. Alternate means of travel will have to become more realistic, for thirty people commuting on an express bus will put out far less pollutants than thirty people driving individually. Well-organized car pools and staggered working hours can have a positive effect, but mass transit systems in urban areas will have to be part of the solution, as will increasing reliance on alternative forms of engines.

From all of this discussion of possible improvements or replacements for the present internal combustion engine, it can be seen that there is no shortage of ideas. However, you and I are involved in a dilemma of time. Can advances be made fast enough to offset the rising pollution potential from our automobiles? Will it be necessary to legislate strict control of emissions, at least temporarily, by setting legal standards for lower octane rating for gasoline, lower engine horsepower, rules as to when and where the automobile may be driven, taxes for gasoline at an even higher rate or perhaps taxes for automobile emissions? Can we change our transportation habits to include effective mass transit routes? These questions will all have answers before the end of the twentieth century.

1. Methane, CH_4, composes 0.00015 percent by volume of our atmosphere. What is that in ppm? (Check your answer with Table 1.)

2. If water vapor makes up 26,000 ppm of the atmosphere on a particular day, what percent is that?

3. The total tonnage of all atmospheric pollutants in 1968 was estimated to be 263 million tons. How does this compare with the total for 1969 which was 281 million tons? What was the percent change?

Use these data for questions 4 and 5.

Million Tons of Air Pollutant

Year	Sulfur oxides	Carbon monoxide	Nitrogen oxides
1940	22	85	7
1950	24	103	10
1960	23	128	14
1970	34	147	23

Source: Environmental Protection Agency

4. Which of the types of air pollutants has had the greatest percentage increase for the period 1940–1970?

5. In 1969, 34 million tons of sulfur oxides, 154 million tons of carbon monoxide and 22 million tons of nitrogen oxides were emitted to the atmosphere. What short-range trends are evident in the time period 1969–1970?

6. A cyclone collector can remove particles of from five to twenty-five microns minimum size. How effective would this be in reducing aerosols in the atmosphere? (See Table 2.)

7. Copper can be oxidized to form either of two oxides:

$$Cu + O_2 \longrightarrow Cu_2O \qquad \text{copper I oxide (also called cuprous oxide)}$$

$$Cu + O_2 \longrightarrow CuO \qquad \text{copper II oxide (also called cupric oxide)}$$

For each reaction, balance the equation and identify the substance oxidized, the oxidizing agent, the substance reduced, and the reducing agent. What is the final oxidation state of copper in each case?

8. What is the difference between combustion and oxidation?

9. What products are formed by the complete combustion of any hydrocarbon? The incomplete combustion?

10. What happens to hydrocarbon molecules during the "cracking" process? Why is this an industrially important process?

11. If a person is exposed to carbon monoxide concentrations of 500 ppm for two hours, what symptoms could be expected? Would you be exposed to this concentration in most cities?

12. Sulfur and oxygen each have six electrons in their outermost principal quantum level. They form two covalent oxides. Draw electron dot diagrams for each compound.

13. Write an equation showing SO_3 reacting in H_2O to form sulfuric acid. What is the oxidation state of sulfur in each compound?

14. If iron pyrite (FeS_2) is not removed from coal before it is burned, oxygen will combine with both the iron and the sulfur to form iron (III) oxide, Fe_2O_3, and sulfur dioxide. Write a balanced chemical equation to represent this reaction.

15. As a sunny day progresses in a large city, the air may become more and more discolored. What components of pollution are responsible? Why would the color development be greater on a sunny day?

16. From the information given in these two equations, which acid is stronger — nitrous or nitric?

$$HNO_2 \xrightarrow{\longleftarrow} H^+ + NO_2^- \qquad HNO_3 \xleftarrow{\longrightarrow} H^+ + NO_3^-$$

nitrous acid   nitrite radical   nitric acid   nitrate radical

17. What is the oxidation state of nitrogen in each of the acids given in question 16?

18. Are isooctane and n-heptane isomers? Why or why not?

19. Ozone, O_3, is a different molecular form of oxygen gas, O_2. Such a set of molecular forms of the same element but different numbers of atoms per molecule are called allotropes. How do allotropes differ from isotopes?

20. Explain why SO_2 in the air would cause misleading readings for oxidants if the iodide test is used.

21. How would atomic oxygen react with a reactive hydrocarbon such as ethylene, $CH_2{=}CH_2$? What might the final oxidation product be if nitrogen dioxide gas were also present in the atmosphere?

22. Early control measures for air pollution centered around control of carbon monoxide and hydrocarbons. In light of what we now know about the chemistry of photochemical smog, why did these measures meet with only partial success?

23. Tetraethyl lead contains four bonds to ethyl groups, arranged symmetrically around the central lead atom. Sketch this molecule in two dimensions; in three dimensions.

24. Storage batteries such as are used in automobiles produce energy by means of this reaction.

$$Pb + PbO_2 + 2\ H_2SO_4 \underset{\text{recharging}}{\overset{\text{discharging}}{\rightleftharpoons}} 2\ PbSO_4 + 2\ H_2O$$

a. Explain why you have to add acid to your battery from time to time.

b. During recharging of a storage battery, what chemical changes are taking place?

25. If a fuel, tested in the standard engine with standard procedures, had the same knocking properties as 5 percent heptane and 95 percent isooctane mixture, what would be the octane rating of the fuel? Would the fuel be more likely to contain straight-chain or branched-chain hydrocarbons?

Study Questions – Group B

1. For each of the following atmospheric pollutants, give the main source and the second most important source by weight. Choose from transportation, fuel combustion in stationary sources, industrial sources, solid waste disposal, and miscellaneous sources of emission.

a. Carbon monoxide   c. Nitrogen oxides   e. Sulfur oxides

b. Hydrocarbons   d. Particulates

2. Sodium sulfite scrubbing is another method under study in both the United States and Japan for removal of SO_2. The SO_2 is reacted with a solution of sodium sulfite, $Na_2SO_3 + H_2O$, to produce sodium bisulfite, $NaHSO_3$. The $NaHSO_3$ solution is then removed and heated in order to regenerate the original sodium sulfite for reuse; a concentrated, mixed stream of SO_2 and steam is a byproduct.

a. Write the equation for this reversible reaction.

b. What factors will influence the potential widespread use of this process?

3. Perfecting fuel cells may be an important step in providing alternate sources of energy for the future. The main impetus for development of the fuel cell came from the space program, for here the cell is useful not only as an energy source but also for its production of water. The most common type of fuel cell utilizes hydrogen and oxygen gases which are fed into a solution of potassium hydroxide. (This type of fuel cell is also known as a Bacon Cell.) Find out how this cell works and explain its chemical principles. You may also want to find out about the newer hydrogen iodide fuel cell.

4. In 1875, experiments were being carried out to determine if a gasoline-powered engine could be used to propel a vehicle. The following statement was entered in the Congressional Record for that year:

Never in history has society been confronted with a power so full of potential danger and at the same time so full of promise for the future of man and for the peace of the world. The dangers are obvious. Stores of gasoline in the hands of the people interested primarily in profit would constitute a fire and explosive hazard of the first rank. Horseless carriages propelled by gasoline engines might attain speeds of 14 or even 20 miles per hour. . . . the development of this new power may displace the use of horses, which would wreck our agriculture. . . . the discovery with which we are dealing involves forces of a nature too dangerous to fit into any of our usual concepts.

From a vantage point of 1975, respond to this writer.

5. A new 1000 MW power plant must be built in your community, but whether it is to use fossil fuel or nuclear fuel has not been decided.
   a. Set up a "public hearing" to hear arguments for both sides. Make specific assignments ahead of time so that statements can be prepared accurately, reflecting the points of view of such participants as the project engineer, representative of AEC, citizens groups, and so on, perhaps even including a hysterical environmentalist! (Who will eventually make the decision?)
   b. Assume the power plant is not needed until the year 2000. This time set up a panel discussion dealing with various alternative sources of power. Schemes represented should include fusion reactors, solar, tidal, geothermal, hydroelectric, and wind power, but you need not limit yourself to this list. For each type try to find the current state of research, whether it will be able to furnish 1000 MW of power by 2000, applicability for your particular area, economic feasibility, and possible environmental effects. For an overview of alternate energy sources, see: Hammond, Allen L. "Energy Options: Challenge for the Future." *Science* 177 (September 1972): 875–76.

6. William D. Ruckelshaus, administrator of the Environmental Protection Agency, has stated that achievement of federal air pollution standards by 1975 may require drastic changes in everyday living. What are some of these changes? Be specific as to the effect a proposed change would have on air quality. How can these changes be brought about?

7. One of the best places to bring about improvement in the environment is in your own immediate area. The starting place is to gather all the necessary facts, such as:

a. What is the quality of the air where you live?
b. Does your city or town meet federal standards?
c. What industrial and stationary sources are present?
d. What geographic features hinder air movement?
e. Are the citizens concerned about air quality in your area? If so, what action is being taken? If not, should there be some action?

Suggested Readings

Brodine, Virginia. *Environmental Issues: Air Pollution*. New York: Harcourt Brace Jovanovich, 1973.

> This new book surveys the entire air pollution question. It is well written for the general reader: the author is the consulting editor of *Environment* and has written many articles about air pollution for that magazine. (Some of the material in this book appeared in Jan/Feb and May, 1972, issues of that journal. Has there been any progress in combating air pollution? What are the health effects and the environmental effects? How do we set standards? Where do we go from here? These, and many other questions, are considered in this book.

Esposito, John S. *Vanishing Air*. New York: Grossman Publishers, 1970.

> For a thorough introduction into the politics of air pollution, this carefully researched book would be excellent. The result of a Ralph Nader Study Group investigation on air pollution, you will learn a great deal about the relationships of industry and government in the fight to end the "environmental violence" of air pollution.

Madeiros, Robert W. "Smog Formation Simplified." *Chemistry* 45:1 (January 1972):16–18.

> A short article that compactly presents a simplified picture of the chemistry of photochemical smog. An excellent companion for studying Part Four of this chapter.

Stern, Arthur C., ed. *Air Pollution*, 2nd ed. 3 vols. New York: Academic Press, 1968–69.

> This is the standard reference for a serious study of air pollution. It has been updated fairly recently but you might also like to consult current journals such as *Environmental Science and Technology* for the last word on our understanding of the chemistry of photochemical smog. If you have a particular question or interest about the effects, interactions, or chemistry of a particular air pollutant, try the Stern volumes first.

Chapter 6
Chemistry of the Water Environment

The water, like the air, is a dynamic system that has received enormous environmental insults as the result of man's activities. In a sense there is just one form of pollution, water pollution, for eventually almost all materials find their way into the largest environmental sink on earth, the oceans.

We will first look at some of the special properties of water that enable it to play such an important role in life processes. The sources and characteristic pollutants added to the waters are enumerated, leading in Part Two to a discussion of some of the major problems associated with water quality today. Dissolved oxygen content, one important method of determining the health of a body of water, will be explained, and some of the special problems of ocean contamination discussed.

In Part Three we will examine the treatment of water for municipal use, and the processes used for desalination, sewage and industrial waste water renovation. Planned and current governmental action abating water pollution and some success stories conclude this discussion.

Part One: WHAT'S DOWN THERE?

Water is perhaps the most important and versatile chemical compound known. It is essential for life processes, for it is an integral part of animal and vegetable tissues. Early civilizations were always established near a supply of this life-giving substance, and even today, water is a determining factor in the placement of industry and agriculture. Water is both abundant and scarce, for although three-fourths of the earth's surface is covered by water, the distribution is uneven.

The Hydrological Cycle

Since the mid-seventeenth century, it has been recognized that water takes part in an endless circulation pattern called the hydrological cycle. The processes involved in this ecological pattern are shown in Figure 1.

This is nature's recycling system. No water is ever "lost" but rather transferred from one location to another by the processes of evaporation, condensation, precipitation, and runoff. Even though the percentages of water found in each reservoir are constant over all, there is continual movement within this dynamic cycle.

The worldwide dilemma of obtaining fresh water is emphasized by looking at the pattern of water circulation. Less than 1 percent of the entire earth's water supply is found in surface and ground waters, the usual sources for man's use. In sharp contrast, over 97 percent is found in the salty oceans, quite unusable for many purposes. In comparatively recent times, a new alternative has developed, in that it is possible to remove the salt from seawater in order to obtain the necessary fresh water supply (see Part Three). In any case, the wise management of this important resource is essential.

As the astronauts have noted from their vantage point in space, the abundance of water on the Earth is the most striking feature of our planet. Seventy-one percent of the earth's surface is covered with oceans and another 3.5 percent by polar ice caps; the remaining land is often temporarily covered by clouds. Where is all of the water on earth found? This figure shows the relative distribution of the earth's entire water supply as well as the processes that transfer water from one location to another.

Figure 1. The Hydroglogical Cycle

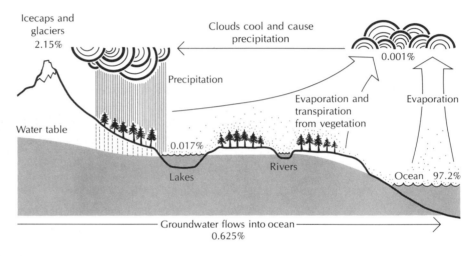

Icecaps and glaciers 2.15%

Clouds cool and cause precipitation

0.001%

Precipitation

Water table

Evaporation and transpiration from vegetation

Evaporation

0.017%

Lakes

Rivers

Ocean 97.2%

Groundwater flows into ocean 0.625%

Physical Properties of Water

Water is chemically and physically a very interesting substance. It seems quite familiar, but many of its properties are unique and unexpected when it is compared to similar compounds. The beauty of the exceptional nature of water lies in the way that each unusual property is intricately woven into the pattern of life processes.

Let us compare water, a compound of hydrogen and oxygen, with the other compounds formed between hydrogen and the elements of the oxygen family, Group VIA (see Table 1). Note that there is more than one way that water, H_2O, does not follow the pattern of the other three compounds. The trends for the melting and boiling temperatures are reversed, and the water's heats of fusion and of vaporization are very much larger than those for the other compounds. To understand the reasons for these values, one must understand the molecular structure of water, so this must be the starting point for the rest of the discussion.

Structure of the Water Molecule

The familiar formula H_2O shows a ratio of two hydrogen atoms for every oxygen. As we discussed earlier, hydrogen and oxygen each exist in three isotopic forms, so actually the formula stands for a large number of compounds. However, since isotopes usually have very similar chemical properties, we can consider the different isotopic variations of water all together as one chemical entity. In each case the oxygen atom and the hydrogen atom share electrons to form a predominantly covalent bond. Oxygen, however, is a more electronegative element than hydrogen, and therefore the shared electrons are closer to the oxygen than to each hydrogen. This makes the oxygen atom negative, relative to the hydrogen. The hydrogen atom has a relatively smaller part in the shared electrons and is therefore positively charged with respect to the oxygen

Table 1. Physical Properties of the Hydrogen Compounds of Group VIA Elements

Formula	Color	Mol. wt	Melting point (°C)	Boiling point (°C)	Heat of fusion (cal/g)	Heat of vaporization (cal/g)
H_2O	Colorless	18.0	0.00	100.0	80.0	540.0
H_2S	Colorless	34.1	−85.5	−60.3	16.7	131.0
H_2Se	Colorless	81.0	−65.7	−41.3	7.4	57.0
H_2Te	Colorless	129.6	−51	−2.3	−	42.8

Figure 2. Structure of the Water Molecule

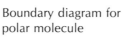

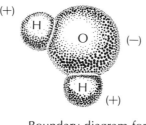

Electron configuration

Hydrogen   1s¹   H·

Oxygen   1s²2s²2p⁴   :Ö:

H :Ö:
H
Lewis structure

104.5°
Actual
bond angle

(+)
H
O   (−)
H
(+)

Boundary diagram for
polar molecule

atom. The hydrogen-oxygen-hydrogen bond angle is 104.5°. This non-linear structure, having regions of uneven pull on the shared electrons, makes water a polar molecule. These relationships are illustrated in Figure 2.

Hydrogen Bonding

The strongly polar nature of water is responsible for the formation of a very important type of bond, called the hydrogen bond. This type of bond comes about only between polar molecules and is common in compounds containing hydrogen combined with the elements oxygen, fluorine, or nitrogen. When bonded to such highly electronegative elements, the hydrogen atom is almost like a bare proton. Thus the hydrogen atom can be attracted to the negative region of an adjacent polar molecule. The weak bond that results between the electropositive hydrogen and the elctronegative atom is called a hydrogen bond. The hydrogen bonding in liquid water is shown in Figure 3 with the dotted lines representing this bond. Solid lines indicate covalent bonds; the strength of the hydrogen bond is only a fraction of the normal attractive force of a covalent bond.

The hydrogen bonding serves, in effect, to form a linkage of a hydrogen atom between two highly electronegative atoms; in this case the hydrogen is now associated with two oxygen atoms. The size of the electronegative atoms is important in determining whether or not this

Figure 3. Hydrogen Bonding in Liquid Water

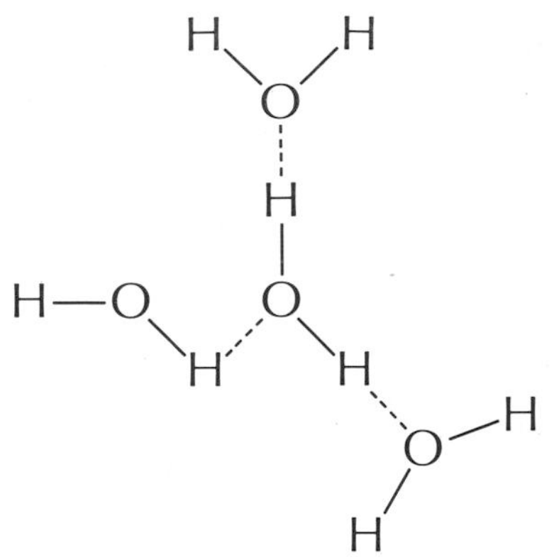

— Electron pair covalent bond
---- Hydrogen bond

phenomenon occurs. In compounds with larger atoms, the electron cloud is very diffuse, and the hydrogen atom will not approach the other molecule very closely. Thus only a very weak, or no, hydrogen bond is formed.

Effects of Hydrogen Bonding

Even though the strength of the hydrogen bonding is only a fraction of the normal attractive force of a covalent bond, it is enough to appreciably change expected properties. As heat energy is added to liquid water, it does not all go towards increasing the kinetic energy (energy of motion) of the molecules; some of it must go towards breaking apart the hydrogen bonds as well. This means that water has a very high heat capacity. Compared with substances without hydrogen bonds, a large amount of heat is required to increase the temperature of water by a certain number of degrees. This property has great effect on the environment, for water plays an important temperature-moderating role on nearby land. If the temperature of water fluctuated rapidly with the sun's heat energy, the climatic effects would be very great. In addition, aquatic life forms which depend on slowly changing temperatures within a well-defined range would no longer be able to survive.

Because of water's ability to absorb heat, it makes a good heat-transfer agent, and therefore water and steam can be used to heat buildings or to exchange heat in industrial applications. Also, a higher temperature than might otherwise be expected by comparison with other hydrogen-group VIA compounds must be reached before the molecules receive enough heat to actually reach the boiling temperature, and a large heat of vaporization must be supplied at that temperature to give the molecules enough energy to leave the surface of the liquid.

Figure 4. The Influence of Hydrogen Bonding on Boiling Points

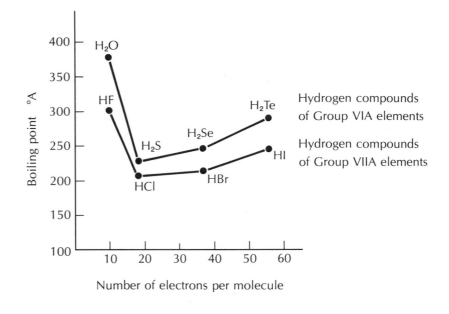

Hydrogen compounds of Group VIA elements

Hydrogen compounds of Group VIIA elements

**Figure 5.
Hydrogen Bonding in Ice**

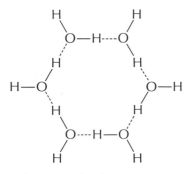

— Electron pair bond.
---- Hydrogen bond.
Bond length = 0.99 Å for covalent bond.
 1.77 Å for hydrogen bond.

The light spheres represent oxygen, the dark spheres hydrogen.

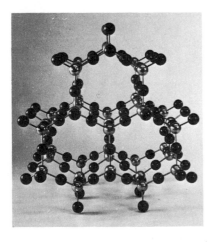

The pattern which we have seen in the hydrogen compounds of the oxygen family can also be seen in the group VIIA compounds with hydrogen. The trends for the boiling points are shown in Figure 4, comparing the two groups of hydrogen compounds.

Only the first member of each group is small enough and electronegative enough to bring about appreciable hydrogen bonding, so that the properties of these compounds do not follow the pattern of the others in the group. In the case of HF, the hydrogen bonding is so strong that hydrogen fluoride exists in the molecular form H_2F_2 with a structure of alternating covalent and hydrogen bonds. In the gaseous phase, hydrogen fluoride has been found to exist in even larger groups of two to six units, depending on the temperature.

We have seen that hydrogen bonding leads to a high boiling point and a high heat capacity. At the other end of the temperature range, hydrogen bonding also plays a role. When water freezes into ice, a regular hexagonal pattern of molecules results, held in position by the hydrogen bonds. The structure is shown in Figure 5. The melting point for water is considerably higher than expected, for energy is needed to break apart the hydrogen-bonded ice formation.

In most substances, the solid form is more dense than the liquid.

This is not true of water. The crystalline structure of ice contains a large proportion of empty space, so ice at 0°C is actually less dense than liquid water at 0°C. The transition to an open structure increases appreciably below 4°C, so the maximum density for water occurs at 4°C even though the freezing point is 0°C. It is difficult to visualize what our world would be like if ice did not float on the warmer water beneath it; fish populations that presently thrive under the insulating blanket of ice in the wintertime would clearly be the first victims if water's unusual properties were not the rule.

When ice is added to a liquid, the liquid cools due to the absorption of heat by the ice cube as it melts. This process can be reversed; freezing water releases heat energy, for heat must be withdrawn from water at 0°C to change it to ice at 0°C. This physical law can have a unique application in preventing frostbite on susceptible young plants.

When severe frost conditions threaten new leaves in vineyards in the early spring, a fine spray of water is used to prevent damage by keeping the leaves at a safe 0°C, the ice-water equilibrium temperature. Temperatures much below that would damage the new leaves, but the presence of the water helps to prevent further cooling of the leaves for no ice will form until all the water has reached 0°C. Then, any ice formation will be accompanied by the release of heat, protecting the new growth from the damaging below-zero temperatures.

This simple system has several advantages over conventional methods such as "smudge pots" and wind machines: no air pollution results, no electrical power is needed, and there is the added advantage of having the sprinkler system available during the summer months for irrigation and cooling. Therefore a reliable and low-cost system is designed on the basis of a simple physical fact.

Water as a Solvent

Water has been called "the universal solvent," with considerable justification, for substances that are themselves polar or ionic are readily soluble in water. In some cases, the solubility results from the relative strength of two attractive forces; if the attraction of the polar water molecule for ions is greater than the ions' attraction for each other, the substance readily goes into solution. For example, crystalline sodium chloride, when added to water, will break apart into its component ions due to the pull of the water molecule. The excellent solubility of many ionic substances in water is responsible for the salinity of seawater.

The attractive forces between water and another polar substance may be enough to cause a chemical reaction rather than just a breaking apart of electrostatic bonds. Such a reaction occurs when gaseous hydrogen chloride is added to water.

$$H{-}O \atop H \quad + \quad H{-}Cl_{(g)} \longrightarrow \left[H{-}O{-}H \atop H \right]^{+} \quad + \quad Cl^{-}$$

hydronium ion   chloride ion

This solution reaction forms an aqueous solution of hydrochloric acid.

Water's ability to form solutions with polar substances is of particular importance in biological systems. It is estimated that 70 to 75 percent of the human body is water, with water being essential for the transport of nutrients and the elimination of wastes. The essential organic compounds found in biological systems contain carbon-oxygen and nitrogen-hydrogen atom groups; these are particularly suited for hydrogen bonding. Therefore, the interaction of the water with these substances is essential for their transport.

Unfortunately, the solubility of many substances in water has a great effect on the environment. The present state of a number of our waterways can be explained by the fact that many of the materials present in polluted waters are actually in solution. Other categories of pollutants are not really dissolved but rather are temporarily suspended. Such substances move through the water either by convection patterns or are carried along with the currents. As is the case in the atmosphere, the components of pollution react and undergo changes once in the water, creating new chemical forms and making analysis and removal more difficult.

The possible discovery of a new form of water called polywater was the subject of much debate and experimentation from 1968–71. The "new water" was first brought to light by Russian researchers who reported changing water vapor in thin capillary tubes into a dense, viscous liquid that freezes into a glassy solid at temperatures considerably below the freezing point of normal water. Yet it cannot be made to boil at laboratory temperatures. The water molecules were thought to be joined together in large polymer-like clusters.

Present understanding of "polywater" is that it is not a new substance but rather a special case of capillary action. Capillarity is the tendency of liquids to rise along a surface of a solid material and is caused by the hydrogen bond formation. Water inside a tube will be attracted by the nitrogen or oxygen atoms in the tube itself and in defiance of gravity, the liquid is pulled up the tube. This mechanism occurs, for example, in circulation of the blood and the feeding of plants from their roots. If there is no liquid reservoir, an isolated capillary or "isocap" is formed. In an isocap, the dissolving power of water is greatly magnified due to the tendency of the vapor to extract normally insoluble ions from the walls of the capillary tube to serve as nuclei for condensation. Thus polywater may simply be a complex solution of water and mineral substances leached out of the glass surface.

To some observers this entire controversy was just a replay of an old controversy between scientists around 1770. (See J. R. Partington, *A History of Chemistry*, Vol. III, 379–81.) Who says that history doesn't repeat itself?

Sources of Water Pollution

Even the definition of polluted water provides some problem, but generally it is taken to mean water that is unsuited for its intended use. Water considered polluted may be actually contaminated, that is, so impaired in quality that a health hazard is created, or it may be, for example, just too salty for irrigation use. Pollution may also be an aesthetic judgment. We can all recognize some signs of polluted water, such as visible oil slicks, floating foam, offensive odors, and changed clarity and color. As with air pollutants, some of the worst offenders are not visible.

The sources of man-made water pollution are not hard to identify: manufacturing, domestic wastes, agricultural and urban runoff, acid mine drainage, and watercraft all play a role. The relative significance of these sources is hard to completely define for several reasons. We do not have complete information about the characteristics and amounts of industrial waste material being added to our water. A generally accepted figure in the United States is that manufacturing generates roughly three times as much waste materials as do the sewage systems in our country. This comparison is less than straightforward, since different types of materials are placed in the water. Table 2 gives estimated data on waterborne wastes from industrial and domestic sources.

Classes of Polluted Water

The pollutants found in water can be a problem because of their biological activity, their physical form, or their chemical nature. Such a classification serves as a useful way to look at pollutants and their effects. For example, chlorinated hydrocarbons from pesticides or plastics can enter a water system and become widely distributed throughout an ecosystem. Soluble inorganic compounds may contain radioactive isotopes discharged from a nuclear fuel reprocessing plant. Both the hydrocarbons and the radioactive compounds are examples of chemical pollutants.

Storm drains may also serve to carry sewage. Untreated domestic wastes add many organic pollutants to the water and present a health hazard. *(Phiz Mezey)*

Many factories and mills use the waters of the Androscoggin River. At Lewiston, Maine, unsightly foam coats the water. The river contains a variety of organic and inorganic pollutants having a high biological oxygen demand.

Mining operations at Leadville, Colorado, produce a stream of discolored water, yellow with an unsightly load of iron hydroxide. Sulfuric acid is another damaging chemical often found in mining waste water.

Table 2. Estimated Volumes of Industrial and Domestic Wastes before Treatment

Industry	Waste-water volume (billion gallons)	Process water intake (billion gallons)	BOD[e] (million pounds)	Suspended solids (million pounds)
Food and kindred products	690	260	4,300	6,600
Meat products	99	52	640	640
Dairy products	58	13	400	230
Canned and frozen food	87	51	1,200	600
Sugar refining	220	110	1,400	5,000
All other	220	43	670	110
Textile mill products	140	110	890	N.E.[f]
Paper and allied products	1,900	1,300	5,900	3,000
Chemical and allied products	3,700	560	9,700	1,900
Petroleum and coal	1,300	88	500	460
Rubber and plastics	160	19	40	50
Primary metals	4,300	1,000	480	4,700
Blast furnaces and steel mills	3,600	870	160	4,300
All other	740	130	320	430
Machinery	150	23	60	50
Electrical machinery	91	28	70	20
Transportation equipment	240	58	120	N.E.
All other manufacturing	450	190	390	930
All manufacturing	[a]13,100	3,700	22,000	18,000
For comparison: Sewered population of United States	[b]5,300	—	[c]7,300	[d]8,800

[a]Columns may not add, due to rounding.
[b]120,000,000 persons times 120 gallons times 365 days.
[c]120,000,000 persons times 1/6 pound times 365 days.
[d]120,000,000 persons times 0.2 pound times 365 days.
[e]BOD will be discussed in the next section.
[f]N.E. = no estimate.

Source: 1st Annual Report of Council on Environmental Quality, 1970, 32. The values are for the year 1964 and are the most recent available. The next comprehensive National Waste Assessment is scheduled for 1977.

Physical water pollution refers to suspended matter such as sand or pulp as well as to floating foam or wood chips. These physical pollutants, as is the case with the other classes, may be added naturally to the waterway or placed there as the result of man's activities. Several of the types of biological pollutants are not easy to classify as to natural or man-made. Algae may be present naturally, but nutrients added by man can cause abundant algal growth with serious results for the quality of the water. Further examples of each type of water pollutant—chemical, physical, and biological—are given in Table 3.

In addition, it is useful to further classify water pollutants as either degradable or nondegradable. Biodegradable (or simply degradable)

Table 3. Classification of Water Pollutants

Type	Examples
Chemical	
Organic	• Oil, dyes, synthetic detergents. chlorinated hydrocarbons, phenols, carboxylic acids, carbohydrates, sugars
Inorganic	• Acids, alkalies, chlorine, metallic salts, nitrates, phosphates, sulfates, bicarbonates, hydrogen sulfide, radioactive isotopes
Physical	
Floating matter	• Foam, scum, wood, leaves
Suspended matter	• Silt, sand, gravel, metal pieces, cinders, rubber, wood chips, paper, pulp, solid sewage material, animal carcasses
Thermal effects	• Heat added
Biological	
Pathogenic forms	• Bacteria, protozoa, fungi, algae, viruses, and parasitic worms that produce disease
Algae	• Excess growth caused by excess nutrients; decay uses oxygen
Aquatic weeds	• Growth uses needed water, such as salt cedar plant

materials are those that can be broken apart into smaller chemical units by natural physical, chemical and biological processes. These smaller units, perhaps even single elements, can more easily reenter natural cycles. Examples of degradable materials are domestic sewage, oil, present detergents, and cellulose. Many other materials will never be broken down or will change only very slowly. Such nondegradable substances are chlorinated hydrocarbons used as pesticides, aluminum cans, and plastics. Some of the effects of these materials on the aquatic environment are discussed in the next section.

Part Two: WHAT PROBLEMS DO THESE POLLUTANTS CAUSE?

The original threat from water pollution was the spread of disease, such as the typhoid epidemics that London experienced in the mid-nineteenth century. Although poor sanitation and contaminated waters still pose a problem in certain areas of our world, waterborne epidemics are largely a thing of the past in developed countries. Instead, water pollution has come to be regarded from a more sophisticated viewpoint. The concern is now focused on the effects that varying amounts of toxic chemicals can have on humans and on other forms of life, as well as on the economic results.

The increased concern for water pollution can be traced to several phenomena, particularly the growth of industry and urban areas. This, together with increased pressure for water-oriented recreation, due to population increases and increasing leisure time, has created a new awareness of the part that water plays in our lives. No one cares for the way that water looks or smells when covered with oil, and no one wants to fish in polluted waters. Yet some of the changes can be more subtle, such as changing of ecological cycles to favor a less desirable type of fish or the filling of underground wells with saline water when fresh water is removed too quickly. Small streams, great lakes, and the oceans have felt the effects of man's activities.

Measuring Dissolved Oxygen: BOD

In order to compare the effects of waste discharges into water systems, some standard of measurement is needed. Instead of analyzing each waste discharge and reporting its chemical composition, it may be more important to indicate the effect of the discharge on the over-all water quality. One such useful measurement of water quality is based on the amount of dissolved oxygen present. It is desirable for water to be high in dissolved oxygen, as the gas is necessary for the existence of fish and other aquatic life. A level of 5 to 7 mg/liter usually indicates healthy water. In addition, this dissolved oxygen is essential for purification processes normally carried on in water by microorganisms. These organisms use organic matter in the water as food, breaking down, or biodegrading, the complex organic matter into simple end products that can then be utilized by other organisms. Such a breakdown of organic matter by microorganisms in the presence of oxygen is called aerobic decay.

If the available dissolved oxygen has been used up and decomposition continues, it must proceed without oxygen or anaerobically. It is highly undesirable to have anaerobic decay only, since it tends to produce large amounts of sludge and noxious gases such as hydrogen sulfide. Another product of anaerobic decay is methane, CH_4, which is known as "swamp gas," for it is often formed in such areas. It is highly flammable and, if it accumulates in a trapped area, can explode. A comparison of the products of aerobic and anaerobic decay is shown in Table 4.

If large amounts of organic materials are suddenly added to a water system and start to decay, a demand is placed on the amount of dissolved oxygen, for the bacteria and other aerobic microorganisms present will utilize the oxygen at a much faster rate than normal. This demand for oxygen can be used as a standard to compare effects of different sources of pollution on water quality. In order to make meaningful comparisons, the conditions must be specified. Therefore, the biochemical oxygen demand or BOD is defined as a quantitative measure of the amount of oxygen used by a sample of polluted water during a five-day incubation period at 20°C. This test is accomplished by taking a sample to be tested and diluting it with fully oxygenated water (9 mg O_2/liter of H_2O at 20°C) and then chemically determining the initial amount of oxygen

Table 4. Comparison of the End Products of Aerobic and Anaerobic Decay

Compounds containing:	Will decay aerobically to give:	Will decay anaerobically to give:
C	CO_2	CH_4
P	H_3PO_4	PH_3
N	NH_3, HNO_3	NH_3, amines
S	H_2SO_4	H_2S

Table 5. Examples of BOD Values

Residential community sewage before treatment	150–390 mg/liter
Milk processing, canning wastes	5000–6000 mg/liter
Wood pulping	Up to 15,000 mg/liter
Wool scouring process	More than 20,000 mg/liter

present. After five days in the dark, the oxygen content is again determined. The difference in oxygen content gives an indication of the BOD. In the course of this time period, probably only 70 to 80 percent of all possible degradation has actually occurred, but standardizing the test at five days is a practical measure to save time and does allow comparisons between water samples.

In the BOD test there are several types of materials that may possibly be contributing to the oxygen demand. Raw or settled sewage is apt to be high in carbon-containing compounds which are used as a source of food by oxygen-using aerobic bacteria. Oxidizable nitrogen from nitrites, ammonia, and organic nitrogen compounds are also present in sewage and in effluents that have been biologically treated, and this uses more oxygen. Certain chemical reducing compounds may also use up oxygen in the BOD test, particularly Fe^{+2}, sulfite, and sulfide ions. Some examples of BOD values are given in Table 5.

Measuring Dissolved Oxygen: COD, TOC

Another test which measures the effect of waste materials on dissolved oxygen and therefore measures water quality is the chemical oxygen demand or COD. Instead of using oxygen itself for the degradation, this test uses strong oxidizing agents such as chromic and sulfuric acid to oxidize compounds, thus providing a measure of the oxygen equivalent of that waste water. This procedure has the advantage of being rapid, although the method may exclude some important degradable compounds such as acetic acid. More importantly, it includes other compounds that are not biodegradable under normal water conditions, such as cellulose. Therefore, the values for COD are usually higher than BOD values.

Total organic carbon or TOC is still another useful measure of over-all water quality. This new method uses a rapid combustion process to change all carbon available to CO_2, which is then measured using the technique of infrared spectroscopy. The amount of CO_2 produced then can be related to the oxygen equivalent of the water.

Figure 6. Oxygen Content in Polluted Waters

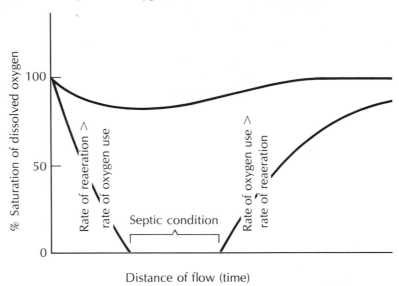

This small stream in New Jersey contains an almost solid mat of algae. Nutrients making their way into the water have stimulated excessive growth of algae. The surface layer cuts out sunshine and oxygen for the waters below and uses up dissolved oxygen in decaying.

CHEMISTRY OF THE WATER ENVIRONMENT

All three of these methods for looking at the demand for oxygen are important, for they will help to predict the resulting condition of the water after waste is added. If the rate of oxygen use is very high, the water may not be able to replace the lost oxygen quickly enough through natural processes. Running water has a capacity to absorb oxygen from the air; this process is known as reaeration. Reaeration replenishes the water's supply of oxygen for the aerobic bacteria. High use of oxygen may go beyond this capacity. This will cause septic conditions, in which the dissolved oxygen falls to zero and anaerobic decay takes place. If no further demand for oxygen is placed on the water, the percentage of oxygen may again rise. Some of these relationships are shown in Figure 6.

As important as the dissolved oxygen is as an indicator of water quality, it does not give the full story, by any means. The BOD and other parameters do not give any indication of specific compounds present, particularly whether or not toxic chemical or bacteriological agents are in the water. Other factors that are commonly monitored are the water's pH and temperature, total dissolved solids, specific ions of interest, pesticide and radioactive content, along with such obvious characteristics as color, odor, and turbidity.

Eutrophication

If the water system is a lake or a slow-moving stream, it becomes important to measure the levels of nutrients present. Phosphorus and nitrogen compounds are examples of nutrients essential to soil and water systems as a source of food, but a large influx of these compounds into a waterway causes excessive growth of algae and aquatic plants. Lakes that have been overenriched by nutrients are called eutrophic meaning "well nourished." The process of enrichment is called eutrophication.

The most visible result of eutrophication is an "algal bloom" producing a mat of algae covering the water's surface. The thick layer of algae has several effects on water quality. As the sun's rays can no longer reach the bottom part of the layer, the algae begins to decay, using dissolved oxygen in the process. Taste and odor of the water may also be affected. Some fresh water algae produce toxic materials when they decay; members of the cyanophyta or blue-green algae group, the most primitive form of algae, are most likely to decay into toxic materials. Algae differ in their toleration of pollution, and a shift from green to blue-green algae usually indicates increasing eutrophication. Similarly, a shift to all one type of algae is not an encouraging environmental indication as diversity is one sign of a healthy ecosystem.

Although eutrophication can and does occur naturally, it is usually a slow process, brought about, for example, as a lake's basin fills with sediment. Man's activities have contributed in large measure to speeding up eutrophication. In particular, the use of high-phosphate detergents has received considerable attention. In order to understand the reasons behind the use of phosphate detergents and their relationship to the problem of eutrophication, we first will look at the chemical differences between soaps and detergents and their methods of operation.

Soaps

Soaps are the sodium or potassium salts of long-chain organic acids. A common example would be sodium stearate.

$$
\underbrace{CH_3-(CH_2)_{16}-C}_{\substack{\text{Nonpolar}\\\text{end of molecule}}} \overset{\displaystyle\overbrace{\phantom{CH_3-(CH_2)_{16}-C}}^{\text{Stearate ion}}}{\underset{\underset{\substack{\text{Polar end-}\\\text{ions present}}}{O^-\quad Na^+}}{\overset{O}{\diagdown}}}
$$

Soap derives its cleaning ability from the fact that one end of the molecule is polar and therefore will dissolve in water; it is said to be the *hydrophilic* or water loving part of the molecule. The long-chain hydrocarbon end has a structure similar to that of grease and oil and therefore is a good solvent for those substances, which do not dissolve in water. That end is termed *hydrophobic* or water fearing. The dual nature of this molecule enables it to act as an emulsifying agent; such an agent allows two substances that normally will not mix (grease and water) to be suspended in each other, since the emulsifying agent is attracted to both substances. Thus one end of the molecule can dissolve in the water as the other end dissolves in the grease or oil, holding it in suspension long enough to be rinsed away.

The main drawback of soap as a cleaning agent is that in "hard" water (water containing ions of calcium, magnesium, and sometimes iron) the soap will react to form an annoying scum or precipitate instead of emulsifying the dirt. The calcium and magnesium compounds of soaps are not soluble. This reaction uses up some of the soap, so excess must be used in order to achieve the cleaning power desired. In addition, the scum must be disposed of.

$$
2\left[CH_3-(CH_2)_{16}-C\underset{O^-}{\overset{O}{\diagup}}\right] + Ca^{+2} \longrightarrow \left(CH_3-(CH_2)_{16}-C\underset{O}{\overset{O}{\diagup}}\right)_2 Ca \downarrow
$$

This disadvantage of soap can be overcome by the use of a water-softening compound such as washing soda, sodium carbonate. The carbonate reacts with the ions responsible for the hardness to form a precipitate.

$$Ca^{+2} + CO_3^{-2} \longrightarrow CaCO_3 \downarrow$$

Unlike the gummy, floating curd that results from the reaction between soap and calcium ion, this precipitate is rather granular and settles harmlessly to the bottom of the washing machine.

Soap has another disadvantage, but this one is shared with most detergents as well. Since laundry tends to be acidic due to the presence of perspiration, a reaction can take place with soap that reduces its effectiveness.

$$CH_3-(CH_2)_{16}-C\underset{O^-}{\overset{O}{\big<}} + H^+ \rightleftharpoons CH_3-(CH_2)_{16}-C\underset{OH}{\overset{O}{\big<}}$$

Stearic acid

Since the hydrophilic end no longer contains charged ions, the molecule is less effective as an emulsifying agent.

Detergents

Synthetic detergents were first formulated in Germany in the 1930s and were introduced into the United States in the 1940s. Their solubility and lack of precipitate even in hard water played a large part in their public acceptance. Detergents now outsell soap by a five to one ratio. Like soap, detergents have both a hydrophilic and a hydrophobic end of the molecule; there are several types of structures that meet this requirement.

The first type of detergent to be formulated was anionic detergents. For several years, these were the only type of synthetic product that could effectively be used for cleaning, and they remain the principal type in production today. Anionic detergents are so called because the charged end of the molecule that is attached to the hydrocarbon group is an anion (negatively charged). A common example of one of the hundreds of anionic detergents is the class known as the ABS or alkyl benzene sulfonate detergents. Their structure is:

$$R-\!\!\!\left\langle\!\!\bigcirc\!\!\right\rangle\!\!-SO_3^- Na^+ \qquad R = \text{alkyl group, } C_{12}-C_{18}$$

Hydrophobic end   Hydrophilic end

Cationic detergents, in which the attached charge group is a cation (positively charged) are commonly of this type:

$$\underbrace{R\text{———}}_{\substack{\text{Hydrophobic}\\\text{end}}}\underbrace{N^+(CH_3)_3Cl^-}_{\substack{\text{Hydrophilic}\\\text{end}}} \qquad R = C_{16}$$

This class is in general more expensive to produce than the anionics but may have other properties that enhance their use, such as germicidal function. Some cationic formulations are used as fabric softeners.

Nonionic detergents, as the name implies, do not have a charged end but do have a polar area as the hydrophilic part of the molecule. An example is:

$$\underbrace{CH_3\text{—}(CH_2)_8\text{—}\langle\bigcirc\rangle\text{—}}_{\substack{\text{Hydrophobic}\\\text{end}}}\underbrace{(OCH_2CH_2)_{10}\text{—}OCH_2CH_3}_{\substack{\text{Hydrophilic}\\\text{end}}}$$

Nonionic detergents are used primarily as wetting agents or emulsifiers and do not account for a very large share of the detergent industry at this time.

Prior to 1965, one of the main problems connected with detergents was their slow rate of biodegradation. This condition produced masses of unsightly foam in rivers used for the discharge of domestic wastes. All detergents are now required to be readily biodegradable. The change was technologically possible in a short period of time due to the discovery that straight-chain hydrocarbons were more easily attacked by bacteria than were branched-chain formulations. By chemically altering this basic alignment, the cleaning properties remained unchanged but the problem of long-lasting foam was solved.

As originally developed, no detergents by themselves could match soap in cleaning power; their public acceptance was based originally on their favorable characteristics in hard water. Although detergents did not precipitate in hard water, some of their action was lost in reacting with the calcium and other hardness ions present. It was soon discovered that the performance of detergents could be greatly enhanced by the addition of a large percentage of sodium tripolyphosphate, $Na_5P_3O_{10}$. The phosphate serves as a filler to lessen the cost of formulation and also to adjust the pH to alkaline as is desirable in cleaning acidic laundry. However, the main function of the phosphate is to react with the calcium and magnesium ions present, keeping them bound in a variety of soluble complex ions. (In performing this function, sodium tripolyphosphate is said to be a sequestering agent for the metallic ions present.) Adding phosphates therefore has the effect of increasing the cleaning power of detergents because the water is softened by the presence of the phosphates.

In addition to being unsightly, foam can serve to transport potentially harmful organisms and other pollutants. Recent laws requiring detergents to be biodegradable should make this scene less frequent. *(Nicholas R. Keough)*

Phosphates and Eutrophication

Phosphates have been added to commercial detergents since 1945, but only in the late 1960s did they come under attack as a possible cause of accelerated eutrophication in lakes and other waters. It soon became clear that the entire eutrophication process was a typical example of a complex web of life distorted by man's actions without knowledge of the effects. Nutrients needed for the growth of plant life include carbon, hydrogen, oxygen, sulfur, potassium, calcium, magnesium, nitrogen, and phosphorus, as well as trace amounts of other organic and inorganic materials. Of these, only nitrates, phosphates, and carbon dioxide have been studied in any detail. Any one of these three nutrients can set off an algal bloom, assuming the other two are present in sufficient amounts. Since carbon dioxide is available from the air and nitrogen can be fixed from the air by blue-green algae, the focus for the control of total nutrients was placed on phosphorus. This emphasis was confirmed in early studies showing the ratio of phosphorus to nitrogen was the growth-limiting factor for algae. If all phosphates were removed from household detergents in the United States, about 280 million pounds of phosphorus would be kept from surface waters; it is estimated that 680 million tons would still reach the waters from such sources as municipal and industrial waste waters, urban runoff, agricultural fertilizers, and rainfall. The relative importance of the sources of phosphates varies with the specific location, however, so that in some places, phosphates from detergents and other domestic uses may provide up to 70 percent of the total amount placed in a water system. The confusion over the role of phosphates continues; reduction in phosphorus in some water systems has produced marked improvement in water quality.

Phosphate Substitutes

Unfortunately for the consumer, some of the replacements for phosphates in detergents have proven to be highly alkaline, and the caustic nature of alkaline substances is irritating to eyes, skin, and respiratory tract. Particularly harmful have been those products containing sodium metasilicate. The reason behind the alkalinity of these formulations can be seen by looking at the reaction that occurs in water.

$$Na_2SiO_3 \ + \ 2 \, H_2O \ \rightleftharpoons \ 2 \, NaOH \ + \ H_2SiO_3$$

Sodium metasilicate   Sodium hydroxide   Metasilicic acid

The metasilicic acid produced in this reaction is a weak acid and only a low percentage of the molecules are ionized into hydrogen ions that are the characteristic of an acid. Sodium hydroxide, on the other hand, is highly ionized into sodium ions and the hydroxide ions characteristic of

Manufacturers have responded quickly to actual or threatened limitations on the phosphate content of detergents. However, replacement products have caused problems also. (*The Gold Seal Company.*)

an alkaline substance. The reaction therefore produces more hydroxide than hydrogen ions, giving the resulting solution an alkaline pH.

Another substitute for phosphates is the sodium salt of NTA, nitrilotriacetic acid. This substance, $N(CH_2CO_2Na)_3$, has the following structure.

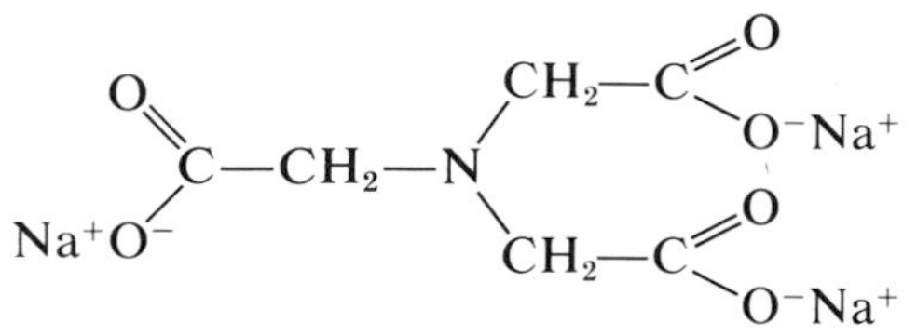

NTA has many potential advantages as a phosphate replacement. It is inexpensive to produce, is readily biodegradable, and forms soluble complexes with calcium and magnesium that are stable at alkaline pH. However, further testing showed that NTA was equally adept at complexing mercury, lead, cadmium, and arsenic. This would have the effect of placing these toxic metals into solution where they could enter different ecosystems. Incomplete evidence as to the possible carcinogenic (cancer-causing) and teratogenic (birth-defect causing) effects of these complexes on man has lead to the withdrawal of NTA pending further tests. This government action in late 1970 put a sudden halt to a booming segment of the detergent industry and further emphasized the need to test materials before they are allowed widespread introduction into the environment.

Other additives are commonly used in detergents to accomplish specific goals. *Enzymes* attack protein stains which are resistant to removal by detergents or soaps. Blood, urine, meat juices, tea, and chocolate stains can be eliminated, but enzyme detergents produce allergeric reactions in susceptible people, including the workers who must breathe the flourlike dust of the enzymes. *CMC* (carboxymethylcellulose) is a water soluble derivative of cellulose used to keep the dirt in suspension so preventing its redeposition on clothing. *Optical brighteners* are organic molecules that absorb ultraviolet light and then reradiate the energy in the visible wavelengths. The exact nature of the brighteners differs with geographic location. In North America, blue-white is the accepted hue for cleanliness, so compounds must be chosen so that the energy is radiated in the blue end of the spectrum. In South America, manufacturers seek to produce a red-white coloration as that is the culturally accepted color for clean. Optical brighteners by themselves do not insure that clothes are clean; they only help us to perceive them as clean.

Ocean Dumping

At one time enrichment was a problem only for fresh water systems, but increasing instances of algal blooms and other alterations in local conditions have been reported in estuaries, bays, and in the ocean itself above the continental shelf. These changes are apparently the result of our policy of minimal controls over ocean dumping. The volume of wastes dumped into the once seemingly infinite oceans is rapidly increasing, and the trend can be expected to continue. Urban areas are running out of capacity for waste disposal in conveniently located land, short-term costs favor ocean dumping, and the political problems involved in obtaining new landfill sites are increasingly difficult to solve. (The problems of solid waste disposal are discussed in more detail in Chapter Nine.) Some of the types and amounts of ocean dumping are given in Table 6.

As may be seen from this table, approximately 80 percent of all material dumped is the result of dredging operations. This material is not just inert mud and dirt, for much of it comes from the bottom of water bodies into which industrial, municipal, and agricultural wastes have been

Table 6. Types, Amounts, and Costs of Wastes Dumped at Sea

Type of waste	Pacific coast[a] annual tonnage	Atlantic coast[a] annual tonnage	Gulf coast[a] annual tonnage	Total tonnage	Estimated cost
Dredging spoils	7,320,000	15,808,000	15,300,000	38,428,000 (80%)	$15,533,000
Industrial wastes[b]	981,300	3,013,200	696,000	4,690,500 (10%)	8,193,000
Sewage sludge[c]	0	4,477,000	0	4,477,000 (9%)	4,433,000
Construction and demolition debris	0	574,000	0	574,000 (<1%)	430,000
Refuse and garbage	26,000	0	0	26,000 (<1%)	392,000
Explosives	0	15,200	0	15,200 (<1%)	285,000
Total	8,327,300	23,887,400	15,996,000	48,210,700	$29,266,000

Source: Chemical and Engineering News, November 30, 1970, p. 40. Data from Dillingham Corp.
[a]Figures for 1968 for 20 coastal cities.
[b]Includes chemicals, acids, caustics, cleaners, sludges, waste liquors, and oily wastes.
[c]Tonnage on wet basis.

dumped for a long time. The United States Army Corps of Engineers reports that 34 percent of the total material dumped after dredging is polluted, judging by such indicators as BOD and COD and measures for oil and grease, phosphorus, nitrogen, iron and silica, and other metallic elements.

The wastes dumped from industrial sources vary greatly because of the diversity of production methods and type of industry, but waste acids account for the largest amount (58 percent). Effluents from refineries, pesticide manufacturing, and paper mills also are important. Cyanides, heavy metals, mercaptans (those smelly sulfur compounds) and chlorinated hydrocarbons have been identified in industrial wastes.

Sewage sludge (see Part Three) is a byproduct of municipal waste-water treatment; at the present time, most of it is disposed of on land or is incinerated. Some areas, for example, the New York harbor and Los Angeles, discharge sludge by pipeline into the ocean. Where this practice is followed, the three greatest causes for concern are once again the concentrations of heavy metals, the high oxygen demand caused by organic material, and the possibility of harmful bacteria remaining active.

The other sources of wastes going into the ocean are relatively small at the present and may constitute only a local problem, as for example in New York City, which disposes of construction and demolition debris by towing 3000- to 5000-ton barges nine miles off shore and sinking them. In some areas, inert solid wastes such as cars and tires are inadvertently serving a new function: schools of fish have chosen the dumped material as desirable living space, presumably for the protection offered from larger predators. Limited experiments are under way to determine more about creating new fish habitats in this way.

Explosives continue to be disposed of at sea, including unserviceable and obsolete shells, mines, solid rocket fuels, and chemical warfare agents (but not biological agents). The United States has not disposed of radioactive wastes at sea since 1962, but some other countries continue this practice.

Oil Spills

Sometimes the ocean dumping takes place as the result of an accident, such as an oil spill. Oil on the water is a problem of the post World War I years and perhaps one of limited duration until our natural supplies are depleted. Nevertheless, the increased capacity of tankers makes the possibility of a huge spill more threatening. Public attention has been focused on this water pollutant by such disasters as the breaking up of the Torrey Canyon, pouring thousands of gallons of crude oil into the western end of the English Channel in 1967, and the Santa Barbara oil leakage from offshore wells in 1969. Besides these well-publicized

Oil pollution of the waters of the world—where does it all come from? Estimates released by the Environmental Protection Agency show that over 5 million metric tons or 1.5 billion gallons of crude oil or petroleum products were spilled in all water systems in 1970. The figures also reveal that by far the major contribution to this amount is from motor and industrial oils that make their way into surface waters after use.

Much of the public's concern about oil pollution centers on the effects of oil washing up on the beaches. Even though this is the most unpleasant effect for the public, the oil can be just as damaging to marine organisms while it is still in the water system. There are several methods now in use to contain and recover the oil in an attempt to prevent it from fouling the beaches. Bacteria capable of digesting hydrocarbons can be added to the water to help biodegrade the oil. This process utilizes the dissolved oxygen in the water. There are also substances such as Sorb-Oil © that will soak up the oil so that it will not wash up on the beach or into important waterways. The oil can be reclaimed from the absorbent. The simplest and oldest method to remove oil from shallow areas is to soak up the oil with straw, collect, and then burn the straw.

This offshore oil tanker is transferring oil by an underwater pipeline to storage tanks at an onshore power plant. The use of larger and larger tankers increases the magnitude of possible damage from spills or leaks.

Using straw to recover oil from beaches. (*Klink*)

events, unknown numbers of small leaks and constant small amounts from tankers flushing their tanks at sea add oil to the marine environment. Thor Heyerdahl, in his trans-Atlantic ocean trip in 1970, reported seeing large areas of oil, together with plastics and other evidences of man's activities, miles from any land.

Most of the oil tankers carry material in the form of crude oil. Crude oil is a complex mix of hydrocarbons with a wide range of molecular weights. The different hydrocarbons behave in different ways when spilled into sea water. Up to 25 percent of it will evaporate, mainly aromatics, including such fractions as xylene, benzene, and toluene. The aromatics are known to be the most toxic of the hydrocarbons. What is left usually drifts into tarry lumps and may be transported large distances by horizontal ocean currents. This residue is subject to photo-oxidation and bacterial action with poorly understood long-term effects. Recent evidence shows that these tarry surfaces are ideal for collecting pesticide aerosols, thus concentrating toxic materials and making them available for entry into the marine food chain. Some residues eventually find their way to the ocean floor, and little is known of their effects there.

In the case of a large oil spill, efforts are made to contain and recover the spill to minimize environmental damage (and to recover the oil—a major investment). Various methods to accomplish this have been

Oil Pollution in the Waters of the World

Percent of total	In metric tons	Source
67.2%	3,300,000	•Used motor and industrial oils[a]
10.7%	530,000	•Tankers, normal operations
10.1%	500,000	•Oil from bilges of other ships, excluding pleasure craft
6.0%	300,000	•Refineries, petrochemical plants
2.0%	100,000	•Tanker and ship accidents
2.0%	100,000	•Nonship accidents
2.0%	100,000	•Offshore production, normal operations

[a]If your garage serviceman drains and changes the oil for your car, where does the used oil go? If the same job is done at home, where does the oil go?

tried, and more are now under development. One of the simplest is to place straw or other absorbent material such as rice hulls or fiber products on the spill to soak up the oil. The absorbent material must then be removed and disposed of, probably by burial or burning. In some cases, the oil can be reclaimed from the absorbent material. Powdered chalk or other agents can be placed on the oil to form particles heavy enough to sink. Oil may be ignited but usually does not burn very completely. Booms, barges, and skimmers contain the oil so that it can be vacuumed off the surface. Barriers of air bubbles are being tried instead of physical barriers to contain oil, but neither method works well in rough waters.

Various chemical dispersants have been tried, particularly detergents derived from long-chain acids. The detergents should act as emulsifiers and cause the oil to agglomerate, making it easier to pick up. This practice has been largely stopped since the Torrey Canyon incident, for the detergent may have caused more problems than it helped solve. The detergents killed limpets which normally would have helped remove the oil by browsing on the rocks on inflicted beaches. Another factor in that case was that the detergents were dissolved in toxic aromatic hydrocarbon solvents before use.

Some of the newer methods of retrieving oil are the use of oil soluble ferrofluids and accelerated microbial biodegradation. In the first method, an iron-containing material soluble in oil is added to the spill and then an electromagnet can be used to remove the oil. In the second, the natural biodegradability of hydrocarbons is enhanced by use of a mixture of some twenty organisms selected to metabolize the hydrocarbon rapidly with no toxic products. The most promising type of bacteria are a type called the pseudomonas: tests have shown them capable of breaking down 50 to 75% of oil into smaller, harmless compounds within forty-eight hours.

These methods would, of course, become unnecessary if losses were stopped at their source. For example, it was estimated that in 1969, 10^6 tons of oil were lost to the sea in production and transportation accidents. It is clearly of economic as well as purely environmental concern to reduce these spills.

Effects of Pollution on the Oceans

Is the purposeful or inadvertent practice of ocean dumping cause for concern? As we grow in ecological sophistication, we have to disregard as inaccurate a romantic view of the "bottomless, unutterably vast and timeless" nature of the ocean. Marine pollution has already damaged the environment and endangered humans in several areas. Many beaches and bays have been closed for swimming, lifeless zones have been created in certain water bodies, visual quality is often unpleasing, there have been kills of fish, and it is estimated that one fifth of the nation's shellfish beds have been destroyed by pollution. Therefore, our present practices have already affected marine life, human health, and economics. With projected increases in dumping, the problems will continue to grow in importance.

A popular misconception about the ocean is that it is safe to dump wastes in it away from the coast because they will drop to the bottom and stay out of the accessible environment "forever." This may actually happen for a number of solid, nonsoluble wastes, if "forever" just means a few hundred years. However, as noted previously, floating and suspended wastes can be carried great distances by horizontal currents and winds. In most cases this happens much more quickly than the vertical movement of wastes to the bottom. In addition, many substances react with the water, which helps to keep them in suspension. Pollutants can then enter living systems and be concentrated through normal biological pathways.

The tiny phytoplankton, the bottom of the food chain, act as a great biological blotter and soak up trace metals and nutrients. The phytoplankton utilize some of the ingested substances as part of their normal processes, but amounts that are in excess of their requirements or foreign to their systems are either excreted or stored. Those excess substances that are water soluble tend to be eliminated, but many organics and metals that are only slightly soluble in water are very fat soluble and therefore are deposited in fats of the host system. At each of the subsequent steps

Figure 7. The Food Chain in the North Atlantic

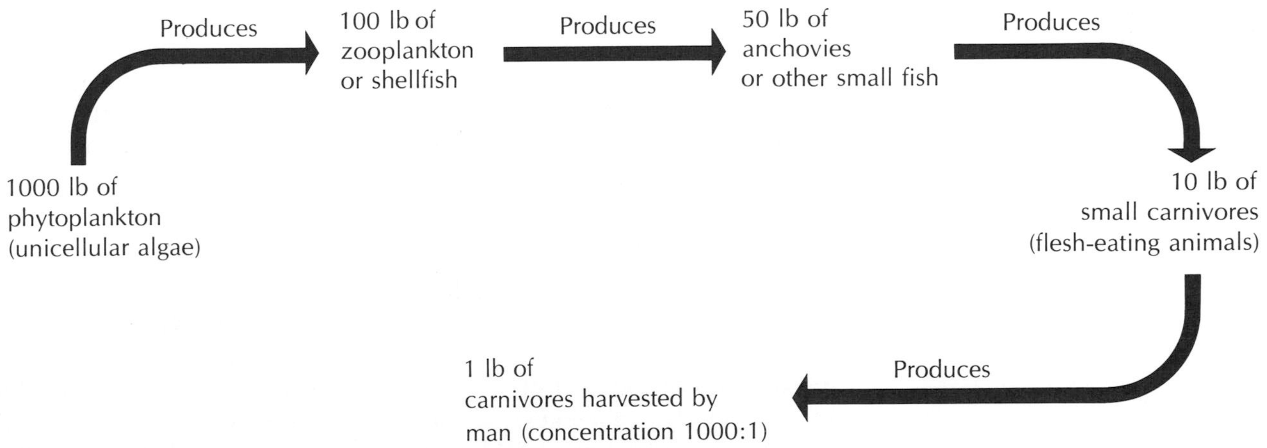

1000 lb of phytoplankton (unicellular algae) → Produces → 100 lb of zooplankton or shellfish → Produces → 50 lb of anchovies or other small fish → Produces → 10 lb of small carnivores (flesh-eating animals) → Produces → 1 lb of carnivores harvested by man (concentration 1000:1)

Table 7. Phytoplankton Concentration of Some Heavy Metals

Metal	Concentration factor (phytoplankton to surrounding water)
Aluminum	100,000
Cobalt	1,500
Copper	30,000
Iron	45,000
Lead	40,000
Radium	12,000
Zinc	26,000

of the food chain, any contaminants that have been stored in the lower member will also be stored in greater and greater concentration in the next step until a very high biological magnification has taken place. The generalized process of concentration is indicated in Figure 7 for one type of food chain.

The result of such a chain is the concentration of heavy metals, pesticides, and other waterborne contaminants. Even though the surrounding water may be relatively low in a toxic metal, even the organisms lowest on the food chain may have concentrations from several hundred to several thousand times greater, as shown in Table 7.

Many metals are now present in local areas in toxic quantities, and biological concentration increases the possible harm at every step of the chain. For example, copper is present in concentrations ranging from 300 to 2000 ppm in sewage sludge, as opposed to a natural seawater concentration of 0.003 ppm. Concentrations of 0.1 ppm have been shown to inhibit photosynthesis in kelp and to kill soft clams. Several factors common to many types of waterborne metal contamination can be illustrated by considering mercury as a case study.

Mercury: An Unexpected Peril

The modern history of public concern for the properties of mercury began in the early 1950s when fishermen of Minamata, Japan, their families, and pets were stricken with a mysterious set of symptoms: constriction of the field of vision, loss of vision, progressive weakening of the muscles, numbness, paralysis and in several cases, coma and death. The small town of Minamata is located on a bay on the most southerly of the main Japanese islands. The town thrived on two industries, fishing and chemical manufacturing. Subsequent investigations of this tragedy, called "Kibyo" or "strange illness" by the residents, clearly showed the cause to be the large amount of mercury discharged into the bay in the manufacturing of PVC, the plastic polyvinylchloride. Measurements of the silt near the plant showed mercury concentrations of 2000 ppm and of the water itself between 1.6 and 3.6 parts per billion (seawater would normally have a concentration of 0.1 ppb). The fish that constituted the main protein source of the daily diet for these people contained 5 to 20 ppm; 0.5 ppm is the concentration for fish allowed by the United States Food and Drug Administration.

The concentration of mercury in fish has created problems in this country as well. In late 1970, millions of cans of tuna fish were removed from the shelves after tests showed mercury concentrations over 1 ppm. Subsequent tests of swordfish found levels up to 1.50 ppm and the Food and Drug Administration warned the public, particularly children and pregnant women, not to eat this fish. The swordfish is a large predator near the top of the marine food chain and is therefore a likely type of fish to show accumulation of toxic materials. Even the size of the tuna correlates with the amount of mercury present for in FDA tests, small tuna (less than 26 lb) had an average of 0.13 ppm mercury, large tuna (more than 50 lb) had an average concentration of 0.25 ppm and the highest concentrations of mercury were reported for the 100-pound Skipjack tuna, 1.12 ppm. Fish from fresh water systems in the United States and Canada have shown even greater concentrations of mercury. For example, Walleye pike from Lake Erie and the St. Clair River had mercury concentrations from 1.40 to 3.57 ppm; restrictions on fishing have been imposed in this and similar areas.

Other incidents have continued to keep mercury in the news. There have been outbreaks of mercurial poisoning in Iraq, Pakistan, and Guatemala due to the improper use of mercury-coated seeds. Grain seeds are commonly coated with organic mercury compounds to protect against harmful soil microorganisms. Such seed is meant to be planted and not used for feed, but the Huckleby family in New Mexico were stricken in 1969 after eating pork derived from hogs which had been fed mercury-coated seed. Tragically, even their unborn child became blind, showing the teratogenic effects of mercury. In 1972, the natives of the remote Pribilof Islands of Alaska were advised to give up eating seal livers, their traditional delicacy, because of dangerously high concentrations of mercury. Evidently the seals ingested mercury-contaminated fish as they migrated through the waters off California. Game birds and wild life have been reported poisoned in Sweden; restrictions have been placed on fishing and the sale of fish in Canada. What is this chemical that has such toxic properties and is so widespread?

Table 8. Important Uses of Mercury

	U.S. consumption in thousands of pounds	
	1959	1969
Electrolytic preparation of chlorine and sodium hydroxide by the use of mercury cells (chlor-alkali process)	443	1575
Electrical apparatus • "Silent" light switches, neon tube light, rectifiers, highway lights, radio batteries, fluorescent lights	677	1417
Paint • Antifouling paints to resist seaweed and barnacles	75	19
• Mildew-proof paints—use in latex-based paints	192	721
Industrial controls • Thermometers, manometers, pressure gauges	468	531
Dental preparation • Amalgams for fillings	139	232
Industrial catalysts • Production of urethane, polyvinyl chloride (PVC is the single most widely used plastic in the world.)	73	225
Agriculture • Organic mercury compounds protect seeds against organisms causing fungus, rot, and disease	243	204
General laboratory use • Catalyst for chemical reactions • $HgCl_2$ (corrosive sublimate) can be used to preserve specimens, sterilize instruments • Laboratory instruments, thermometers, etc.	84	115
Pharmaceuticals • Diuretic in treating congestive heart failure • Historically used for treating syphilis • Use in mercurochrome; germ-killing properties • Skin disease treatment	130	55
Paper and pulp industry • Phenyl mercuric acetate prevents green slime and mold (also used in swimming pools) • Prevent bacterial growth	331	42
Amalgamation and purification of metals • Bonds to other metals (except iron and platinum) to form solid solutions called amalgams • Must separate amalgams by electrolysis	20	15
Total usage	2,875 ($\times 10^3$)	5,251 ($\times 10^3$)

Data: U.S. Bureau of Mines

Properties and Uses of Mercury

Mercury has been known since medieval times for its fascinating chemical and physical properties. It is the only metallic element that is liquid at room temperature. It does not occur abundantly in the earth's crust but is widely distributed. Most of it is in the form of the mineral cinnabar, HgS. This bright red ore was mined at least two or three millenia ago in China and Peru and used as a pigment. Mercury's ability to kill germs has been acknowledged since 400 B.C. The physicians of the medieval period were the first to extract mercury by heating cinnabar, and used mercury to produce medicines. They were carrying out this reaction:

$$HgS + O_2 \longrightarrow Hg_{(l)} + SO_{2(g)}$$

These uses produced little over-all threat to the general environment, although there was some danger to the workers, since mercury vapor is harmful if inhaled. Mercury compounds still are used safely to treat various infections and disorders, although their use is declining.

Mercury is widely used in industry now, so large amounts of mercury are being redistributed and concentrated in the environment, and this aspect must be evaluated with respect to harmful effects. Some of the important uses of mercury are given in Table 8. The values are given for two years, ten years apart, so that patterns of increasing or decreasing use can be identified.

Many of these uses reflect the unique properties of the element mercury, such as its ability to conduct electricity and yet be a fluid. Thus, it is placed in devices requiring movable electrical contacts. Although its conductivity is actually rather poor compared to other metals, its mobility is a great advantage. Mercury's amalgamation property was the basis for gold extraction from its ores, and many miners were well acquainted with the properties of "quicksilver," as they termed liquid mercury in its elemental form.

Environmental Exposure to Mercury

Not all forms of mercury are harmful: liquid mercury itself is not toxic. The vapors are very corrosive and can cause irritation and destruction of lung tissue. Chronic exposure to mercury vapor is not a general environmental problem but is serious for miners or industrial workers. They may receive enough inhaled mercury vapor to produce such symptoms as tremors, inflammation of the gums, and general irritability. Mercuric nitrate, $Hg(NO_3)_2$, is used in processing felt, and vapors from this chemical may cause similar symptoms.

Since mercury is a trace constituent of coal and petroleum products, burning fossil fuels releases mercury into the air. This is a general problem, for it has been estimated that 10^5 metric tons of mercury have been released into the environment since 1900 from this source, approximately equal to the estimated losses from agricultural and industrial consumption for the same time period. For comparison, the earth's seawater is estimated to naturally contain 10^8 metric tons of mercury, but the concentration varies considerably from place to place.

A large percentage of the mercury used by man will eventually make its way into the environment. Some industrial uses at least have the potential for developing total recycling of the mercury (chlorine-soda manufacturing and electrical equipment uses for example) but in other uses the mercury will be distributed into the environment (in paints, agriculture, pharmaceuticals, pulp and paper, and mining). These dissipative uses of mercury are the ones that present the greatest challenge to control. This is particularly true in light of new evidence about the mobility of mercury once in the environment.

Mercury's Surprising Mobility

The movement of mercury in the environment and its concentration in the food chain are greatly facilitated by the fact that many forms of mercury can be converted in natural systems to alkyl mercury forms, particularly methyl mercury (CH_3Hg^+) and dimethylmercury ($(CH_3)_2Hg$). This was a surprise to investigators in the early 1960s who first found evidence for these reactions, and not a pleasant surprise at that. The soluble inorganic salts of mercury and the phenyl (aryl) mercury compounds are toxic but are not nearly as dangerous as the alkyl forms which can attack brain cells, causing permanent injury. In particular, the body cannot metabolize the monomethyl mercury form and thus it remains in the body for a relatively long time (biological half-life of 70 days) to cause damage. The mercury in the monomethyl mercury molecule has a strong attraction for sulfur found in sulfur-hydrogen linkages in proteins (especially enzymes) and thus the mercury is bound in cell membranes, altering the cell's proper functions. (Arsenic and lead exhibit similar activity.) The alkyl mercury compounds contain mercury firmly bonded to carbon atoms and are not easily degraded, thus retaining their activity for a period of several weeks to several years.

Waterborne mercury is available for methylation primarily through the mercuric ion, Hg^{+2}, which stays in the water system by its equilibrium reaction with the water and by the fact that it is rather inert to oxidation by the air. Some of the pathways of reaction are indicated in Figure 8.

The exact mechanism for the methylation is now the subject of intense research effort, and many alternatives have been proposed. It is known that both enzymatic and nonenzymatic reactions occur; aerobic systems are favored, but conversion to methyl mercury can take place

Figure 8. Chemical Conversion to Alkyl Mercury Compounds

$$Hg^{+2} + H_2O \rightleftharpoons HgOH^+ + H^+$$
$$HgOH^+ + H_2O \rightleftharpoons Hg(OH)_2 + H^+$$

Reactions between Hg^{+2} and water

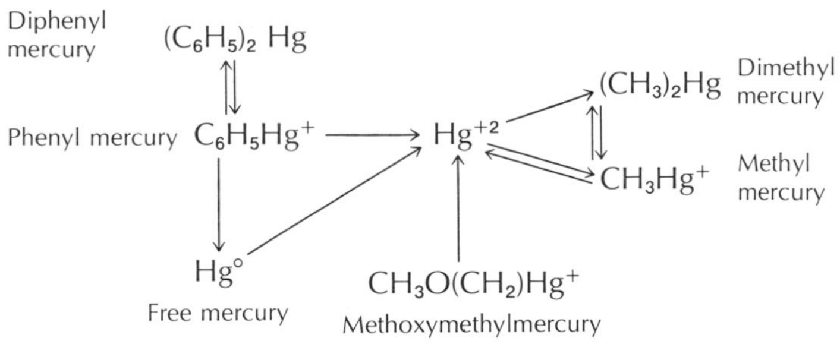

Diphenyl mercury $(C_6H_5)_2 Hg$

Phenyl mercury $C_6H_5Hg^+ \longrightarrow Hg^{+2}$

$(CH_3)_2Hg$ Dimethyl mercury

CH_3Hg^+ Methyl mercury

Hg° Free mercury

$CH_3O(CH_2)Hg^+$ Methoxymethylmercury

under anaerobic conditions also. Microorganisms in chickens seem to convert mercury right in their systems, but it is not known if other mammals or fish do this. Similar methylation has been shown to occur for arsenic, selenium, and tellurium.

From all of this, what lessons are to be learned? One result is an appreciation of how little we know about the natural cycles of mercury and therefore the ways in which man alters those cycles. We still do not know if mercury is also methylated in ocean floor deposits or if there are ways to detoxify current deposits in inland waterways or to decrease human body burden. Even our knowledge of background concentrations was scanty; earlier measurements in seawater showed Hg concentrations of 0.03 to 2.0 ppb, but modern analytical techniques yield averages closer to 0.1 ppb. Is this just the effect of discovering what has always been true due to the use of more sensitive and accurate instrumentation?

Whether or not certain regions have always contained high levels of mercury or other heavy metals, the fact remains that concerns about the health effects of toxic metals are legitimate, and concentrations must be continually monitored and practices altered so that harmful levels are not reached. Further research is needed to determine toxic levels, and particularly the effect of continued, low-level exposure, including possible synergisms. Industrial discharges of mercury can be reduced largely by study and implementation of necessary recycling or process changes. All of this is particularly important in the case of mercury, since the difference between tolerable natural background levels and levels of harm is very small, estimated to be only a factor of ten in populations depending heavily on fish as their source of protein. The entire mercury episode has emphasized once again that the wisest course of action is to try to understand the natural processes involved and then act in conformance with that knowledge. Panic is not needed, but extensive research is essential.

Thermal Pollution

Public concern about thermal pollution is relatively new as compared with other types of air and water pollution. Since nuclear power plants generate more waste heat than fossil plants, the recent growth of nuclear power has served as a focus for the problem.

In the past, engineers have solved the problem of how to dispose of waste heat by drawing on available natural water supplies. Proximity to lakes, rivers, and the ocean has been a major factor in siting both nuclear and fossil-fuel power plants. The effects of temperature increases on prevailing ecosystems are not specifically known, although some generalizations have been reached for particular organisms. Changes are most noticeable in a relatively closed system such as a lake where changes in algae population and fish reproduction and survival rates have been observed. Since gases are less soluble at higher temperatures, the oxygen necessary to the life of aquatic animals is less available. Higher temperatures speed up metabolism of the fish, as well as giving them false climatic cues as to when to start reproduction cycles. This may lead to their death if they are swept into cooler water where food supplies are not ready.

Rather than putting heat directly into aquatic environments, cooling towers and ponds are finding increasing use. A cooling pond simply contains the water until a desired reduction in temperature has taken place, but a tower is designed to break the water up into small droplets and cool it in a natural or forced draft of air. Common designs are shown in Figure 9. The cost of such towers must be considered, and it is not inconsequential. For example, for a power plant with an installed capacity of 800,000 kilowatts of power, it is estimated that a total investment of 5 to 13 dollars per gallon of cooling water might be necessary. Cooling towers are also subject to problems of corrosion, chemical scale, fouling due to silt, and microbiological attack. Both towers and ponds require increased land area for the site. It should be realized that at best, cooling towers and ponds represent an exchange of thermal aquatic addition for thermal air addition. If the number of cooling towers becomes large in any one area, undesirable atmospheric effects might be expected.

Beneficial Uses of Waste Heat

Another approach to thermal pollution is to treat the heat as an opportunity for byproduct recovery instead of as a problem in waste disposal. If the rejected heat can be utilized for other purposes, economic

Three huge natural draft cooling towers of the typical hyperbolic form are part of the Tennessee Valley Authority's Paradise Steam Plant in Kentucky. Each tower can vent a ton of water vapor per minute and is 437 feet high.

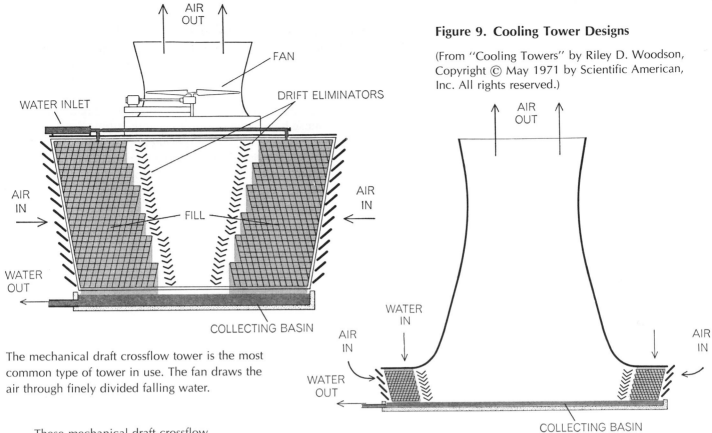

Figure 9. Cooling Tower Designs

The mechanical draft crossflow tower is the most common type of tower in use. The fan draws the air through finely divided falling water.

The hyperbolic natural draft tower depends on the height and shape of the structure to set up an air flow between cooler, drier air outside the tower and warmer, moister air within the tower.

These mechanical draft crossflow cooling towers serve a power plant near Colorado Springs. There are two six-cell units used to cool heated water from the generating station at the left of the picture.

as well as environmental benefits will result. One workable suggestion is to combine power plants with desalination facilities or other industrial applications. The waste heat might be used for residential heating in some areas. Experiments have shown that the heat can be used for growing vegetables in a controlled environment.

One of the most promising avenues for utilization of heated water is aquaculture. The Japanese have been researching aquaculture for many years and their experience as well as other experiments using the heated water to farm lobster and shrimp have shown initial success. At present, these uses do not account for more than a small fraction of waste heated water. Instead, they represent future large-scale alternatives to thermal pollution problems.

Part Three: OBTAINING PURE WATER

Drinking Water

Contamination of water by heavy metals is of increasing concern not only in its ultimate sink, the ocean, but also in drinking water systems. Drinking water contamination by cadmium, arsenic, chromium, cobalt, lead, and zinc has been reported, and questions of synergistic effects and the subtle physiological effects of small amounts of toxic metals remain largely unanswered. The health of those using a water supply must be protected from excess exposure to dissolved metals and organic compounds as well as from pathogenic bacteria. To accomplish this, municipal water treatment plants have been built to test and then treat the water supply.

A municipal water supply is derived from groundwater, rivers, or lakes or is delivered by pipeline from upland supplies. The basic chemical composition varies considerably, particularly with regard to dissolved salts. The purposes of treating water before use are to make the water both safe and aesthetically pleasing for the consumer. This means controlling the color, odor, amount and type of solids, and the bacterial quality of the water. These goals are accomplished in a typical treatment plant by the steps outlined in Figure 10.

The most basic concern is to safeguard the health of those drinking the water. Therefore, disinfection must be carried out. The most common method of disinfection is adding chlorine, although other oxidizing agents have also been used experimentally. The disinfection usually is done in several stages of the treatment process for maximum effect. Strict bacteriological control as standardized by the Public Health Service must be maintained.

An extensive survey carried out in 1970 by the Bureau of Water Hygiene investigated water quality in 989 systems serving 18.2 million people and found that most drinking water met present standards. Still, there were some disquieting discoveries, including hazardous amounts of metals and high bacteriological levels. The lack of systematic testing for synthetic organic compounds was emphasized in the report and probably will lead to an updating of the federal standards.

Some people attempt to control the quality of the water they drink by buying bottled water, while others use this service for health or taste reasons. Less than one percent of all homes in the United States now use bottled water, but industry spokesmen expect this percentage to rise sharply in the next decade unless water pollution is controlled more effectively than it has been to date. Because of the increase in consumption, the Food and Drug Administration has decided to establish federal standards for bottled water. Still, it will pay to investigate the company offering different types of bottled water. At least one firm simply took tap water and ran it through a carbon filter to give the customer a better tasting but expensive product.

Suspended matter is removed more efficiently if chemicals are added to aid in the normal settling process. The process of coagulation is generally used for this goal and involves forming a *floc*. This is a light, fluffy precipitate that slowly forms and becomes heavy enough to settle, taking the suspended matter with it. Removal of the suspended matter increases the clarity and purity of the water. The chemical used for coagulation is aluminum sulfate, $Al_2(SO_4)_3$, also known as alum or filter alum. Ferrous sulfate, $FeSO_4$, and ferric chloride, $FeCl_3$, are also sometimes used. This coagulation reaction is an example of an ionic reaction. The floc is produced by this reaction:

$$Al_2(SO_4)_3 + 3\ Ca(OH)_2 \longrightarrow 2\ Al(OH)_3 \downarrow\ +3\ CaSO_4$$

$$\text{floc}$$

If the water is sufficiently alkaline, this reaction will proceed directly, but in some cases, either CaO or $Ca(OH)_2$ is added to the water to facilitate the reaction and to adjust the pH. The essential ions are:

$$Al^{+3} + 3OH^- \longrightarrow Al(OH)_3 \downarrow$$
$$\text{or} \quad Fe^{+2} + 2OH^- \longrightarrow Fe(OH)_2 \downarrow$$
$$\text{or} \quad Fe^{+3} + 3OH^- \longrightarrow Fe(OH)_3 \downarrow$$

Raw water influent

Screen

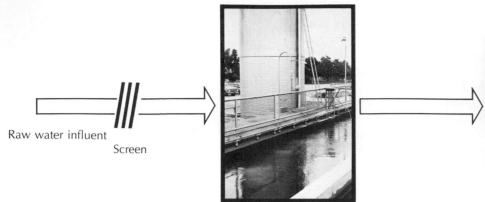

Chemicals are added for coagulation, taste and odor control, softening, pH adjustment, initial chlorination.

Large paddles revolve to insure complete mixing of the raw water and the chemicals added. Flocculation starts slowly in this basin.

Treated water effluent

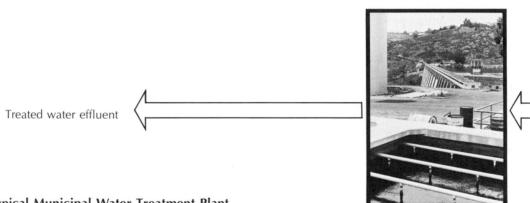

Figure 10. Typical Municipal Water Treatment Plant

The treated water is stored for use in a regulating reservoir. It may be distributed at any time for consumption. The water will be chlorinated one final time before use.

Formed floc settles to the bottom, taking suspended solid with it. The basin must be closed and drained periodically to remove the accumulated sediment.

Chlorination: stabilization chemicals are added if softeners are used in treatment.

Water flows over a size-graded filter. Finely divided anthracite coal may be used as the top layer of the filter. After so many hours of use, the filter is back-washed by reversing the normal flow of the water. Accumulated material is removed from the top of the filter.

At first, the flocculant precipitate is kept from settling as the water and chemicals are stirred in mixing basins. This is to insure good contact between the floc and the suspended matter in the water. After settling is allowed to occur, final remnants of the floc are removed in the filtering process.

Taste and odor control is partially accomplished by the chlorine added for disinfection, but in some cases, more control is needed. This is effected by the use of activated carbon filters, or the use of ammonia, chlorine dioxide, ozone, or potassium permanganate, which is widely preferred for its low cost. Potassium permanganate, a deep purple crystal, dissolves when added to the raw water and turns the supply pink. As the chemical works by oxidizing the odor- and taste-producing substances, the color disappears due to the formation of the insoluble manganese dioxide. This dark brown-black material settles with the floc or is removed by the filters. The reaction is:

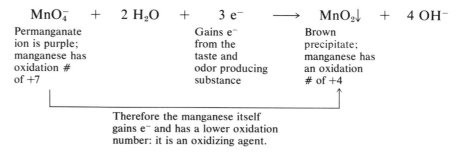

$$MnO_4^- \; + \; 2\,H_2O \; + \; 3\,e^- \; \longrightarrow \; MnO_2\downarrow \; + \; 4\,OH^-$$

Permanganate ion is purple; manganese has oxidation # of +7

Gains e^- from the taste and odor producing substance

Brown precipitate; manganese has an oxidation # of +4

Therefore the manganese itself gains e^- and has a lower oxidation number: it is an oxidizing agent.

After the water is filtered it is usually given another dose of chlorine to complete the disinfection process. The pH must be adjusted to be slightly alkaline for water that is even slightly acid will corrode pipes, adding metallic content to the water and creating an environmental and economic hazard. The water may then be stored or delivered directly to the customer. The final quality of the water must meet federal drinking water standards.

Desalination

Geographic location, population growth, and the accompanying need for increased amounts of fresh water for industry and agriculture create the possibility or reality that severe water shortages will result. A very large supply of water exists in our oceans, but its over-all salt content, 35,000 ppm, renders it useless for most applications. Other supplies of groundwater are classified as brackish (500–3000 ppm salts). Consequently, since 1952, the Office of Saline Waters, established by Congress, has been working on the development of processes for economically converting saline water into fresh water. Many technological possibilities exist, but generally it has been difficult to produce water at a cost comparable to fresh waters from other sources. Unlike the purification of drinking waters, which is mainly concerned with removal of suspended materials, processes for desalting must separate water from dissolved salts. If the water is to be used for drinking, it may then go through exactly the same previously described processes, including disinfection.

Table 9. Known Abundances in Seawater

Element	Milligrams per liter	Element	Milligrams per liter	Element	Milligrams per liter
Chlorine	19,000	Zinc	0.01	Tungsten	1×10^{-4}
Sodium	10,600	Molybdenum	0.01	Germanium	1×10^{-4}
Magnesium	1,300	Selenium	0.004	Xenon	1×10^{-4}
Sulfur	900	Copper	0.003	Chromium	5×10^{-5}
Calcium	400	Arsenic	0.003	Beryllium	5×10^{-5}
Potassium	380	Tin	0.003	Scandium	4×10^{-5}
Bromine	65	Lead	0.003	Mercury	3×10^{-5}
Carbon	28	Uranium	0.003	Niobium	1×10^{-5}
Oxygen	8	Vanadium	0.002	Thallium	1×10^{-5}
Strontium	8	Manganese	0.002	Helium	5×10^{-6}
		Titanium	0.001	Gold	4×10^{-6}
Boron	4.8	Thorium	0.0007	Praseodymium	2×10^{-7}
Silicon	3.0	Cobalt	0.0005	Gadolinium	2×10^{-7}
Fluorine	1.3	Nickel	0.0005	Dysprosium	2×10^{-7}
Nitrogen	0.8	Gallium	0.0005	Erbium	2×10^{-7}
Argon	0.6	Cesium	0.0005	Ytterbium	2×10^{-7}
Lithium	0.2	Antimony	0.0005	Samarium	2×10^{-7}
		Cerium	0.0004	Holmium	8×10^{-8}
Rubidium	0.12	Yttrium	0.0003	Europium	4×10^{-8}
Phosphorus	0.07	Neon	0.0003	Thulium	4×10^{-8}
Iodine	0.05	Krypton	0.0003	Lutetium	4×10^{-8}
Barium	0.03	Lanthanum	0.0003	Radium	3×10^{-11}
Indium	0.02	Silver	0.0003	Protactinium	2×10^{-12}
Aluminum	0.01	Bismuth	0.0002	Radon	9×10^{-15}
Iron	0.01	Cadmium	0.0001		

Figure 11. Solar Humidification

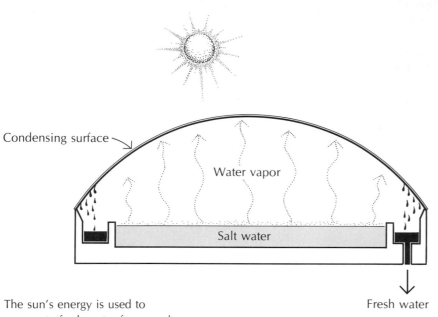

The sun's energy is used to evaporate fresh water from a salt water solution. The vapor is then condensed and collected.

Figure 12. Simple Distillation Apparatus

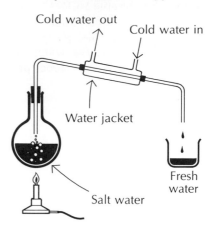

Heat energy supplied by the Bunsen burner boils the water. Cooling water is used to help condense the vapor.

Figure 13. Multistage Flash Distillation Process

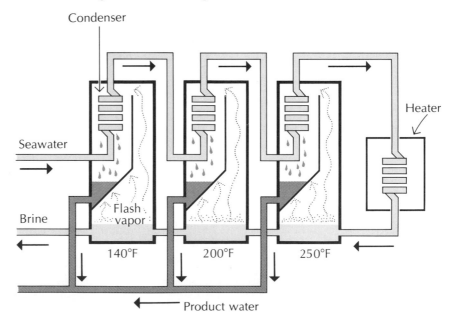

Incoming seawater is first used as a cooling agent. The water is then heated; waste heat from a power plant may be used to supply the energy. The heated seawater then passes into chambers with successively lower pressure, causing flash vaporization.

The starting material for desalting (desalination) processes is an enormously complex solution, probably containing all naturally occurring elements. Table 9 gives the average abundances of elements in seawater in order of magnitude of occurrence. For the most part, the elements are present in ionic form, either as radical ions such as NO_3^-, CO_3^{-2}, or as simple ions such as Cl^-. Metallic ions are usually associated with one or more water molecules. Since the ions conduct electricity, one method used to test for the over-all salinity of seawater is to check the electrical conductivity of the solution. Electrical properties of seawater are also responsible for some methods of separation as well, as we shall soon see. The simplest methods, however, depend on the boiling point differences between pure water and dissolved salts.

Distillation Processes. Ionic compounds have characteristically high boiling points as compared with water. Since antiquity, men have been making use of that observed fact to vaporize water and collect and condense the pure vapors, leaving the salts behind. This process, called *distillation,* has many different possible applications. For example, in the process of solar humidification, rather than boiling the water, the energy of the sun is used to heat it, causing it to vaporize. The water is then condensed by a cooler plastic or glass shield, since these materials do not absorb heat as well as the water. (This is an example of the "greenhouse effect.") Solar humidification is a slow process that requires a large surface area and a reliable climate; only about 0.13 gallon can be produced per square foot of basin per day. This is enough to make this process useful aboard a ship, for example. Figure 11 shows an example of a simple solar still.

If enough energy is added to cause the water to boil, simple distillation occurs. This is a two-step process as was humidification, involving both heating and condensing. A simple distillation apparatus such as you might use in the laboratory is shown in Figure 12.

In order to make distillation economically feasible, some steps must be taken to minimize the energy required. This goal is accomplished in two ways. One is by making use of the fact that water boils at lower temperatures at lower atmospheric pressures. Therefore at the top of Mount McKinley, where the air pressure is only 56 percent that at sea level, water boils at 184°F instead of the usual 212°F (85°C instead of 100°C). (Conversely, water inside a pressure cooker at a pressure double that of sea level boils at 248°F (120°C).) The second way to minimize energy used in distillation is to design the system so that the incoming cool salt water is used to condense the water vapor. This is a double advantage, for the heat absorbed by the incoming salt water means that less energy must be added from some external source later in the process.

These two concepts are illustrated in Figure 13 for a multistage flash distillation apparatus.

The heated seawater goes into the first chamber where the pressure is low enough to cause some of the water to boil instantly or to "flash" into steam. Since that process absorbs heat, it lowers the temperature of the remaining brine, which flows then into the next chamber. The pressure here must be lower than in the first chamber so that the cooler brine will also flash. This process can be repeated several times. In each case, condensation occurs as the vapor comes on contact with coils containing the incoming seawater, bringing about the essential exchange of heat.

Flash distillation now accounts for 98 percent of the total installed capacity for desalination. Economic feasibility improves if the desalting plant is combined with another system that produces waste heat. Commercial desalination plants can be constructed near fossil-fuel or nuclear power plants and therefore utilize the heat energy that remains in steam after it passes through a turbine to produce electricity. This heat energy would otherwise be rejected to the environment. The large (7.5 million gallons per day) plant at Rosarita Beach south of Tijuana, Mexico, uses this energy-saving design.

Related variations on distillation procedures are long-tube flash distillation, multieffect multistage distillation, and vapor compression distillation. In all of these processes, heat recovery is high. All of the

Flash distillation units at Rosarita Beach Desalting Plant provide fresh water from seawater for Tijuana, Mexico. Note the large pipe that crosses the middle of the picture; it brings steam from the fossil-fuel power plant on the same site.

methods share the major problem of scale formation. As pure water is removed, the concentration of minerals increases in the remaining brine. Some of the dissolved minerals begin to precipitate out of solution when their solubility limit is reached. This forms a crust of scale on the heat transfer surface. Also, the higher temperatures cause chemical changes to occur. Dissolved bicarbonate ions will decompose above 160°F, forming the main component of the scale, calcium carbonate.

$$Ca(HCO_3)_2 \xrightarrow[160°F]{\Delta} CaCO_3 \downarrow + CO_2 \uparrow + H_2O \uparrow$$

Soluble   Insoluble

This crust will reduce the effectiveness of the heat transfer or in extreme cases may clog pipes. The crust problem can be minimized by pretreating the water by ion exchange (see page 220) to remove the calcium bicarbonate. The brine or concentrated salt solution acts corrosively on pipes, but new alloys of nickel and titanium have been developed that minimize that problem. The brine produced must be disposed of properly without creating an adverse environmental effect. At the present most of it flows back into the ocean after it is cooled to avoid thermal pollution.

Desalination by Freezing. Desalination may also be accomplished by freezing. This is also a two-step energy process, since heat must be withdrawn to form ice and then the ice melted to form the product, water. As salty water freezes, fresh water ice crystals will be formed first, and the salts will remain in the unfrozen solution. (If you have made ice cubes in an area of hard water, you are already familiar with this method, for the last areas to freeze have such high salt concentration that visible salt crystals will form on your cubes.) This method is promising from an energy standpoint in that roughly one sixth of the energy is required compared with vaporization processes, and furthermore the problems of corrosion and scale are minimized.

In a direct freezing process a sudden expansion of seawater into a vacuum chamber causes flash vaporization. Since rapid evaporation absorbs heat, the temperature of the remaining salt water is lowered sufficiently to cause approximately half of the incoming water to freeze. The resulting ice-brine slurry is pumped to a separation chamber and the floating ice crystals are rinsed and removed.

A secondary refrigerant freezing method differs from the primary system in that a refrigerant, such as butane, is used in the freezing step. Rapid evaporation of liquid butane absorbs heat from the incoming seawater and freezes it. Before discharge, the cool brine may be passed through a heat exchanger to precool the incoming seawater. Final disposal of the brine remains a problem. Such a scheme is shown in Figure 14.

Figure 14. Secondary Refrigerant Freezing Process

Fresh water is separated from seawater by means of freezing. The expansion of butane absorbs enough heat to create a cool ice-brine slurry. The ice crystals are skimmed off the top and remelted to produce fresh water.

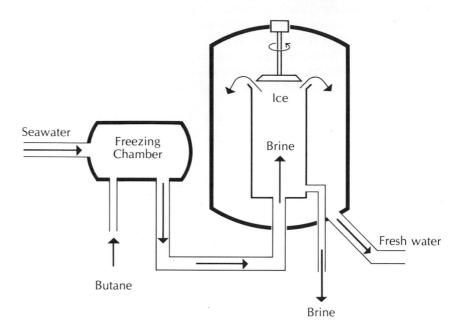

Membrane Separation. There have been several successful desalination processes developed using the principle of membrane separation. The semipermeable membrane may be considered as a selective filter through which some substances can pass freely but others are effectively stopped. There are many natural systems using membrane separations, and there are several important medical applications such as the purification of blood in the process of dialysis necessary for kidney malfunctions. The membranes are commonly made from cellulose acetate and are extremely thin (60 to 70 microns). If pure water and salt water are on opposite sides of such a semipermeable membrane, the pure water normally diffuses through the membrane and dilutes the salt solution. This is an example of osmosis. By applying pressure to the salt solution, reverse osmosis can be made to take place and the water from the salt solution flows through the membrane, leaving the salt behind. This process is sometimes referred to as piezodialysis or PD. Satisfactory separation may take more than one pass through the membrane, increasing cost and time factors. The main advantage of the simple reverse osmosis is that it does not require much energy to accomplish the separation.

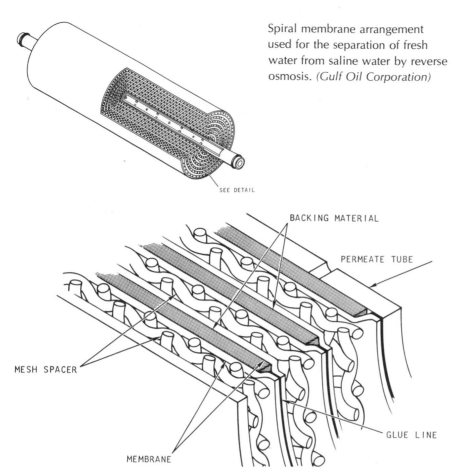

Spiral membrane arrangement used for the separation of fresh water from saline water by reverse osmosis. *(Gulf Oil Corporation)*

SEE DETAIL

BACKING MATERIAL

PERMEATE TUBE

MESH SPACER

GLUE LINE

MEMBRANE

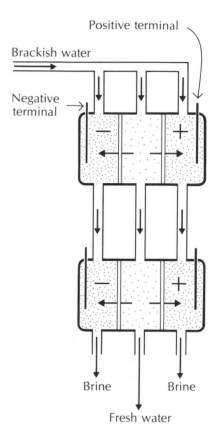

Figure 15. Electrodialysis

Positive terminal

Brackish water

Negative terminal

Brine   Brine

Fresh water

Research on the membrane materials is aimed at increasing their selectiveness and durability. The physical arrangement of the membrane is also the subject of experimentation. Spiral-wound, tubular, and hollow-fiber arrangements have all been tried. The newest of these is the method using hollow, fine fibers which provide a very large working surface of membrane and can withstand great pressures.

Improved desalination results from the addition of an electrical field to the process. If two membranes are used, one which allows the passage of positive ions and one which allows the passage of negative ions, the water between the two membranes will become fresh as the ions move from the region under the influence of the electrical field. Figure 15 shows this process. Of course, the disadvantage of this method is the increased cost for the energy consumed, the amount depending on the salt composition of the feed water.

A closely related process is transport depletion in which nonselective

A cell is divided into three parts by ion-selective membranes. In the presence of an electric field, the positively charged sodium ions move towards the negative electrical terminal; chloride ions are attracted to the positive terminal. Repeated separation leaves fresher water between the two membranes.

membranes are used. The difference in the velocity of ions in solution under the influence of an electric field creates regions enriched or depleted in ions and the product water is drawn from the depleted region. This process uses more power than electrodialysis, but the lower cost of membranes helps to compensate for this. A further variation uses a magnetic field to separate the ions, which are momentarily given higher oxidation states by exposure to ultraviolet or x-ray energy.

Ion Exchange. Chemical methods used to separate salts from water center mainly on ion exchange. The saline water is passed through a porous bed of material having the ability to exchange ions with the solution. The bed material is either a form of natural silicate mineral called a zeolite (approximate formula NaH_6AlSiO_7) or may be a synthetic hydrocarbon network containing postive or negative charges owing to either covalently bonded $—NH_3^+$ or $—SO_3^-$ groups. The most common application is to exchange sodium ions for hardness-causing calcium ions; small units for this purpose, manufactured to place on your faucet, make enough water to use in a steam iron. Ion exchange is illustrated in Figure 16 using Na^+Zeo^- to represent the complex natural zeolite structure.

As the conversion continues, the bed gradually loses its ability to exchange ions and the exchange medium must be regenerated by washing the beds with suitable chemicals. When the material regains its initial composition it may be reused, but regeneration costs limit the application of ion exchange to small volumes of water. Emergency kits for life rafts usually include an ion-exchange unit.

Research, laboratory, demonstration plants, and operating units all show that saline water conversion is technically possible and can be made economically attractive in some locations. Worldwide there are 686 desalting plants either operating or under construction. These will produce almost 250 million gallons of fresh water per day. The Middle East, with a severe need for fresh water at any price, leads the world with 74 plants producing 63 million gallons per day. Experience in Mexico, Russia, Europe, and the Caribbean all show the technical and economic feasibility of the concept. Since many of the same processes can be used with brackish waters, even inland areas with salty underground water supplies can benefit from this technology. Pollution of the incoming water in any location will substantially add to costs, particularly if the incoming water is contaminated with oil. Byproduct recovery of salt, magnesium, and other minerals may also increase economy, but large-scale desalination could turn this into a liability; desalting enough seawater to supply New York City for a year would theoretically produce more than 60 million tons of salt, four times the national use for one year.

Figure 16. Ion Exchange

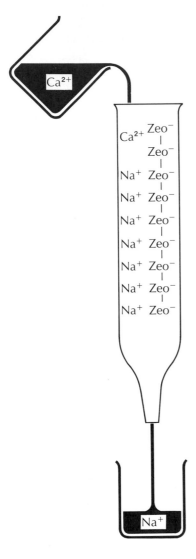

Sodium ions are exchanged for calcium ions in this zeolite water-softening unit.

Reclaiming Used Water

Since pure water will continue to be in demand, other sources are also being considered. It is possible to obtain drinking water from reclaimed sewage, but the cost involved usually prohibits such a use even if the public could be educated to accept such water. Instead, the main purpose of treating sewage is to decompose the organic matter before discharge in order to lower oxygen demand on the receiving waters. Disinfection with chlorine also takes place in most treatment facilities. The three possible treatment steps are shown in Figure 17.

Figure 17. Treatment of Sewage

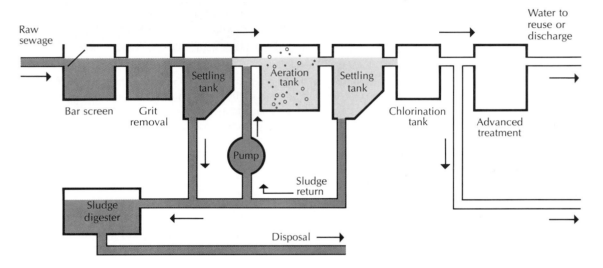

Step one: Primary treatment
- Removes approximately 40% BOD.
- Bar screen catches large objects; others go through grinder.
- Water flows slowly through grit chamber, sand and gravel settle. Can be used for landfill as it contains little organic matter.
- Water stands in settling tank.
- No direct reuse of water possible.

Step two: Secondary treatment
- Can remove 45–55% BOD (total 85–95% BOD removal).
- Aeration helps growth of aerobic organisms (activated sludge process).
- Trickling filters (bed of coarse stones) may replace aeration; organisms on stones feed on organic material.
- Sludge used as landfill or fertilizer; probably high in metallic content.
- Water can be used for irrigation, recreation, industrial supply. Water will still contain dissolved nutrients, some types of organic materials.

Step three: Tertiary treatment
- Most expensive treatment.
- Used to remove organic chemicals, nutrients, and excessive salts.
- May use chemical coagulation, distillation, reverse osmosis, etc.
- Can use water for all uses, including irrigation, industrial supply, groundwater recharge, drinking (if meets Public Health Standards).

A modern sewage treatment plant is not an unsightly neighbor. The sludge digesters on the left and the settling and aeration tanks on the right of this picture carry out the primary and secondary treatment at this plant before wastes are discharged. Since secondary treatment was added on this site, the natural population of the beach has been reestablished and crabs have returned.

Two Success Stories

One of the most advanced treatment plants now serves the south basin on the edge of Lake Tahoe in California. What has come to be called the "Tahoe process" takes effluent from a conventional primary-secondary treatment plant and first removes phosphates by the addition of lime.

$$3\ Ca^{+2} + 2\ PO_4^{-3} \longrightarrow Ca_3(PO_4)_2 \downarrow$$

Nitrogen compounds are removed in an ammonia stripping tower followed by coagulation, filtration, and ion exchange. The water is finally passed through activated charcoal to absorb odor- and taste-causing organics, and chlorinated. The clear effluent water is then piped out of the basin and into a reservoir several miles away which is used for fishing and water-contact sports. Thus the sewage from homes and commercial enterprises is converted into a recreational asset.

Another successful example of water reclamation is the Santee County Water District located near San Diego, California. Starting in 1957, a program of water treatment was planned to allow the community to reuse the expensive water which had to be imported from the Colorado

River. The waste water is treated so that it can meet the demand for recreational facilities, irrigation, industrial uses, and water for fire protection. Several public agencies at all levels of government have provided funds and manpower to help in this pioneering effort. The product water now irrigates a new golf course, has created several small lakes, and is used for boating, fishing, and swimming. The sludge produced is bacteriologically safe and can be used for soil conditioning or fertilizer. Public acceptance has been most enthusiastic for the entire project.

Experimental tertiary treatment units were added at Santee in 1968–69 and for two to three years, produced another valuable product—information. The data gained in these demonstration units are now being evaluated to determine the future usefulness of each type of advanced treatment. Processes tested were filtration, carbon adsorption, electrodialysis, and ion exchange.

Treatment of Industrial Wastes

Much of the same technology developed for the treatment of municipal wastes can also be applied to industrial waste waters. The Environmental Protection Agency estimates that at least half and possibly three quarters of all the oxygen-demanding wastes in the nation's municipal sewerage system actually comes from industry, and therefore a large part of the overloaded facilities can be attributed to industry. Since the federal government partially funds the building of waste treatment

Santee Lakes, near San Diego, California. Reclaimed water is being used to create a popular recreation area. Heavy public use indicates their acceptance of the project.

plants, industry is thus receiving a hidden subsidy in many areas of the country. Some of the problems involved with the treatment of industrial waters are different in that trace metals, acid wastes, and chemicals resistant to degradation may be involved; this is particularly true for such industries as paper, chemicals, petroleum, and coal and metal processing. Thermal pollution may be important too.

In some cases, a double purification may be needed if a high-quality water is required by an industry. Production of bottled beverages or edible food oils may necessitate pretreatment of water coming into the plant as well as purification of the effluent. Since economic considerations are important, minimal treatment of waste has been the rule in the past, but this is changing with increasing federal regulations and with the realization that water reuse and byproduct recovery make treatment more economically favorable. Treatment may be minimized by not discharging wastes into waterways but disposing of them by injection into deep wells, a practice shown to cause mild earthquakes in the Denver area. The salt mines under discussion for the disposal of radioactive wastes may be useful in the future for industrial disposal if geological conditions prove favorable.

Part Four: WHAT'S BEING DONE?

Water pollution has been recognized as a problem with serious economic, health and aesthetic effects. Just as is the case for air pollution, recognition of the problem does not always translate into effective action towards solutions. Localized successes have been achieved in controlling domestic and industrial discharges but the nationwide magnitude of the problem has dictated federal or at least regional coordination of efforts.

Federal Action

The first major federal legislation with respect to the abatement of water pollution was the Federal Water Pollution Control Act of 1956. It was amended and strengthened in 1961, 1965, 1966, and 1972. This act clearly recognizes the states as the major agents in preventing and controlling water pollution and casts the federal government in the role of providing grants for planning and construction of municipal waste facilities, providing technical assistance, supporting research efforts and water resource planning, and administering enforcement and approving standards of water quality. All of the states have now submitted water quality standards for their interstate waters and all standards have been approved; 41 of the 50 states have had standards totally approved and the rest have been accepted with certain exceptions, primarily because the standard for thermal pollution was too lax.

In 1970, the Water Quality Improvement Act gave needed controls over vessel waste discharges. Joint surveillance networks have been established with interagency cooperation of the Federal Water Quality Administration, the United States Geological Survey, and various state pollution agencies in order to gather long-term data for analysis and to monitor possible violations. The 1972 amendments to the Federal Water Pollution Control Act set a deadline of 1985 for the achievement of national water quality standards. Industries are required to use the "best practicable control technology" by July 1, 1977, and the "best available control technology" by July 1, 1983. Municipalities are required to use secondary treatment of wastes by mid-1977 and "more advanced disposal methods" by mid-1983. If a state still cannot meet the water quality standards by 1985, a delay of up to five years could be granted by the Environmental Protection Agency upon request and justification by the governor of a state.

One of the oldest pieces of legislation may unexpectedly prove to be one of the most effective in controlling water pollution. The Rivers and Harbors Act of 1899 (also called the Refuse Act) prohibits discharges into any U.S. navigable waters or their tributaries without a permit from the Army Corps of Engineers. (Exceptions are wastes from runoff and sewage.) The bill also provides that anyone who gathers the evidence to convict a violator receives half the fine levied on the polluter, an incentive that is now being tested legally. The Environmental Protection Agency is enthusiastic about the active use of the long-neglected permit system, for it would give them information about industrial wastes that previously was hard to come by, as well as providing a systematic mechanism to insure compliance with water quality standards. Additionally, the means would exist to upgrade industrial waste quality by regulation before dumping rather than waiting until a violation occurs and prosecuting. The permit system provides for periodic review to ensure the standards are being maintained or improved according to schedule. Responsibility for the permit program has been transferred from the Corps of Engineers to EPA by the 1972 amendments to the Federal Water Pollution Control Act.

We have all heard many stories of waterways that have fallen victim to pollution despite the legislative attempts to reverse the trend. Even Lake Tahoe, with its excellent treatment facility, still faces trouble caused by improper land use, for increased erosion places large amounts of sediment, some of it containing pesticides, into the once crystal clear lake. Is it possible to successfully stop and reverse the processes of destroying a waterway? Let's look at two stories that illustrate that concerned and informed public action can make a difference.

Seattle — Lake Washington's Rebirth

Lake Washington is a large body of water, approximately twenty-two miles long and from one to eight miles wide, lying just east of Seattle. Seattle is bounded on the west by Puget Sound and prides itself on the water-oriented activities that abound in the area. Lake Washington was used for raw sewage outfall in the first part of this century but in the early 1930s the city's sewage was redirected into Puget Sound, temporarily improving the quality of the lake water. Population growth in the area created many smaller towns around the lake in the 1940s. Despite continuous growth in the number of sewage treatment plants, algae growth increased conspicuously as the treated effluent, along with drainage from septic tanks, went into the lake. Particularly troublesome was the growth of a certain algae known to have been associated with the deterioration of a number of European lakes. Seattle was fortunate enough to have local scientists who recognized this danger sign.

Public concern led to the establishment of a Metropolitan Problem Advisory Committee which studied and recommended possible causes of action. They saw that the specific problem was really an area-wide problem of the management of sewage, and thus wisely attacked the problem on that basis. An informational campaign helped to obtain authorization from the voters and "Metro" was established in 1958. Sewage diversion projects were carried out in 1963–1968 and now some of the sewage receives primary treatment at one large plant with an outfall deep in Puget Sound. The rest of the sewage receives secondary treatment and is discharged into a river leading to the Sound. Since the large volume of water in the Sound is replenished four times a year by tidal action, it is thought that the effect of the treated water will be minimal, but study of the Sound for possible adverse effects continues. The lake began to show improvement when about one fourth of the sewage had been diverted; by 1969 some of the deep water had more oxygen than measured any time since 1933. The lake today is a scenic recreational asset for the metropolitan Seattle area.

A successful fight to end pollution of Lake Washington has made this beautiful body of water safe and enjoyable for recreational uses.

Seattle was fortunate in many respects—the lake's problems were recognized and tackled rather early in the eutrophication process and an alternate site was available to receive wastes. For some areas the answer will have to be increased treatment before discharge including the removal of excess nutrients if fresh water bodies are to be restored to health. Still the example is valid, because regional consideration of the interlocking problems of water pollution is the only reasonable and effective way of attacking the problem.

San Diego Bay

Another area that has successfully met the problem of deteriorating water quality is San Diego, California. San Diego Bay has had a colorful history of early Spanish discovery, naval activity dating back to 1842, commercial fishing and canning operations, and recreational boating. It is about fifteen miles in length and varies from one-fourth to two and one-fourth miles in width.

Deterioration of water quality came as the result of waste discharges and became an obvious problem in the mid-1930s. In 1942, a waste treatment plant for metropolitan San Diego was completed but was overloaded by the next year. The same cycle was repeated in 1951, and by 1960 most of the bay was quarantined and off limits for body-contact uses. Algal blooms varied from red to green to brown, and dissolved oxygen levels were so low that game fish all but disappeared. By 1963, a seven-foot deep sludge bed, 200 yards wide and 9000 yards long stretched from the treatment plant outfall.

In that year, the large-scale San Diego Metropolitan Sewerage System was completed. The facility included mainly primary treatment and disinfection, with an ocean outfall. Therefore discharge into the bay of virtually all municipal wastes and a large percentage of industrial wastes was stopped. Water quality in the bay responded almost immediately and within weeks the clarity and oxygen content improved. Fish and wildlife have returned. The sludge bed was gradually diminished in size and is presently confined to a few deposits. Since that time the last major industrial polluter, a kelp-processing company which previously had been discharging considerable organic waste with high BOD and bacterial content, has completed a four-year program to end its pollution, thus further improving the quality of the bay water. Discharges from Naval facilities and to a lesser extent, pleasure boats, have remained the last major problems in the vastly improved San Diego Bay. By July of 1973, all toilet-equipped pleasure boats using the bay will be required to have sewage holding tanks. The Navy has also announced new environmental programs that will benefit water quality in San Diego Bay.

Challenge for the Future

In all areas, the uses of water for recreation, public water supply, aquatic life, agriculture, and industry are constantly in conflict, and as in air pollution, there are many unanswered basic questions. Study is needed on the effects of polluted waters on human health, analytical methods used to detect certain pollutants, the interlocking role of different nutrients in causing eutrophication, and improved methods for waste treatment. Whatever plans are made for the utilization of this important resource, the need is for a comprehensive look at the water basin involved so that no one use jeopardizes the others. Also, as in the case of air pollution, improvement in water quality will mean spending money wisely to attain the desired goals.

Study Questions – Group A

1. Hydrogen exists in three isotopes, ^1H, ^2H, and ^3H. Oxygen also has 3 isotopes, ^{16}O, ^{17}O, and ^{18}O. How many different compounds having the formula H_2O are possible?

2. Why does *one* oxygen atom form a stable compound with *two* atoms of hydrogen?

3. Which compound would require more calories of heat to change an equal weight of it to a vapor at its boiling point – water or hydrogen sulfide?

4. a. From the graph in Figure 4, estimate the "expected" boiling point of water, if it followed the rest of the family's trend.
   b. Change this value to degrees Centigrade and degrees Fahrenheit. The formulas are

   $$°C = °A - 273 \qquad \text{and} \qquad °F = (9/5)°C + 32$$

5. Explain why hydrogen fluoride is a highly polar molecule. How does this account for the observed abnormally high boiling point of hydrogen fluoride compared with other hydrogen compounds of Group VIIA elements?

6. If water freezes, does it absorb heat from the environment or release heat to the environment? Explain.

7. When explaining the solubility of many inorganic substances in water and the solubility of many organic substances in benzene, the phrase "like dissolves like" is often used. What do you think this means?

8. Pulp and paper mills can employ several types of operations to prepare, pulp, and process wood. The bark is often removed mechanically and chipped in preparation for pulping. In the sulfite pulping process,

solutions of sodium bisulfite and excess sulfur dioxide are used to break down the noncellulose portions of the wood. What classes of water pollutants could result from these processes?

9. Explain the difference between a biodegradable and a nonbio-degradable material, giving examples of each.

10. What chemical compounds are typically formed by anaerobic decay? Why are they usually undesirable?

11. What is BOD and why is it a measure of the pollution of a water body?

12. Why are the values for COD higher than those for BOD?

13. Why is a thick mat of blue-green algae on the surface of a lake an undesirable sign? What can cause such an algae layer? What will happen when the algae dies?

14. What distinguishes soaps from synthetic detergents? How is each effective in cleaning?

15. What is an ABS detergent?

16. What is "hard water"? What are the advantages and disadvantages of hard water?

17. The reaction between sodium metasilicate and water (as discussed on page 192) is an example of hydrolysis. Phosphates also undergo hydrolysis with water and also produce an alkaline solution necessary for cleaning of clothes. What does this tell you about the relative degree of ionization of the acid produced (phosphoric acid) and the base produced (usually sodium hydroxide)?

18. Is crude oil a hydrophilic or hydrophobic material? Explain.

19. In the extraction of mercury from cinnabar, is the mercury reduced or oxidized to form the free element?

20. If mercury ions (Hg^{+2}) are present in water, what are some of the chemical products that may result? Of these alternatives, which form is potentially the most harmful to man?

21. What happens to the heat energy from hot water cooled by means of a cooling tower? Why is it desirable to break the hot water up into fine droplets for efficient cooling?

22. Outline the chemical steps involved in treatment of drinking water.

23. Why will treated drinking water often have a greater dissolved mineral content than the incoming water?

24. In the distillation of a saline solution, what basic physical property difference must be present so that distillation can be used to separate the pure water from the dissolved salts?

25. If a person is restricted to a low-sodium diet, should they use a zeolite water softening unit on their water supply? Explain.

Study Questions—Group B

1. The total effect that a particular effluent has on the water quality will depend on other factors than just the BOD. Taking community sewage as an example, what are some of the other influencing conditions?

2. If you try to compare phosphate content of detergents and other household products, you will find a great deal of conflicting data. What are some of the problems involved in reporting the quantitative percent phosphate present? To avoid these problems, some researchers are now using grams per washload as the accepted unit for comparison. What is the analogy for each of these units in reporting concentration of air pollutants?

3. Set up a "panel of experts" to try to predict which will be the next metal to receive the most attention as a pollutant harmful to man. Attempt to find the metal's sources, methods of transport, and fate in the environment. What standards have been set? What are the known medical effects of the metal? You might set up groups to consider arsenic, barium, beryllium, cadmium, copper, and zinc, together with other metals of your choosing.

4. Sorb-Oil is an oil absorbing, biodegradable wood-fiber product that can absorb from 7 to 20 times its weight in oil. It has been used for oil spill control and cleanup, as well as for industrial filters and domestic and recreational applications wherever an oil-absorbent, nonwettable material is desired. Recycled paper such as cardboard boxes and egg cartons can be included in the manufacture of Sorb-Oil. Find out more about this product from the Innova Corporation, 444 Ravenna Boulevard, Seattle, Washington 98115. Report on the chemical and physical properties of this material.

5. You should know how your area treats its water resources. Some of the questions your class might consider are: What is your drinking water supply and how is it treated before use? What methods of sewage treatment are carried out? Where is the treated water discharged? (Try to arrange a visit to water and waste water treatment plants.)

6. What are the industrial sources of water pollution in your area? What types of chemicals must be removed in the treatment of wastes? How is this being accomplished?

7. An interesting way to study the complexities of water pollution is by playing *Dirty Water*, a game developed by Urban Systems, Inc., 1033 Massachusetts Avenue, Cambridge, Mass., 02138. The game shows some of the difficulties in keeping a local body of water in ecological balance while at the same time dealing with the realities of industrial activities. The economic aspect of abatement is also

important. After playing the game, discuss how realistic you feel the game is in learning about the effects of various pollutants on the ecology of the lake and the political-economic aspects of water pollution.

Suggested Readings

Berg, George G. *Water Pollution*. New York: Scientists' Institute for Public Information, 1970.

> Degradation of our waters is such a complicated problem that solutions are difficult to reach. In this workbook, different aspects of the problem are isolated and discussed. Some of the history of water pollution control as well as some current problems are included. Management policies for the future are suggested.

Environmental Protection Agency, Water Quality Office. *A Primer on Waste Water Treatment*. Document 0-419-407, 25 pages, 1971, $0.55.

> This recently revised booklet describes eight basic types of water pollutants and the methods currently used for their removal from waste water. The advanced processes under development for future use are also discussed. A two-page glossary of water treatment terminology is a useful addition. This booklet is available from the Superintendent of Documents, U.S. Government Printing Office, Washington, D.C. 20402.

Goldwater, Leonard J. "Mercury in the Environment." *Scientific American* 224:5 (1971):15–21.

> This article provides an excellent overview of the sources and pathways of mercury in the environment. The possible effects of mercury at different concentrations are presented. The author recommends a comprehensive monitoring system and an active research program to find the true dimensions of the seriousness of the mercury problem. At the same time, he reminds us that the measures he suggests should be applied to all contaminants that threaten our environment.

U.S. Department of the Interior, Office of Saline Water. *New Water*. Document 0-381-844, 36 pages, 1970, $0.60, and *The A-B-Seas of Desalting*. Document 0-306-916, 40 pages, 1968, $0.35.

> The first of these booklets gives general information about the goals of the Office of Saline Water and how they have been implemented. The companion booklet gives more details of the different technical processes used to produce fresh water from saline. Both booklets are clearly written and well illustrated. They may be obtained from the U.S. Government Printing Office.

Chapter 7
Pesticides: Chemical Controls and Their Alternatives

It is estimated that there are about three million species of in-sects—far more than the combined number of animal and plant species. Most of this tremendous number of insects are either helpful or at least innocuous to humans. Roughly 3000 species, or 0.1 percent, of the insects, have become the targets for chemical control. Only 200 have been classed as serious pests. This includes agricultural pests and those that spread human or animal diseases.

The chemical control of pests has met with many successes, including a reduction in disease and short-term increases in agricultural productivity. Despite this, chemical control has not been a wholly positive venture. Most of the pesticides developed are too far reaching in their effects, destroying the beneficial insects along with the pests. Insects also show a remarkable agility in adapting to the new environment by developing resistance to certain chemicals. This necessitates increasing doses and constantly changing formulations. By persisting and concentrating in the environment, pesticides present hazards to many other organisms, including man.

We will examine some of these basic problems. The chemistry and effects of several classes of pesticides are discussed. Some of the more fundamental controls that could arise from taking advantage of biological, biochemical, and behavioral differences between insects and other forms of life are presented. A look at public policy concerning pesticides concludes this study.

Part One: SCOPE OF THE PROBLEM

What is a Pesticide?

A pesticide is a material capable of selectively killing a pest in a biological community. Pesticides are classed depending on the particular use intended: insecticides if insects are the target species, fungicides if controlling plant diseases, herbicides if killing weeds or other unwanted vegetation, rodenticides if destroying vertebrate pests such as rats, mice, gophers, or ground squirrels, germicides if killing germs. This by no means exhausts the list. There are also acaricides, molluscacides, nematocides, and so on. Unfortunately, very few of the pesticides that are practical for use are specific for just the intended pest; some writers prefer the term biocide in order to emphasize the overlapping ecological effects of such compounds. Since pesticide continues to be the term commonly used both by scientists and the general public, we will keep that terminology.

Chemical Control of Pests: Promise and Problems

Perhaps the first usage of pesticides was recorded in 1763 when nicotine extract was used to kill aphids. Other uses were slowly developed, centering particularly on the uses of metallic or naturally occurring plant compounds. The first synthetic chemical pesticide was marketed in 1892; the biggest surge in the development and use of pesticides has occurred in the last twenty years. This phenomenal increase in pesticide use is emphasized by noting that the number of synthetic pesticides has quadrupled, and dollar sales have risen at least 300 percent in this time period. Farm practices have been revolutionized and crop yields increased. Insect-borne diseases such as malaria have been brought under significant control.

Yet new problems have unexpectedly resulted from the seemingly bountiful benefits of pesticides. Resistance to pesticides by some target

The small, fixed-wing airplane is commonly used to apply pesticides. This craft is dusting tomatoes with a mixture of DDT and toxaphene. The picture was taken prior to the recent ban on DDT. *(San Diego County Department of Agriculture)*

species has rendered certain compounds ineffective or has made it necessary to use increasing amounts of the substance, creating both economic and environmental effects. Biological concentration of stable organochlorine compounds now turns their desirable property of long life into a liability. Residues are found in soil, food, and water supplies. Some increases in crop yields have turned out to be very short-term effects, for as natural predators are killed, the target pest may subsequently experience an increased population. Misunderstanding of the ways in which herbicides interact with the weeds they are intended to kill has led to the misuse of these compounds and in some cases to the unexpected failure of crops.

Is Chemical Control the Answer?

Despite these problems, pesticide usage continues to increase. Synthetic organic compounds show both the greatest growth rate and the largest potential for contaminating the environment. Organochlorine compounds (such as DDT), organophosphates (such as malathion) and carbamates (such as sevin) are three important types of organics used; annual consumption in the United States is approximately 800 million pounds per year. The amazing array of synthetic organic compounds is reflected in the fact that more than 900 such pesticides are now known in the United States, dispersed in over 60,000 different formulations. Of this number, approximately 100 compounds in 1000 formulations are commonly used. Inorganic materials containing metals (such as lead arsenate) form part of the total use, particularly as rodenticides, insecticides, and fungicides. Materials derived from petroleum and from plants are also important classes of pesticides. Altogether, the pesticides produced in the United States for both domestic and export use in 1970 amounted to 12,000 million dollars in value. The properties, use, and effects of each of these types of substances will be discussed in the next sections in order to try to find the proper role of pesticides in our ecosystem. Since most research and most public concern has centered on the organochlorine compounds, that will be the starting place.

Part Two: ORGANOCHLORINE COMPOUNDS

As the name implies, organochlorines are basically organic compounds that have been chlorinated, usually with several atoms of chlorine per molecule. Very often there is more than one ring of carbon atoms in the basic structure. All of these compounds are lipophilic and therefore show great affinity for the fatty tissues of animals. This, combined with their persistence in the environment due to rather slow decomposition rates, makes them a serious problem. As a class they are often referred to as the "hard" pesticides. Some of the common organochlorines are listed in Figure 1.

Most complicated organic molecules are known by a common name or set of letters—a glance at the names of some of the compounds in Figure 1 will verify the necessity of such a shorthand! It is also important to have an exact chemical name for these substances to identify and communicate specific information about a compound. Naming these complicated organic molecules is a game that necessarily follows very specific rules; some of the basic ones are illustrated in the case of DDT.

Consumers can choose from a wide variety of pesticides for home use. How do you decide which product is most specific and at the same time safest for your local environment?

Naming Organic Compounds: DDT

DDT is shorthand for *di*chloro*di*phenyl*tri*chloroethane, a name which gives some information about the structure of the compound but is not explicit enough to completely characterize the substance. However, both the expanded version and the correct chemical name shown in Figure 1 give the most important clue last, for the -ethane is the base for the compound.

Pure ethane, C_2H_6, would have the following structure.

$$\begin{array}{ccc} & H & H \\ & | & | \\ H- & C- & C-H \\ & | & | \\ & H & H \end{array}$$

Each carbon has four bonds, three to hydrogen atoms and one to the other

Figure 1. Organochlorine Pesticides

Substance, common name, and chemical name	Structural arrangement	Uses
DDT (1,1,1-trichloro-2,2-bis (p-chlorophenyl)ethane)	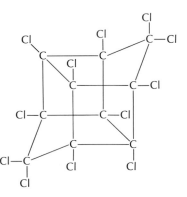	• Malaria eradication by control of mosquito, fly, louse, and flea vectors of human and animal disease • For hundreds of species of orchard, garden, field, and forest pests
Lindane (benzene hexachloride gamma isomer)		• Soil poison • Seed treatment • Toxicant for grasshopper control • Insect-killing shelfpapers
Heptachlor (1,4,5,6,7,8,8-heptachloro-3a,4,7,7a-tetrahydro-4,7-methanoindene)		• Cockroaches, ants, termites, soil insects, grasshopper control
Mirex (1,2,3,4,5,5,6,7,8,9,10,10-dodecachlorooctahydro-1,3,4-methano-2H-cyclobuta-[c,d]-pentalene)		• Stomach poison used in bait • Fire ant eradication program
Dieldrin (1,2,3,4,10,10-hexachloro-6,7-epoxy-1,4,4a,5,6,7,8,8a-octahydro-1,4-endo, exo-5,8-dimethanonapthalene)		• For insect pests of fruit, vegetables, cotton • Soil insects • Seed treatment • Termites • Mothproofing
Toxaphene (chlorinated camphene containing 67–69% chlorine—incompletely characterized at present)	(suggested skeleton structure)	• Broad use for insect pests of cotton, field crops and animals

carbon. If some of the hydrogens are replaced by chlorines, then the location and number of chlorines must be given in the formula:

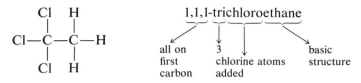

As a general rule, the numbers are kept as low as possible. Thus the name 2,2,2-trichloroethane would not be correct for this molecule, since both carbons are identical.

If two of the hydrogens on the second carbon are then replaced by a phenyl group (a benzene ring minus one hydrogen atom so that a bond can form between the ring and the ethane), then the result would be:

1,1,1-trichloro-2,2-diphenylethane

However, in DDT, each phenyl group has a chlorine attached, and the location of that chlorine relative to the carbon-carbon bond must be clarified. There are three different possibilities for isomers:

(to carbon of ethane)   ortho position (o-chlorophenyl)

(to carbon of ethane)   meta position (m-chlorophenyl)

(to carbon of ethane)   para position   (p-chlorophenyl)

In the case of DDT, the p-chlorophenyl form is the correct structure. Since this entire group is present twice, the prefix *bis* correctly indicates that everything in the following parentheses is taken twice. Therefore the total name now falls into place.

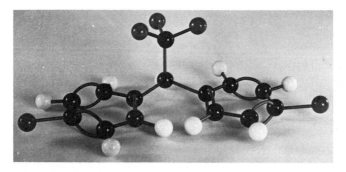

1,1,1-trichloro-2,2-bis(p-chlorophenyl)ethane

Compare this three-dimensional model of DDT with the two-dimensional representation.

There are several more conventions in naming organic compounds that have not been illustrated in naming this compound; there are many other building blocks as well. This example surely will not make you an instant expert, but hopefully it will make you feel a little more comfortable with complicated names. Look carefully at the other chemical names given in this study, and try to compare the name fragments with the pertinent structures in order to gain a little more familiarity with the system.

DDT: A Case Study

Since DDT illustrates many of the properties and problems associated with organochlorine pesticides, we will consider it first and in the most detail. First synthesized in 1874, it was 1939 before DDT's insecticidal properties were discovered. Pure DDT is virtually insoluble in water (1.2 ppb) but is quite soluble in a number of organic solvents, reflecting its lipophilic nature. Several close relatives of DDT also have insecticidal activity, and altogether many hundreds of such compounds have been studied. This illustrates a common practice in pesticide research to date; if a certain organochlorine is shown to have high insecticidal activity, slight variations in structure are accomplished by synthesis and the new compounds tested. Some of the results are shown in Table 1. Economic considerations along with activities are then considered in choosing which compounds will be marketed.

Experimentation with different but similar structures has shown that for maximum activity the para-substituted component should be either a halogen or possibly a short-chain alkyl group. The nature of the atoms substituted on the l-carbon has been chlorine in the most active molecules. Such molecules are readily absorbed through the outer protecting cuticle of an insect and affects peripheral sensory organs to produce hyperactivity, convulsions, paralysis, and death. This absorption is a specific reaction for insects and therefore a direct dose of DDT is relatively nontoxic to higher animals.

Table 1. Effect of Structure on the Toxicity of DDT Analogs

Exact nature of:

X	Y	Z	Common name, if any	LD_{50}* mosquito larva, ppm
Cl	CCl_3	H	DDT	0.070
Cl	CCl_3	Cl		>10
Br	CCl_3	H		0.018
CH_3	CCl_3	H		0.080
CH_3O	CCl_3	H	methoxychlor	0.067
Cl	$HCCl_2$	H	DDD	0.038
Cl	$=CCl_2$	—	DDE	>10
Cl	CCl_3	F		0.092

*LD_{50} means the *lethal dose* for 50 percent of the experimental population. Thus a low value in ppm implies a toxic substance to the insect tested; a high value such as for DDE means the material is not very toxic.

Figure 2. Metabolism of DDT by Insects and Mammals

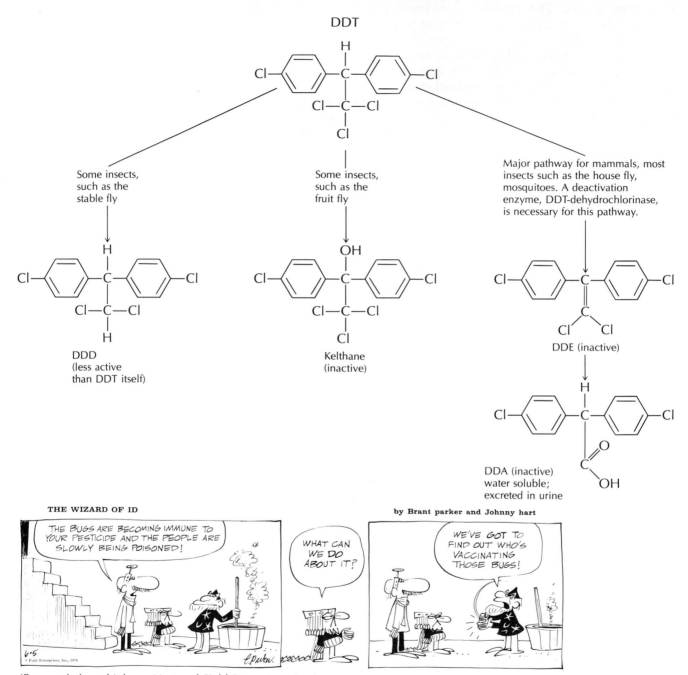

(By permission of Johnny Hart and Field Enterprises, Inc.)

Insect Resistance to DDT. The ability of insects to develop resistance to DDT has been one of the surprises in the use of this pesticide. To understand this behavior, first consider the normal metabolism process for DDT in insects and mammals, as shown in Figure 2.

When DDT is used for the control of an insect pest, those insects which naturally possess larger amounts of the deactivation enzyme survive. Over a period of a few generations, the population soon consists of the more resistant of the species. These insects are able to rapidly convert the DDT to the nontoxic DDE and therefore render the pesticide ineffective. This metabolic pathway is much slower in mammals, but this same evolution of resistance has been demonstrated in mice. The insecticidal activity may be restored to some extent by adding a compound which serves as an inhibitor of the enzyme, thus preventing quick detoxification.

Biological Magnification. The danger to higher animals connected with DDT comes from its ability to evaporate directly from plants and soil into the atmosphere or to cling to water droplets and thus be carried widely into the environment. This mobility, combined with DDT's resistance to oxidation and degradation, and its previously mentioned lipid solubility, are all important in determining the fate of DDT in the environment. All of these factors are evident in explaining the biological concentration (biological magnification) mechanism. Since DDT is not water soluble, much of the residue clings to particles and is transported both by dust and by solids suspended on water. Thus even if the concentration of DDT is very low in the surrounding environment, organisms with high fat or oil content readily absorb available DDT. Then as the tiny plants and organisms are eaten in turn by the next members of the food chain, levels of up to 10,000 times the background concentration can be reached. One such magnification scheme is shown in Figure 3.

One result of biological magnification of organochlorines has been the reproductive failure of several birds of prey, particularly the peregrine falcon, the brown pelican, the Bermuda petrel, the osprey, and the bald eagle. The high levels of DDT found in the fat of these birds is thought to be responsible for the inhibition of a vital enzyme that controls calcium metabolism. Very thin, weak eggshells result. When the nesting bird attempts to sit on the eggs, they break, thus preventing successful reproduction. The exact mechanism of this altered calcium metabolism is now under study.

Other Effects of DDT in the Environment. Even though the effects of DDT on birds have received the most attention, several other results have been noted. Concentrations of only a few parts per billion in water have been shown to reduce photosynthesis and growth in marine

Figure 3. Transport and Biological Magnification of DDT in the Environment

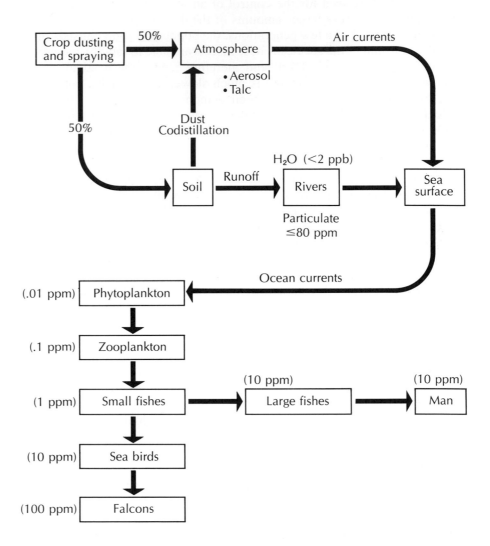

plankton. Such concentrations might be reached in bays receiving agricultural drainage. Declining crab fisheries on both coasts may be linked to the presence of DDT, which is transferred to the crab eggs and is responsible for larval death. A similar transference is known to take place in trout; as DDT in the yolk is used up by the growing fish larva, lethal concentrations are reached. This same effect has been noted for coho salmon.

Direct effects of DDT on man have not been observed. The over-all safety record has been excellent, and DDT's relatively low acute toxicity for animals makes incidences of direct poisoning very rare. It is known that organochlorine residues accumulate in the body fat of man just as they do in other animals on the top of the food chain. Eight to ten ppm DDT has been observed in a study of the United States general public with no ill effects; concentrations up to 600 ppm have produced no gross functional disorders in exposed agricultural workers.

The more subtle effects, as always, are harder to find and more difficult to evaluate. The possibility that such effects occur dictates a policy of keeping exposure to DDT at a minimum. This is reflected in the efforts of the Food and Drug Administration to regulate DDT and other pesticide residues in our food supply. Foods are our source of over 90 percent of our average daily intake of DDT. Other exposures are from air, water, lanolin-based cosmetics, aerosols, fabrics, and tobacco smoke.

There has been some preliminary evidence showing at least a correlation between high DDT levels and health problems such as cerebral hemorrhage, cirrhosis, infertility, and various cancers. The flurry of research activity serves to emphasize how little is really known about the long-term, low-level effect of DDT in humans, even though the lack of acute toxicity is well established.

Although helicopters can deliver pesticides close to the ground, some of the material does not reach the target crop. Residues of chlorinated hydrocarbons build up in local water and soil where they are available for biological concentration. *(San Diego County Department of Agriculture)*

To evaluate the concentration of pesticides in our food supply, the Food and Drug Administration carries out "total diet" studies each year. A balanced diet of foods are purchased in a quantity sufficient to feed the nation's largest appetite, a 17–19 year old male. Dieticians prepare and analyze this food during a two-week period; thirty cities across the nation are used as sampling sites.

Reports from these studies show that a well-balanced diet in the United States contains about 0.02 ppm chlorinated organic chemicals. Acceptable daily intake has been established at 0.01 mg/kg of body weight. The 0.02 ppm from the total diet samples is equivalent to an average intake of only 0.0005 mg/kg. So at the present time, there is a substantial margin of difference between the suggested standard and the actual levels.

This difference is not justification for complacency; the frequency and levels of pesticide residues in the nation's food should be minimized. In particular, foods known to be good carriers of pesticide residues, such as shellfish, fish, eggs, and milk, should be analyzed more regularly to see if they meet standards. Tests have shown that even some human milk has a concentration of 0.1–0.2 ppm of DDT-derived substances and therefore a baby may ingest 0.02 mg of DDT per kg of body weight—double the suggested acceptable intake.

DDT—Judgment by EPA. After many years of controversy, DDT was banned as of January, 1973 for virtually all uses in the United States. The Environmental Protection Agency, after consideration of all the evidence, decided that DDT is uncontrollable in the environment and poses hazards to man due to its persistence in aquatic and terrestrial systems. The uses still allowed (sweet potatoes in storage, green peppers, and onions) account for less than 1 percent of DDT usage in the United States. Due to DDT's importance in fighting malaria-carrying insects in the tropics, exportation of the pesticide is not limited.

The debate over DDT will undoubtedly continue, for in many cases it is not the question of scientific merit which is being discussed. A good deal more heat than light has been present in some of the articles carried in the popular media and even in scientific journals. Few responsible scientists advocate complete withdrawal of all pesticides, and fewer still hail DDT as the "wonder chemical" it was once considered to be. Clearly, there must be a better suiting of need with specific method of control.

The concept of integrated control is now replacing the earlier idea of a broad-spectrum chemical such as DDT that kills all the members of the insect community, for this nonselectivity has been shown to create new problems faster than it solves old ones. A diverse ecosystem usually has greater stability; nature's inherent complicated stability is eliminated by the use of DDT and other broad-spectrum pesticides. Some of the feasible ways of working within nature's own control system will be discussed in Part Four. Until these methods are more fully developed, synthetic chlorinated hydrocarbons other than DDT will continue to be used.

A celery field is being treated with pesticides from a ground rig. This is the most inexpensive type of commercial applicating equipment. *(San Diego County Department of Agriculture)*

Another type of chlorinated hydrocarbon may soon be as well known as DDT, for *PCBs* (polychlorinated biphenyls) share similar chemical structures and properties of solubility in fat, persistence, and concentration in the environment. Unlike DDT, PCBs are not directly sprayed as an insecticide but rather escape accidentally from industrial preparation and usage, or from the incineration of products containing the chemicals.

PCBs represent a variety of compounds formed by replacing hydrogens in a two-benzene system with varying amounts of chlorine.

Biphenyl ring with positions for replacement shown

These compounds are useful industrially for their excellent thermal stability (up to 1600°F) in applications such as coolants for heat transfer systems. Their plasticity (most of the commercial mixtures are liquids or resins) make them excellent solvents for inks and pesticides. Because the PCBs have low vapor pressure, they suppress the evaporation of some of the chlorinated hydrocarbon pesticides but have no insecticidal activity themselves. Another common use is as a plasticizer of vinyl chloride polymer films such as those used in food packaging materials. Tires, brake linings, paints, gasket sealers, adhesives, and carbonless reproducing paper are just a few additional examples of the uses of this versatile chemical.

Although first identified in 1881 and widely used since the 1930s, it was not until 1966 that residues were first noted in fish. Since PCBs are present in lower concentrations than organochlorine pesticides, their similar behavior on the gas chromatograph had been masked by the pesticide residues and thus overlooked. Quickly, residues were identified in birds, water, and sediments; an interim standard of 5 ppm was set by the FDA for food supplies. Poultry and eggs have since been seized and destroyed for exceeding this limit; several deaths resulted in Japan from people ingesting PCB-contaminated rice oil. The Environmental Protection Agency has suggested a maximum limit of 0.01 micrograms PCB per liter of river and lake waters.

Considerable evidence now exists to show that PCBs have similar physiological effects to DDT. As with DDT, acute toxicity is not as much of a problem as the long-term chronic effects; inhibition of enzyme activity appears to be even greater with PCBs, and in fact some of the eggshell thinning attributed to DDT may be due to PCBs or a synergistic combination.

Monsanto Corporation, the only United States producer, is no longer selling PCBs to customers for use in general plasticizer operations where disposal of end-products cannot be controlled. Accordingly, their 1971 production of 20,236 tons is less than half of their 1970 output of 42,527 tons and about the same as their production in 1961. If U.S. users look for substitutes instead of buying from suppliers in Japan, France, or Germany, the concentrations in the United States should begin to decline. The Food and Drug Administration moved in early 1972 to control uses of PCBs in food containers, thus limiting exposure to the public from this source.

Newer Chlorinated Hydrocarbon Pesticides

Some of the pesticides used to replace DDT have been the chlorinated cyclodiene hydrocarbons. Many of these compounds are more toxic than DDT itself, but most biodegrade more rapidly. Cyclodienes are cyclic hydrocarbons with a bridge structure. Examples of this type of insecticide are endrin, aldrin, dieldrin, heptachlor, and chlordane.

Activity and Structure of Chlorinated Cyclodienes. The activities of the chlorinated cyclodienes vary tremendously with the particular shape of the molecules. Some of these closely-related compounds are spatial isomers of each other. Spatial isomers have the same formulas and the same order of linkage for the atoms present; they differ in orientation of the atoms in space. The highest insecticidal activity occurs when a polychlorinated center is close to another site that is strongly electronegative, such as a double bond or an atom of Cl, O, S, or N. This general principle is shown in Figure 4.

A similar relationship exists for aldrin and isodrin, in which aldrin is the endo-exo pair. All four of these molecules have identical structures in the chlorinated part of the molecule. It is thought that their activity is due to the critical fit of these compounds into the pores of nerve membranes. The site for interaction is in the ganglia of the central nervous system, rather than in the peripheral nerves as with DDT. The LD_{50} values for dermal exposure are approximately double the oral values, making these materials more difficult to handle than DDT. Some comparisons are given in Table 2. Note that lindane, which is a simple chlorinated one-ring compound, behaves more like DDT in this comparison of oral and dermal doses.

Table 2 shows that most of the chlorinated cyclodienes are considerably more toxic than DDT and have the added problem of harm caused by dermal exposure. These negative features are partially compensated for by their breakdown time. They are still classed as persistent pesticides, but they do biodegrade somewhat more quickly than DDT. Figure 5 shows the comparative rates.

Table 2. Comparison of Oral and Dermal LD$_{50}$ for Organochlorine Pesticides

Pesticide	LD_{50}, rats mg/kg	
	Oral	Dermal
Endrin	7.5	15.0
Aldrin	39	98
Dieldrin	46	60
Lindane	88	900
Heptachlor	100	195
DDT	113	2510
Chlordane	335	690

Figure 4. Relation of Structure and Toxicity for the Cyclodiene Type of Organochlorine Pesticides

Formula for both dieldrin and endrin: $C_{12}H_8Cl_6O$
Structures:

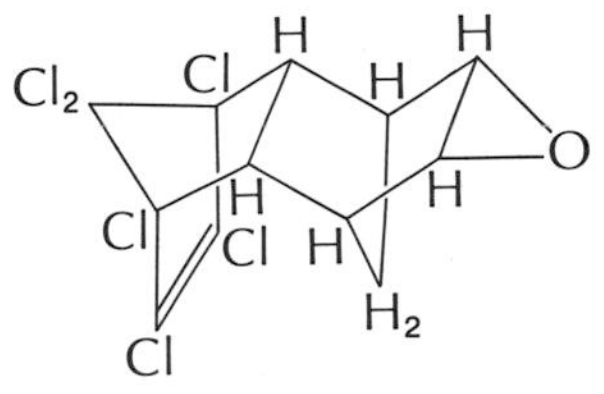

Dieldrin

$LD_{50} = 46$ mg/kg

(oral exposure, rats)

Called endo, exo-isomer

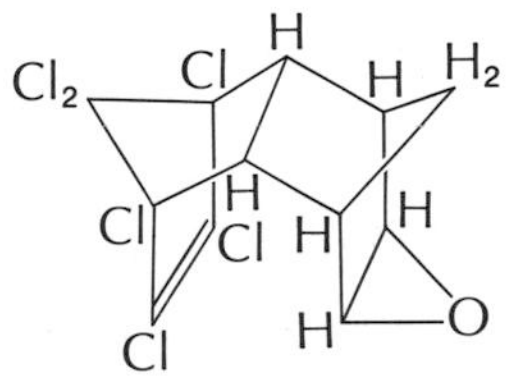

Endrin

$LD_{50} = 7.5$ mg/kg

Highly chlorinated area of the molecule is closer to the oxygen atom in this form of the molecule

Called endo, endo-isomer

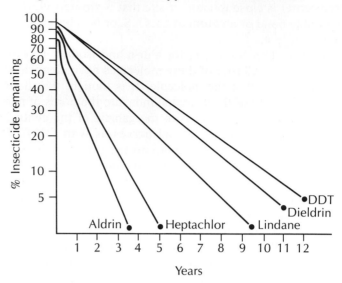

Figure 5. Pesticide Disappearance Rates in Soil

(By permission of Sinauer Associates, Inc.)

Insects also can develop resistance to the cyclodiene compounds, but the phenomenon cannot be explained in the same way as for DDT. Aldrin, for example, is metabolized to dieldrin, which is both more toxic and more resistant to change than the original aldrin. This process occurs with houseflies and many insects; they characteristically display delayed symptoms of intoxication as this change takes place. The specific cause for the observed resistance is not understood at this time.

Phenoxy Herbicides

Some classes of chlorinated hydrocarbons are particularly useful as herbicides. These compounds have raised almost as much controversy as DDT; the class of organic chlorine compounds known as chlorophenoxy (or just phenoxy) herbicides has been used extensively to defoliate forests and destroy crops in Vietnam and Cambodia.

The parent compound for this group of chemicals is 2,4-D (2,4-dichlorophenoxyacetic acid). This is a typical organic acid in that it is a crystalline substance at room temperature. This herbicide and some important related compounds are shown in Figure 6.

Figure 6. Chlorophenoxy Herbicides

Substance, common name, and chemical name	Structural arrangement (2-dimensions)	Uses
2,4-D 2,4-dichlorophenoxy-acetic acid	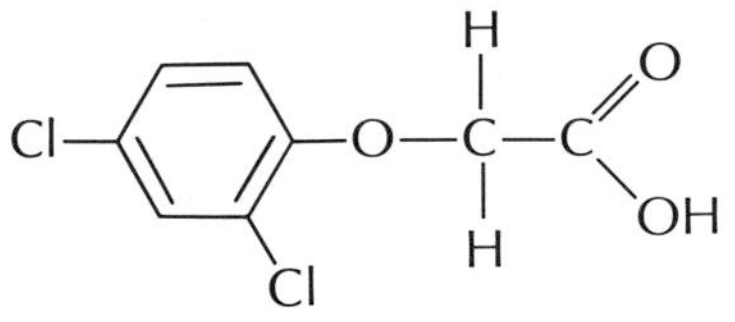	• Control of broadleaf species
MCPA 2-methyl-4-chlorophenoxyacetic acid	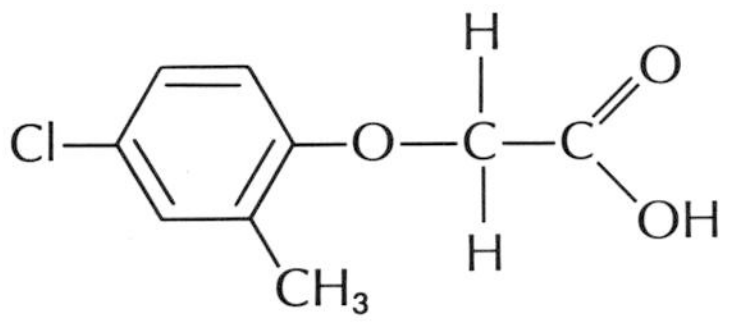	• Used particularly in Europe for weed control in small grains
2,4,5-T 2,4,5-trichlorophenoxy-acetic acid	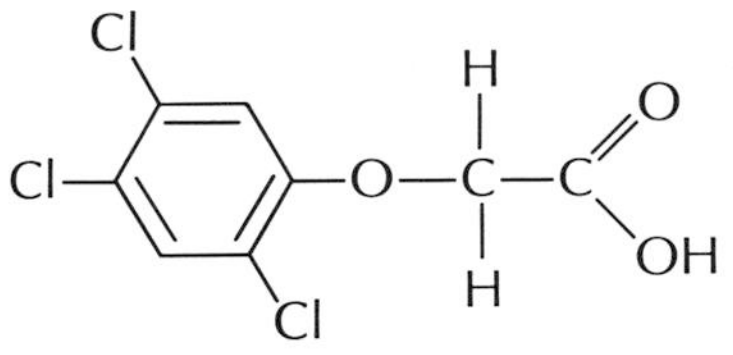	• Woody species and broadleaf species
2,4-DP 2-(2,4-dichlorophenoxy)-propionic acid	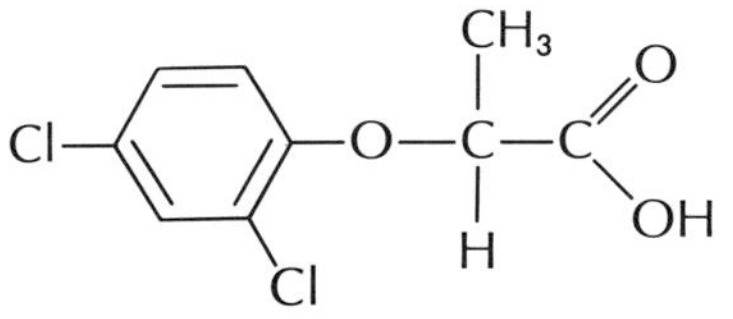	• Brush control on rangelands, rights-of-way, and aquatic weeds
2,4,5-TP (silvex) 2-(2,4,5-trichlorophenoxy)-propionic acid	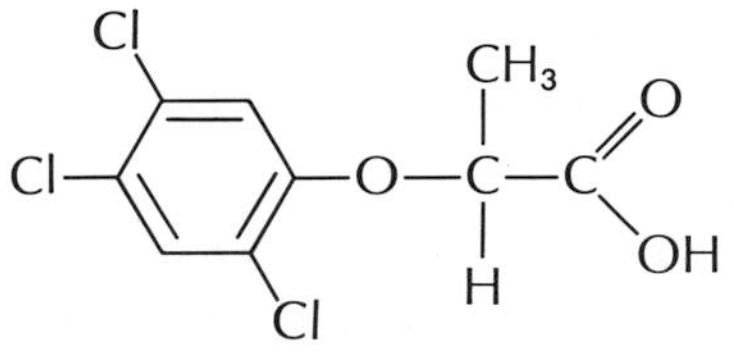	• Control of oaks, maples, aquatic weeds
2,4-DB 4-(2,4-dichlorophenoxy)-butyric acid	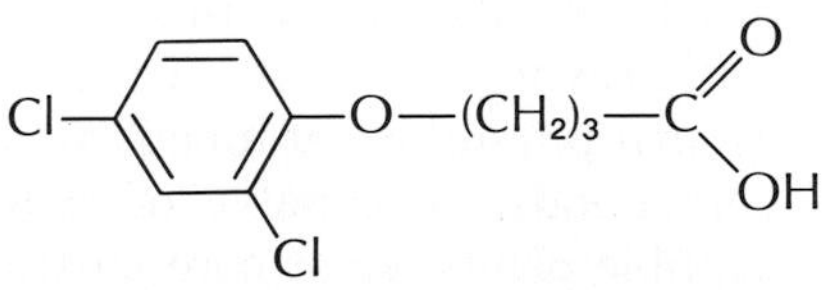	• Weeds in cereal and legume crops

In each case the correct chemical name ends with the proper acid identification.

Acetic acid

$$H-\overset{\overset{\displaystyle H}{|}}{\underset{\underset{\displaystyle H}{|}}{C}}-C\overset{\displaystyle O}{\underset{\displaystyle OH}{\diagup}}$$

Propionic acid

$$H-\overset{\overset{\displaystyle H}{|}}{\underset{\underset{\displaystyle H}{|}}{C}}-\overset{\overset{\displaystyle H}{|}}{\underset{\underset{\displaystyle H}{|}}{C}}-C\overset{\displaystyle O}{\underset{\displaystyle OH}{\diagup}}$$

Butyric acid

$$H-\overset{\overset{\displaystyle H}{|}}{\underset{\underset{\displaystyle H}{|}}{C}}-\overset{\overset{\displaystyle H}{|}}{\underset{\underset{\displaystyle H}{|}}{C}}-\overset{\overset{\displaystyle H}{|}}{\underset{\underset{\displaystyle H}{|}}{C}}-C\overset{\displaystyle O}{\underset{\displaystyle OH}{\diagup}}$$

Herbicides have been used in a roadside maintenance program to clear the area of weeds and grasses. The combination of amitrole and simazine will persist in the soil for three to six months. These materials are not toxic to mammals; both have LD$_{50}$ values above 5000 mg/kg. *(San Diego County Department of Agriculture)*

Substituted for one of the hydrogens has been a phenoxy group which is the familiar phenyl ring (benzene minus one hydrogen) with an oxygen added to link the ring to the acid. The phenyl ring has two or more chlorine atoms in all the common herbicides of this class.

Modifying the Basic Structure. Two types of adaptations are made to increase the ease of application and effectiveness of these herbicides. One is to use the salts (sodium, potassium, and amine) of the acid, which lowers the volatility of the acids. The amine salts are liquids and very soluble in water; they are increasingly used. Esters are another useful formulation. Although they are insoluble in water, they are very soluble in organic solvents and readily emulsifiable in water. The ester forms are the most biologically active of the chlorophenoxy herbicides. This form can wet the cuticle of the plant and aid in penetration into the stomata necessary for effective action. Long-chain esters have been developed with the advantage of lower volatility. The structures of the amine and ester formulations are given in Figure 7.

Method of Action. All of the phenoxy herbicides act to mimic natural plant growth hormones. Artificial introduction of high levels of this hormone in responsive plant tissue causes the cell walls to take up water at a faster rate than normal, producing elongation in the stem, little or no root growth, and leaves that are deficient in chlorophyll. The collapse of normal physiological functions causes the death of the plant. Since these compounds are capable of causing reactions in a wide variety of susceptible plants, great care must be taken to avoid drift. Soil can detoxify

Figure 7. Amine Salt and Methyl Ester of 2,4-D

2,4-D-triethanolamine salt

2,4-D-methyl ester

2,4-D in 1 to 4 weeks; the rate depends on local conditions of soil type, moisture, temperature, aeration, and the exact formulation used.

Environmental Considerations. Since some of the formulations are water soluble, the possible contamination of water supplies used for irrigation, drinking, and watering livestock raises the question of safety. Studies commissioned by the National Cancer Institute and carried out by Bionetics Research Laboratory showed clear evidence of strong teratogenic effects of 2,4,5-T, producing a wide variety of birth defects in mice, rats, and chickens. These studies concluded that 2,4,5-T is "probably dangerous" in concentrations normally used, and 2,4-D was classed "potentially dangerous."

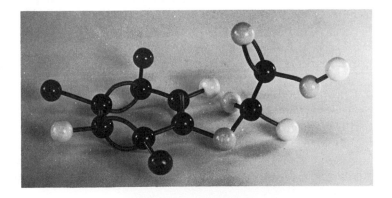

How does the structure of 2,4,5-T differ from that of 2,4-D?

Experiments have suggested that the teratogenic effects of 2,4,5-T may be due in part to the presence of an impurity, TDD. Chemically TDD is 2,3,7,8-*tetra* chloro*dibenz-p-dioxin*. The structure is:

$$Cl\text{---}\underset{O}{\overset{O}{\bigcirc\bigcirc\bigcirc}}\text{---}Cl$$

This impurity is formed as a side product in the main production reaction for 2,4,5-T. TDD is teratogenic and exceedingly toxic; its presence has caused a severe skin rash called chloracne in workers producing 2,4,5-T. Accidental inclusion of TDD in animal feed in the late 1950s caused significant losses to poultry farmers. Concentrations of the contaminant have been reduced from a range of 5–32 ppm TDD in 1965 to less than 1 ppm in 2,4,5-T produced in 1969.

The EPA has suggested a limit of 0.1 parts of this dioxin per million parts 2,4,5-T while further research continues. TDD is not as easily degraded in the soil as are the herbicides themselves, and there is some apprehension that it could accumulate in the food chain in the manner of other stable chlorinated hydrocarbons. If the still-active herbicides, with or without dioxin contaminants, were to get into the water supply, present methods of treatment such as chlorination, reaction with potassium permanganate, or precipitation with lime and alum would not remove the soluble formulations. A standard of 0.1 mg of all chlorinated phenoxy herbicides in one liter of drinking water has been established.

Since concentrations of phenoxy herbicides used in Vietnam (20–30 lb/acre) have been considerably higher than domestic uses, evidence of human health damage and widespread ecological damage might be expected to appear there first. From 1962 to 1969, over four million acres of land were treated with 100 million pounds of herbicides, largely "Agent Orange" (a 50–50 mixture of 2,4-D and 2,4,5-T) and "Agent White" (80% 2,4-D, 20% picloram). Over 468,000 acres of cropland were treated. Biologists have agreed that damage to the mangroves is irreversible, and that undesirable bamboo will take over the area. Several rubber plantations in Cambodia have been eliminated by the drift of herbicides. Several previously unknown birth defects have been noted, but statistical proof linking these to phenoxy herbicides is hard to come by in a country with so many other problems. In light of all the biological damage, the use of 2,4,5-T was suspended in 1970 in Vietnam. The use of 2,4,5-T (in lower application concentrations) is still permitted in the United States, except near aquatic areas, around homes, and on certain food crops. Known incidents of damage from herbicides have taken place in Globe, Arizona (1969) and in the Rio Grande Valley in New Mexico (1971).

Phenoxy herbicides are not the only available compounds for killing unwanted plants and also are not the only ones with possible environmental effects. Inorganic arsenic compounds have been used for years as persistent soil sterilants, active for up to eight years in dry areas. Cacodylic acid is such a compound. Amide herbicides, such as propanil, and the benzoic acid herbicides (picloram and dicamba) are also in widespread use.

Part Three: ORGANOPHOSPHATES AND CARBAMATES

Organophosphates

About the same time as the discovery of the insecticidal properties of DDT, the biological activity of organophosphorus compounds was established by the chance exposure of a researcher to such a compound. Strong effects on the nervous system were noted, and the possibilities of using this type of molecule as an insecticide were investigated rapidly. It is now estimated that more than 100,000 different organophosphorus compounds have been synthesized and insecticidal properties evaluated; of these, approximately 40 are commercially successful. Figure 8 shows some of these compounds that are widely used.

Structure and Activity. As a class, the organophosphates all have structural features in common, as may be seen in Figure 8.

$$\begin{array}{c} R \\ \diagdown \\ P\text{—}X\text{—}R'' \\ \diagup \\ R' \end{array} \overset{Y}{\underset{\parallel}{}}$$

- R and R′—usually short chain hydrocarbon or hydrocarbon and oxygen groups
- X,Y—either S or O
- R″—X—usually the group that is metabolized by insect

The central phosphorus atom is very electrophilic and is the key to observed physiological effects. The phosphorus attracts the enzyme cholinesterase (ChE) and prevents it from performing its usual function, which is to break down the chemical acetylcholine after it has carried an impulse from one nerve fiber to the next. The result is a buildup of acetylcholine and a barrage of extraneous nerve impulses which disrupt normal functions. It is as though the vast electrical system of the insect's brain had been short-circuited. The result can be hyperactivity, tremors,

Figure 8. Organophosphate Pesticides

Compound, common name, and chemical name	Structure	Uses and Comments
Parathion O,O-diethyl O -p-nitrophenyl phosphorothionate	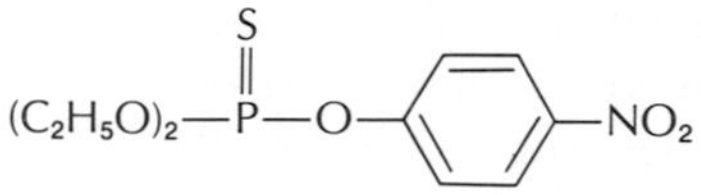 $(C_2H_5O)_2-\overset{\overset{S}{\|\|}}{P}-O-\langle phenyl \rangle -NO_2$	• Most widely used of this class • Garlic odor • High-toxicity to warm blooded animals • Broad spectrum insecticide • Originally used on potato beetle
Methyl parathion O,O-dimethyl O-p-nitrophenyl phosphorothionate	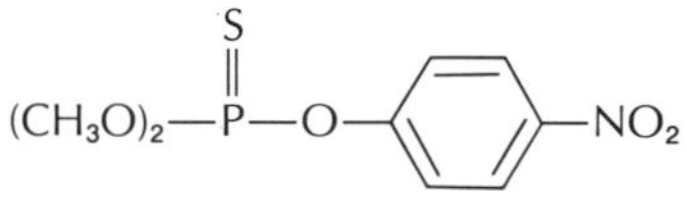 $(CH_3O)_2-\overset{\overset{S}{\|\|}}{P}-O-\langle phenyl \rangle -NO_2$	• Less stable in storage • Shorter residue time • More toxic against aphids and beetles than parathion • Less toxic than parathion to warm blooded mammals
Malathion O,O-dimethyl S-(1,2-dicarboxy ethyl) phosphorodithioate	$(CH_3O)_2-\overset{\overset{S}{\|\|}}{P}-S-\overset{\overset{H}{\|}}{C}-\overset{\overset{O}{\|\|}}{C}-OC_2H_5$ $H-\overset{\overset{|}{C}}{\underset{H}{|}}-\overset{\overset{O}{\|\|}}{C}-OC_2H_5$	• Household, home garden, vegetable, and fruit insect control • Control of mosquitoes, flies, lice
TEPP tetraethyl pyrophosphate	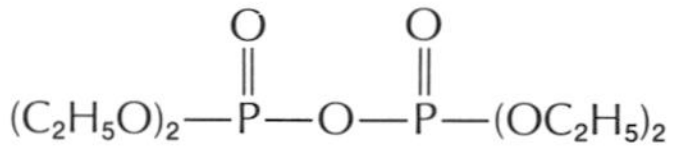 $(C_2H_5O)_2-\overset{\overset{O}{\|\|}}{P}-O-\overset{\overset{O}{\|\|}}{P}-(OC_2H_5)_2$	• Particularly rapid breakdown • Can be used on edible crops before harvest
Sulfotepp tetraethyl dithionopyro-phosphate	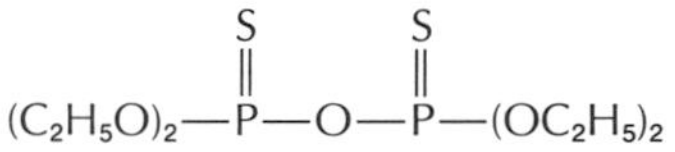 $(C_2H_5O)_2-\overset{\overset{S}{\|\|}}{P}-O-\overset{\overset{S}{\|\|}}{P}-(OC_2H_5)_2$	• More stable than TEPP • Useful as an aerosol or smoke for control of greenhouse pests
DDVP or dichlorvos O,O-dimethyl-2,2-dichlorovinyl phosphate	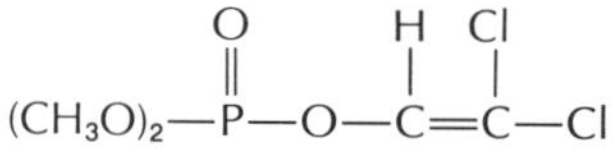 $(CH_3O)_2-\overset{\overset{O}{\|\|}}{P}-O-\overset{\overset{H}{\|}}{C}=\overset{\overset{Cl}{\|}}{C}-Cl$	• Baits and aerosols for rapid knockdown of flies, mosquitoes, moths • Fumigant for household pests • Active ingredient in "pest strips"
Systox (demeton) Mixture of 2 parts O,O-diethyl O-2-(ethylthio)—ethyl phosphorothiomate	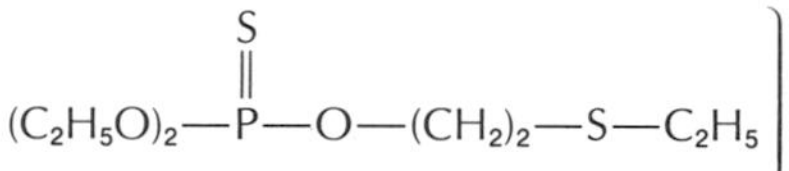 $(C_2H_5O)_2-\overset{\overset{S}{\|\|}}{P}-O-(CH_2)_2-S-C_2H_5$	• Long lasting systemic insecticide; absorbed by roots, stems or foliage
With 1 part O,O-diethyl S-2-(ethylthio)-ethyl phosphorothiolate	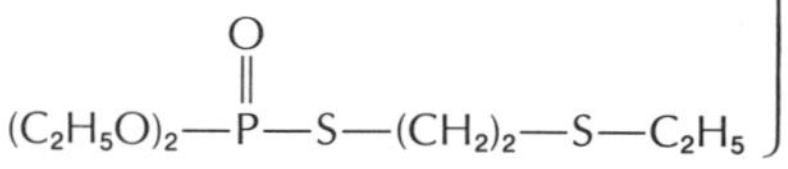 $(C_2H_5O)_2-\overset{\overset{O}{\|\|}}{P}-S-(CH_2)_2-S-C_2H_5$	

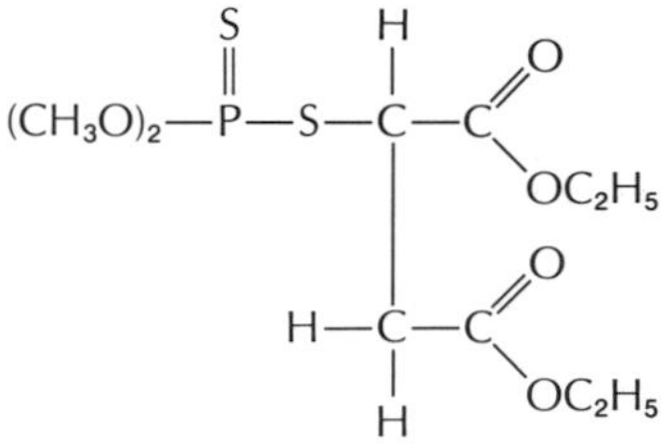

convulsions, paralysis, and death. In some cases the physiologically active compound is not the organophosphate itself but rather closely related compounds produced by metabolism in the insect.

Since the target enzyme, cholinesterase, also plays a vital role in higher animals, the organophosphates are acutely toxic to man as well as wildlife. This property has led to the development of "nerve gases," which are simply organophosphates acting as anticholinesterase agents. The general public knows little of this unpleasant aspect of the application of chemistry to military purposes. Early in the 1950s the powerful agent GB was developed in this country. This is an odorless colorless, volatile gas that can kill in minutes in a dosage as small as 1 mg. It is nonpersistent in the environment. The gas is also known as sarin, the original German name. Chemically it is isopropylmethyl-phosphorofluoridate, with structure:

$$
\begin{array}{ccccc}
 & H & O & & H & H \\
 & | & \| & & | & | \\
H- & C- & P- & O- & C- & C-H \\
 & | & | & & | & | \\
 & H & F & & | & H \\
 & & & & | & \\
 & & & H- & C-H & \\
 & & & & | & \\
 & & & & H &
\end{array}
$$

Presumably it is no longer in production today, but the amount of this material stockpiled is unknown.

By the late 1950s another anticholinesterase agent, GD (also known as soman), was developed. This persistent, liquid agent is chemically 1,2,2-trimethylpropylmethylphosphorofluoridate.

$$
\begin{array}{ccccc}
 & H & O & & H & H \\
 & | & \| & & | & | \\
H- & C- & P- & O- & C- & C-H \\
 & | & | & & | & | \\
 & H & F & & | & H \\
 & & & H_3C- & C-CH_3 & \\
 & & & & | & \\
 & & & & CH_3 &
\end{array}
$$

Closely related is VX which has much lower volatility than GB and is effective for a longer period of time. It is also lethal in 1-mg doses, approximately 1/50 of a drop. Presumably VX is still being manufactured, although on a smaller scale than in previous years. The only known antidote to nerve gas poisoning is atropine which must be administered a few minutes after exposure.

(San Diego County Department of Agriculture)

(San Diego County
Department of Agriculture)

Pesticide safety is an extremely important question for the person actually making the application. For the worker, the potential for harm is largely determined by the initial toxicity of the material. Chlorinated hydrocarbon pesticides such as chlordane (LD_{50} is 335 mg/kg) or DDT (LD_{50} is 113 mg/kg) do not require extraordinary safety precautions for the applicator. This worker dispenses a liquid pesticide formulation from a truck spray rig and does not wear any protective garments. Normal good housekeeping procedures will serve to limit exposure. Incidence of accidental worker contamination is very low. However, the long term effects of chlorinated hydrocarbons in the environment due to accumulation and concentration are important to consider.

The situation is quite different for highly toxic pesticides such as parathion (LD_{50} is 6 mg/kg) or TEPP (LD_{50} is 1 mg/kg). These organic phosphates can produce serious symptoms even with very low doses. Inhalation and even dermal exposure must be avoided. The workers in the picture on the right are in the process of decontaminating a truck in which parathion was spilled. They require rubber gloves and over-shoes, goggles, respirators, and disposable coveralls. Accidental contamination of farm workers is a serious concern. Strict controls must prevent reentry into sprayed areas for the time necessary until the pesticide has lost its high toxicity. These pesticides do not accumulate in the environment.

Production of anticholinesterase compounds can be questioned on tactical, political, medical, and moral grounds. They constitute an environmental danger not only if actually used for the intended purpose, but also due to other factors connected with their production. Field testing is also hazardous, as evidenced by the sheep kill in 1968 after a cloud of nerve gas was carried by air currents from the Dugway Proving Ground in Utah. Storage sites such as the one directly in the flight path of the Denver Airport provide another possible source of accidental exposure. In addition, there is some evidence that shows organophosphates become more toxic upon storage, thus further complicating the problem. Disposal of unwanted supplies has been carried out in the Rocky Mountain Arsenal's deep disposal wells; this practice was blamed for a series of Denver earthquakes. Disposal at sea has also been accomplished. Detoxification of GB is possible by treatment with a strong alkali and presumably VX could be rendered harmless before disposal.

Toxicity of Organophosphate Pesticides. Many organic phosphates have a higher initial toxicity than chlorinated hydrocarbons. For example, LD_{50} for rats (in mg/kg) is 1 for TEPP, 6 for parathion, 15 for methyl parathion, and 1500 for malathion. The wide range of these figures points out another feature of this class—they are one of the most versatile groups of compounds known. By taking advantage of differences in the detoxification process for insects and mammals, compounds safer for humans have been formulated for a particular class of insects. Malathion is therefore about 1/30 as toxic as parathion for insects, but only 1/250 as toxic to mammals, making malathion safer for the applicators as well as an effective insecticide. However, the more toxic organophosphorus compounds must be handled with great care to avoid exposure. Rubber gloves, goggles, a respirator, and protective clothing should be utilized by agricultural workers using TEPP or other of the very toxic compounds.

Since chlorinated hydrocarbon usage is declining, increased use of the organophosphorus compounds has led to a higher incidence rate of systemic poisonings for the agricultural workers. Figures are hard to come by; one federal official estimated 200 deaths per year in the United States due to organic phosphates. Another source found 216 pesticide-related poisonings in 1968 in California; 4/5 of these were due to the organophosphates. Incidents are probably under-reported due to lack of knowledge and suitable laboratory testing facilities on the part of doctors who may see the victims. Since the most susceptible group is migrant farm workers, it is even more likely that they never receive any medical help but instead return to work with what has been termed "orange-pickers' flu." (Low-level symptoms are nausea and headaches.) California has recently adopted some stricter rules about reentering an area that has been sprayed with agents such as parathion. This time period may be up to 45 days in the case of heavy spraying. Most of the organic phosphates have a short span of toxicity as compared with the chlorinated hydrocarbons. Furthermore, since the organophosphorus compounds are rapidly decomposed by the body, they are not stored and cannot accumulate in man or in the food chain.

Carbamates

Structure and Activity. Carbamate insecticides, relative newcomers to insecticidal use, act in a similar way to the organophosphates. Their structural arrangement is quite similar to that of acetylcholine, and therefore carbamates also have a high affinity for the enzyme cholinesterase. In every case, the common molecular feature is an ester of carbamic acid.

Carbamic acid:

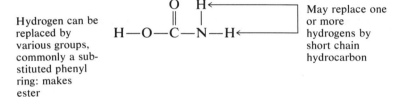

Hydrogen can be replaced by various groups, commonly a substituted phenyl ring: makes ester

May replace one or more hydrogens by short chain hydrocarbon

This structural feature is shown in Figure 9.

Toxicity of Carbamates. Like the organophosphates, carbamates are not accumulated in the system but are rapidly degraded and eliminated. They vary widely in toxicity, with oral LD_{50} (in mg/kg) to rats being 540 for carbaryl, 100 for Baygon, 60 for Zectran, 50 for matacil, 54 for isolan, 65 for dimetilan and 1.0 for Temik. Atropine is effective as an antidote for this class of compounds also. Dermal toxicity may be very low, such as 4000 mg/kg for carbaryl and 1000 mg/kg for Baygon. Carbaryl is particularly toxic to honeybees and great care has to be exercised to prevent eliminating this beneficial insect when using all the carbamate insecticides.

One of the advantages of using carbamate insecticides is that their activity can be increased by adding small amounts of compounds that will act together with the carbamates with synergistic effects. Piperonyl butoxide, sesoxane, and propyl isome have been successfully used in this way. They seem to be effective because they help to prevent rapid detoxification and thus can give the carbamates a greater total activity. Most of the carbamates useful as insecticides are also effective as molluscacides. Related formulations are useful as herbicides and fungicides.

Figure 9. Carbamate Pesticides

Compound, common name, and chemical name	Structure	Uses
Isolan 1-isopropyl-3-methyl pyrazolyl-(5)N,N-dimethyl carbamate		• Baits for house flies and fruit flies • Effective against aphids • Systemic action
Dimetilan 2-(N,N-dimethylcarbaryl)-3-methylpyrazolyl)-(5)-N,N-dimethylcarbamate		• Baits for house flies and fruit flies
Carbaryl (Sevin) 1-naphthyl N-methyl-carbamate		• General purpose Insecticide • Can be useful for 100 or more crops, esp. cotton, forage, fruits, vegetables
Zectran 4-dimethylamino-3,5-xylenyl N-methylcarbamate		• Broad spectrum snails, slugs, and lepidopterous larvae
Aminocarb (Matacil) 4-dimethylamino-3-tolyl N-methylcarbamate		• Broad spectrum snails, slugs, and lepidopterous larvae
Temik 2-methyl-2-(methylthio)-propionaldehyde O-(methylcarbamoyl)-oxime		• Systemic action— seed and soil treatments
Baygon 2-isoprop oxyphenyl N-methylcarbamate		• Flies, mosquitoes, cockroaches, ants • Useful in malaria-control program

Integrated pest control is a blend of all methods necessary to achieve effective control and to minimize environmental damage. Chemical, biological, and cultural methods are used to combat the citrus wooly white fly, a serious economic pest for the growers of southern California. A serious infestation could wipe out entire citrus and avocado groves. The illustrations (at right) show various stages in the life cycle of this tiny fly. The pupal stage is responsible for the characteristic cottony appearance found on the underside of this leaf. Also note the circular pattern of eggs. Although the adults are very small in size, they are voracious eaters and can totally defoliate a citrus tree.

The San Diego County Department of Agriculture is carrying out an integrated program of pest control. County inspection and spraying with diazinon (LD_{50} is 92 mg/kg) and oil helps to save single trees. Since diazinon is particularly toxic for ducks and geese, care must be taken to prevent direct or indirect contamination by this organic phosphate. The pesticide rapidly biodegrades in the environment.

Biological control with two species, eretmocerus and amitus, has been most successful in groves. In the damper climate of Florida, a fungus growth is also used as a biological control, but this will not work in southern California. Agricultural inspection of citrus fruit, including check stations on major highways, helps to minimize the spread of the pest into new regions.

(San Diego County Department of Agriculture)

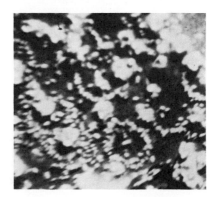

Part Four: ALTERNATIVES

A "perfect" pesticide would achieve complete control of the target pest, would be unique in affecting that pest only, would be nonpersistent, nontoxic, and biodegradable or would otherwise lose its identity in the environment. In addition it would have to be economically competitive. Most alternatives to synthetic chemical pesticides do not yet meet all of these criteria. As more research is accomplished and the true cost of chemical control is assessed, a larger number of approaches will be utilized. Many of the methods that have been successful so far have been based on some characteristic of the insect's own natural ecological cycle.

Pathogens, Parasites, and Predators

The number of destructive insects is reduced by the natural forces of insect disease, parasites, and predators. For example, pathogens such as fungi, bacteria, and viruses can be introduced to cause insect disease if enough is known about the possible effects in other species. Parasites and predators can similarly be imported in larger numbers and this is sometimes a useful method of control, particularly if an insect pest was accidentally introduced into a new area without its natural enemies. This method has recently received a good deal of attention from home gardeners trying to control aphids by the use of ladybugs or the praying mantis. The natural enemies of the gypsy moth, which was inadvertently released in the United States over 100 years ago, have been imported in large numbers, but these parasites and predators have not been as successful in adapting to a new environment as the gypsy moth itself. Such "friendly insects" are maintained in breeding colonies and are useful when released in the spring to combat low-level infestations of the pest moth.

Sterilization Strategies

A more sophisticated approach uses the insect itself for its own destruction. A major livestock pest, the screw worm, was eradicated in Florida by application of the principle of releasing sterile male insects. Insects were raised in the laboratory, sterilized by radiation, and released at the appropriate time to compete with the natural fertile population in mating. To be effective, large numbers of the insects must be reared to achieve the desired "overflooding" of the natural population; a major problem has been producing a sufficient number of healthy insects to adequately compete. Nevertheless, this approach is thought to be useful for low-level infestations of several insects, including such economically threatening pests as tropical fruit flies, codling moths, pink bollworms, boll weevils, and cabbage loopers. It may be that this method will have its greatest value when used in conjunction with other types of control.

Insect Hormones: Pheromones

Researchers are finding many ways in which insect hormones can be useful in pest control. One useful group of compounds is the pheromones—chemicals secreted by one individual to affect the behavior of another member of the same species. Pheromones, the principal means of communication between insects, can be used for sending alarms, marking trails, or attracting a mate. Controlling the mating behavior of the insects through the use of appropriate pheromones can cause a reduction in the species. For most insects, the pheromones are secreted by the females and detected by the antennae of the males, which are sensitive only to pheromones from their own species. Similar species may emit closely related compounds, but other variations, such as the time of release, help the males to respond specifically to the signals of its own species.

Pheromones have been used successfully to control the gypsy moth in some areas. The sex attractant of the gypsy moth was fully characterized in 1970 (cis-7, 8-epoxy-2-methyl-octadecane) and synthesized. It is known as disparlure. Traps containing this compound, slowly released by means of a wick, are placed in the infested fields. The males fly to the trap and are lured into the hollow cylinder which is coated inside with a sticky flypaper-type substance. These males are thus unavailable for reproduction, reducing the size of the next generation of the pest. A similar natural system has been used in the past with ten female moths per trap. Use of the purified synthetic attractant allows each trap to be 20,000 times more effective at a similar cost if the number of traps is large enough (>70,000). The traps have also been used in smaller numbers simply as a way to count pests present in a crop area and therefore to adjust the spraying program.

A variation of this approach is called the "confusion technique" in which large amounts of hydrophobic paper containing the sex attractant or a synergistic mixture of attractants is dropped over an area. The attractant odor so permeates the air that the males are no longer able to find females and mate. Naturally, this application must be exactly timed if it is to work. Tests on 40-acre sites using 300,000 strips of paper have been successful in areas of light infestation, and studies continue. (The paper used is biodegradable so there is no problem about the littering of the landscape!)

Attractants other than sex attractants are also being investigated. Since insects also respond to cues of light, sound, and possibly to radiation level, these means might be useful in control strategies. Blacklight traps, for example, can attract enough of the tobacco

Hundreds of thousands of these gypsy moth traps are scattered throughout the eastern United States each year. The pheremone contained in the traps attracts the pest, providing data on pest spread and population levels. Also note the leaf damage caused by the moths. *(United States Department of Agriculture)*

hornworm so that smaller amounts of insecticide are needed. The bollworm and cabbage looper are also lured by blacklight. Flashes of light can cause an insect to develop too soon, and they die from cold weather or lack of food.

Juvenile Hormone

Disruption of natural growth cycles is also accomplished with hormones which work on a principle different from the attracting function of the pheromones. Hormones found useful in this approach are the juvenile hormones (JH) and the molting hormones (called ecdysones). The importance of these hormones was first studied for silk worms. The entire life cycle of such an insect is intricately regulated by hormones; normal development can be altered by the introduction of synthetic hormones at the proper time. For example, insects have their cuticles (skeletons) on the outside and must periodically shed the cuticles in the process of growing. This is called molting. Ecdysones must be present in order for the resorption of the old cuticle and the production of the new cuticle to take place. The juvenile hormone must be present in the early stages to prevent early maturation; JH must not be present at later stages or the insect will undergo inappropriate transformations and metamorphize into giant larvae and immature adults. Such forms usually die quickly. A typical life cycle and the hormones that must be present at each stage of development is shown in Figure 10.

This scheme then becomes a plan for control. The introduction of hormones at an inappropriate time in the life cycle will produce an extended stage of development, an intermediate (such as an adult with pupal characteristics), or a deformed adult, and usually leads to the speedy death of the abnormal insect.

Is Juvenile Hormone the Perfect Pesticide?　In order to use JH successfully, the life cycle of the insect to be controlled must be studied with care, and the stages causing the most damage identified. For example, adding JH to cause longer or extra larval stages would hardly be appropriate if this immature stage is the most destructive, even if the insect dies without reproducing. Therefore as with pheromones, timely application is very important, possibly requiring multiple applications in some cases. Earlier problems of JH's stability and potency in the field are now largely overcome as demonstrated with the aid of field tests taking place against mosquito larvae.

The similarity between the structure of natural juvenile hormone and some successful synthetics is shown in Figure 11. The similarity in structure leads some scientists to believe that insects will also be

Fig 10. Hormonal Control of Insect Growth, Development, and Reproduction

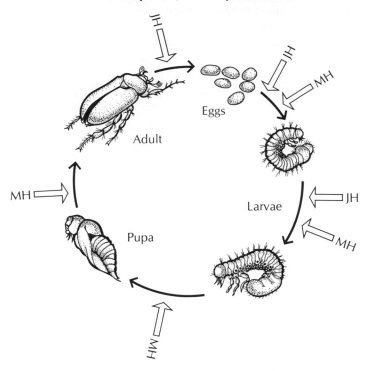

Adult

Eggs

Larvae

Pupa

JH

MH

JH

MH

MH

MH

MH   Molting Hormone
JH   Juvenile hormone

able to develop resistance to excess hormones as efficiently as they have done with chlorinated hydrocarbons. If this happens, the usefulness of JH will be greatly diminished.

One of the biggest problems associated with JH is that not all of the possible spatial configurations have insecticidal activity. The need for stereo-selective or specific production methods that also are economically feasible remains an important limitation. After this, a long series of toxicology, carcinogenicity, and teratogenicity studies must be completed before JH takes its place as a major aid in controlling pest populations. Early studies with rats, mice, rabbits, dogs, and fish seem to confirm the expected lack of toxicity. Since insect hormones are quite different from animal hormones, there should be little environmental danger associated with these methods.

Figure 11. Structure of Natural and Synthetic Juvenile Hormone

Compound: Producer	Structure	Relative potency	LC$_{50}$[a] (ppm in water)
A (USDA)	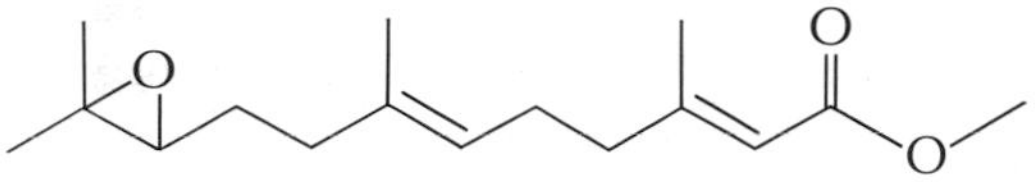	1.0	0.21
B (natural JH)	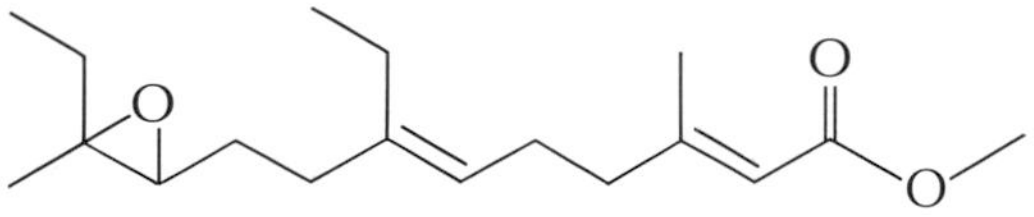	1.4	0.15
C (USDA)	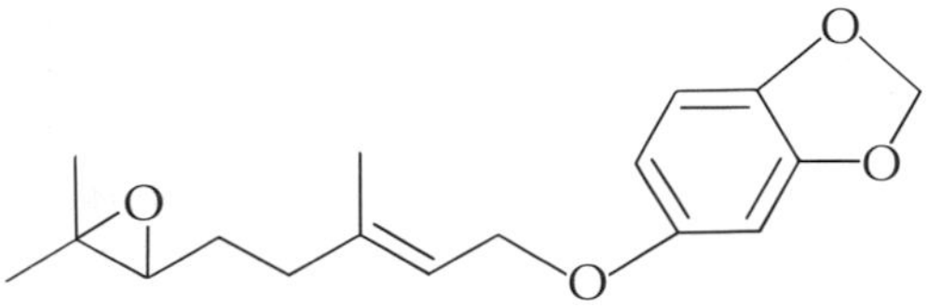	70	0.0030
D (Stauffer)	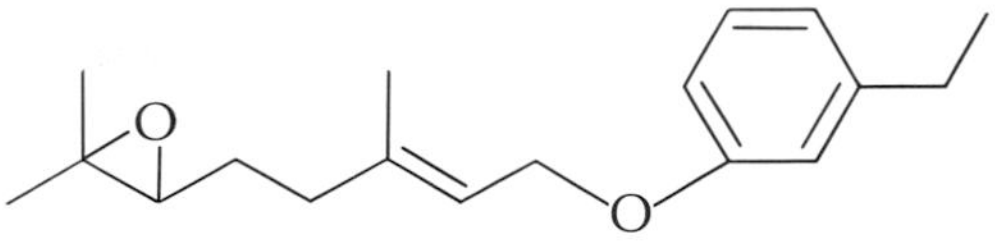	450	0.00047
E (Zoecon)	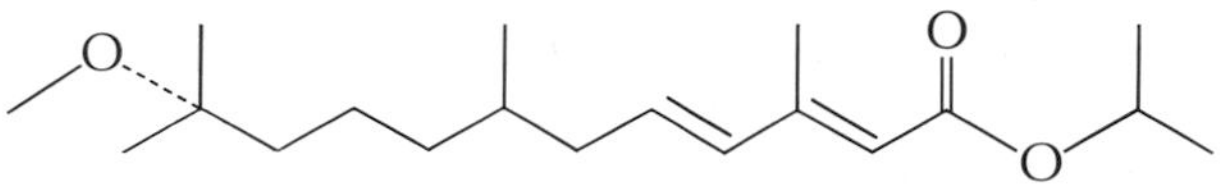	1900	0.00011

[a]Lethal concentration for 50% control of mosquitoes.

Source: Chemical and Engineering News, (November 29, 1971), p. 33.

Gene Infusion

Genetic changes, either in the selective breeding of insect-resistant crops or the breeding of insects that are susceptible to either poisons or diseases, present still other options in planning a program of pest control. Gene infusion, as these methods are called, usually requires extensive research over a long period of time. Crop alteration has been successful in some cases, such as in the development of alfalfa immune to aphid attacks and wheat immune to the Hessian fly. Gene infusion for insects would overcome the problem of developing immune mechanisms in the susceptible insects. The susceptible insects must be released in large numbers, much like the sterilization technique discussed earlier, in order to compete with the normal populations.

Natural Insecticides

Since many plants are insect resistant, it is a logical line of reasoning to try to find the natural compounds which the plants use to defend themselves against insect attacks. There are a few well-known insecticides that are derived from botanical species but there are probably many more compounds that could be useful if the active substances were identified.

Naturally occurring insecticides cannot be looked upon as a panacea to solve the problems of the overuse of synthetic pesticides, for there are some problems here too. Nicotine, for example, is known to have toxic effects for man. Some of these plant materials are expensive to produce or are not as specific as one might wish. The development of resistence may emerge as a problem for plant-derived materials as well. All of these compounds simply add to the options available.

There are several well-known insecticides of plant origin such as the rotenoids, (primarily rotenone), tobacco alkaloids (nicotine sulfate is an example), and unsaturated isobutylamides. Even garlic oil has been shown to be effective against the larvae of mosquitoes, houseflies, and other insect pests. One of the oldest and best known of the natural insecticides is the class of compounds known as pyrethrins.

Pyrethrins. The pyrethrum flower is a daisy-like member of the chrysanthemum family. Originally grown in China, it was introduced to the United States in 1876 but does not thrive in North America. ("Painted daisies" are a related ornamental species widely available in the United States.) Most of the present crop is grown in Kenya, Tanzania, Uganda, Zaire, Ecuador, and Japan. The flower is dried and ground, and the active insecticidal compounds, the pyrethrins, are extracted. The activity is attributed to a mixture of six constituents, each of which is basically a cyclopropene ester of an organic acid. The structures are shown in Figure 12.

Activity and Toxicity. Pyrethrins act by paralyzing insects, probably by blocking the conduction of nerve impulses. These compounds are particularly valuable for their specificity to insects and their lack of toxicity to birds and animals, whether applied dermally or orally. The oral LD_{50} (mice, in mg/kg), is from 330 to 720 for the pyrethrins. For rats, the corresponding value is around 200. (Compare these values with LD_{50} for insects given in Table 3.) The activity can be increased by synergism, piperonyl butoxide being commonly used. It is established that the

Figure 12. Structures of Naturally Occurring Pyrethrins with Insecticidal Properties

Basic structure

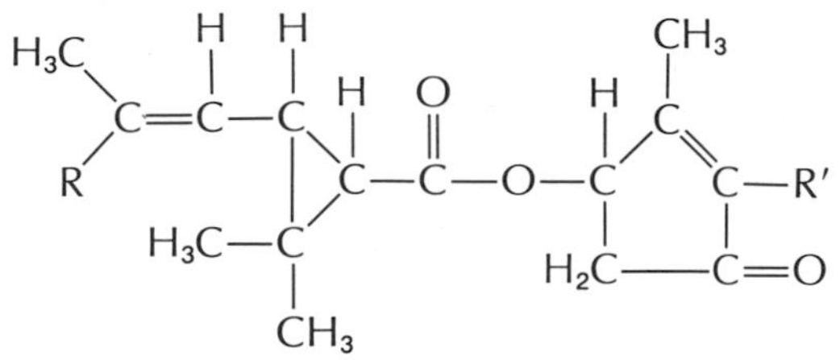

Name	R =	R′ =
Pyrethrin I	—CH$_3$	—CH$_2$CH=CHCH=CH$_2$
Pyrethrin II	—C(=O)OCH$_3$	—CH$_2$CH=CHCH=CH$_2$
Cinerin I	—CH$_3$	—CH$_2$CH=CHCH$_3$
Cinerin II	—CH(=O)OCH$_3$	—CH$_2$CH=CHCH$_3$
Jasmolin I	—CH$_3$	—CH$_2$CH=CHCHCH$_3$
Jasmolin II	—C(=O)OCH$_3$	—CH$_2$CH=CHCHCH$_3$

synergists function by inhibiting detoxification of the pyrethrins, consequently increasing the persistence and toxicity of the compounds. Some comparative toxicities are given in Table 3. It is difficult to isolate the pyrethrins in pure form directly from the pyrethrum extract; since Jasmolin II was only identified in 1962 and Jasmolin I after that, toxicity data is not readily available comparing all six pyrethrins.

Insects can develop resistance to pyrethrins due to reduced absorption of the insecticide or increased metabolism rates. The effectiveness is usually restored or at least increased by use of an appropriate synergist. As may be seen from Table 3, the presence of the synergist increased the toxicity of Cinerin I by a factor of 60 and the toxicity of Cinerin II

Table 3. Comparative Toxicities for Pyrethrins

Pyrethrin	LD_{50} mg/fly, female, topical
Pyrethrin I	0.548
Pyrethrin II	0.942
Cinerin I	2.168
Cinerin II	2.345
Cinerin I + synergist[a]	0.036
Cinerin II + synergist	0.106

[a]Synergist = sesamex

by 22 times. Pyrethrin I, when synergized with sesamex, increases in toxicity to match that of Cinerin I with synergist, even though the original toxicities are quite different.

Integrated Control

Various "cultural" measures are often used by the enlightened farmer to insure continued productivity of the soil without the excessive use of synthetic pesticides. Soil conditioning, rotation of crops, and improved sanitation practices can often avoid pest problems. Crop moratoriums may be necessary in some areas, thereby eliminating a pest by eliminating its food. A preferred target crop may be planted to lure the insects away from the economic crop or mixed plantings used to cut down on the concentration of a pest-attracting crop. Some of these methods may be carried out in conjunction with a vastly modified spraying program in which only necessary amounts of synthetic pesticides are used after partial control by biological methods has been achieved. Ultra-low-volume spraying, which makes possible the effective distribution of a reduced amount of pesticide, is a new development designed to permit decreasing usage of synthetic chemical pesticides.

The increasing interest in "organic gardening" parallels growing concern over the use of persistent pesticides. The advocates of growing food without chemical fertilizers or pesticides reason that these compounds are self-defeating since the fertilizers aren't necessary in a good soil and the pesticides only destroy the bulk of the pests, leaving the hardy insects to breed.

The center for most of the organic gardening information is a small experimental farm in Emmaus, Pennsylvania called the Five Hills Organic Farm. The experience gained there has been shared by means of their magazine, *Organic Gardening*. Using odor-free chicken droppings as fertilizers and huge compost piles of manure, leaves, grass, and sludge, the soil supports a large population of microscopic soil organisms and earthworms, providing a rich base to support healthy, insect-free plants. Laboratory tests have shown that the nutritive value of the crops is higher than that of "chemically-grown" plants.

This isn't the case for all organic farms, for it may take several years to convert mistreated soil into a soil that is healthy and thriving. Twenty or thirty years may be necessary to free it of chlorinated hydrocarbon residues. The greatest successes have been with small farms and city gardens. Huge monoculture farms, necessary for feeding large numbers of people, violate the basic ecological principle of diversity and probably could not convert to true "organic" growing.

Part Five: PUBLIC POLICY

The pollution of our biosphere by persistent pesticides has not been so much the result of negligence as it has been of ignorance of the long-range results of pest control. The need for more research, better planning, and adequate regulation for the safe control of pests is well established. What is not at all clear is how this higher level of ecological sophistication will be accomplished. Certainly agricultural production must continue, but this must be balanced as always with the risks involved.

Federal Control

The Insecticide, Fungicide, and Rodenticide Act of 1947 has been the only basic federal legislation covering the use of pesticides. This act requires that pesticides be registered with EPA (formerly with the Department of Agriculture); this registration is not granted unless scientific studies show the product can be used both safely and effectively.

The Federal Pesticides Office is now one of the five program offices of EPA and was created to unify separate programs formerly under three departments: Agriculture, Interior, and Health, Education, and Welfare. The main functions of the EPA pesticides office are in regulatory actions such as the establishment and enforcement of standards and the processing of registration applications. Some parts of the registration process were kept in the parent agency, and therefore the Food and Drug Administration retains control over enforcing food residue standards. Agriculture retains its function of conducting studies to determine exactly how effective (or ineffective) a specific pesticide is in a specific application. Interior will continue to monitor residues in wildlife and fish.

EPA would like to further strengthen the existing act with provisions that would increase their regulatory powers as well as include the public in decision-making processes. The proposed changes would also tend to diminish the influence of the agricultural chemical industry, sometimes referred to as the agri-chemical complex. The 1972 Congress took one step in this direction by passing a bill which establishes two categories of pesticides. The general-use category would include those products designed for household use, and for interior application, and those substances for which an antidote is available. The restricted-use category would be for those substances with a high proportion of toxic compounds, designed for dilution before use, and includes substances that could be used only with skin protection or inhalation equipment. A pesticide in this category would have to be applied under direct supervision of an approved pesticides applicator.

A proposed third category, the "use-by-permit only" category, was

Fruits and vegetables are regularly checked by the state or county department of agriculture for visible signs of insect damage. In the laboratory, tests will be made to see if recommended levels of pesticide residues are being exceeded. *(San Diego County Department of Agriculture)*

eliminated in last-minute compromises but may be established in the future. It would be for substances that showed persistence and concentration in the environment. Products in this category could be used only by obtaining a written license. This class is particularly important to regulate now that DDT has been banned. Some states already have a similar system, but the systematic use of such categories could end a great deal of confusion which presently exists from state to state due to a myriad of different regulations.

A pesticide may be placed under a cancellation notice by EPA, such as that issued in January of 1971 for DDT. This means that a manufacturer can continue to ship, sell, and have his products used for permitted applications while the safety is under review. It took one and one-half years for a full-scale review of DDT: similar times are expected for other compounds. During this time, a panel of experts from the National Academy of Sciences helps the EPA to decide what ultimate course of action should be taken. Experts in all related fields are asked to testify. If the evidence justifies, a suspension order can be issued which terminates all uses immediately in cases of "imminent hazard to human health."

Improper disposal of partially used or empty pesticide containers creates an environmental hazard. The containers should be kept under lock and key until empty and then disposed of in a certified landfill area. In some regions they can legally be burned. *(San Diego County Department of Agriculture)*

In the case of DDT, six months time was allowed to help ease the transition to other pesticide control methods. Other compounds that have been under administrative review by EPA include aldrin, dieldrin, 2,4,5-T, and Mirex.

The Role of the States

As is the case for water and air, much of the responsibility for regulation will lie with the states acting under the guidelines established by EPA. States are encouraged to set more restrictive standards and procedures. DDT, for example, was totally banned in New York, Wisconsin, and Michigan before the federal government took action. California has excellent licensing and reporting procedures for pest-control operators.

Public Pressure

As the negative aspects of agricultural chemicals come under public scrutiny, pressure from the public to ban the use of persistent pesticides becomes more evident. The EPA has now taken the first step with DDT. It is well to remember, however, that if persistent chemical pesticides are being banned, the replacements must be ready. If the replacements are very toxic, short-lived materials, proper safeguards must be taken to insure safety for the user and the public.

If the replacement is to be biological control, then we can expect to see a continuation of the present shift in research towards finding effective and selective biological procedures. The need for more information as well as the availability of funds will continue to be one of the limiting factors in carrying out these programs.

A healthy sign is that more and more of the new research efforts are being accomplished by university or government agencies; this may help to eliminate one problem that has, in the eyes of many observers, led to the overuse of chemical pesticides in the past. The companies developing pesticides were of course in the business of selling them. The representative who contacted the farmer and advised him on the latest products available and the amounts necessary for control was usually a salesman with limited knowledge of the hazards or chemical properties of the substances. As is true for the Atomic Energy Commission, it usually is not the best situation if the same agency or authority is in charge of both promoting and regulating something, be it atomic power or the safe use of pesticides.

As research continues and public attitudes change, the future will bring decreasing emphasis on synthetic chemicals and increasing reliance on natural controls. The aim is clearly to try to find a more workable balance between the needs of man and the health of the ecosystem.

1. Draw the chemical structure for DDT and write the chemical name underneath the structure. Circle the parts of the structure and parts of the name that correspond. Connect the circles with arrows to make the relationship clear.

2. The compound DDE is structurally very similar to DDT. Compare the structures of these two substances. Write a correct chemical name for DDE.

3. DDD, another product of the metabolism of DDT, is chemically known as 1,1-dichloro-2,2-bis(p-chlorophenyl) ethane. Why is this compound known as DDD? Why is the same compound also abbreviated TDE?

4. Why is milk a good carrier of DDT? Would you expect cream or skim milk to have a higher concentration of DDT?

5. Why is heptachlor a reasonable shorthand name for the compound shown in Figure 1?

6. What does the prefix dodeca- mean?

7. Phenol is a compound closely related to benzene. Its formula is C_6H_5OH. What class of compound is this? Its structure is:

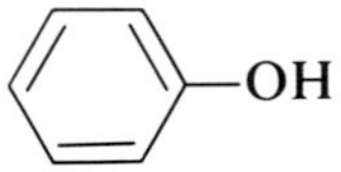

Draw structures to illustrate the three possible positions in which one chlorine atom could replace one of the hydrogens of the ring to form chlorophenol; label the forms appropriately.

8. If aldrin has a LD_{50} (oral exposure, rats) of 39–60 mg/kg, would you expect isodrin to be more or less toxic? Why?

9. Would you expect endrin to be more soluble in water or in organic materials such as fats? Why?

10. Another common organochlorine pesticide is chlordane. Its structure is:

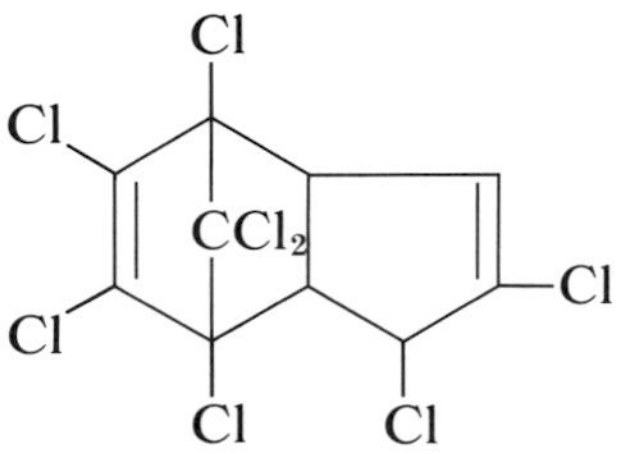

a. What structural difference is there between chlordane and heptachlor? (Despite this slight difference, the two pesticides are quite different in properties; heptachlor is a typical organochlorine pesticide and is persistent in the environment, but chlordane is short-lived.)

b. For both of these compounds, explain why they are classed as chlorinated cyclodienes.

c. The oral LD_{50} for heptachlor is 100 mg/kg (rats) and for chlordane is 335 mg/kg (rats). Which compound is more toxic to rats? Explain your reasoning.

11. How many different isomers are possible if one chlorine atom is added to the basic PCB structure? How many if two atoms are added? (Hopefully this would be enough for you to see the complexity of the mixture of PCBs, but if you are really ambitious, find the total number of isomers possible for all degrees of chlorination.)

12. What physical and chemical properties of PCBs make them industrially useful?

13. 2,4,5-T can also be formulated as an amine salt or as a methyl ester. By comparison with Figure 7, draw structures for these two compounds.

14. Why is it desirable to develop formulations of herbicides with low volatility?

15. Would you expect 2,4-D to be water soluble? Why isn't the methyl ester of 2,4-D water soluble? Since the amine salt is very soluble, what information does that give you about the nature of the amine salt?

16. Marijuana is a broadleaf plant. Which phenoxy herbicides could be used to destroy this crop?

Use this table of data for questions 17–19. It shows selected toxicity information for some organophosphorus compounds.

Compound	LD_{50} fly mg/g	LD_{50} rats mg/kg
Dicapthon	1.6	400
Chlorthion	11.5	1500
Ronnel	2.7	1740
Fenitrothion	2.6	500

17. Which compound is the most toxic to the fly?

18. Which compound is most likely to be harmful to man?

19. Which compound shows the greatest proportional margin of safety in treating flies without harm to man?

20. Consider the graph shown in Figure 5. The straight-line nature of most of the graph seems to predict that zero percent of the pesticide will remain in the soil in less than four years for aldrin, for example. Does that mean that the pesticide is 100 percent biodegraded in that time? What mechanisms remove pesticides from the soil?

21. To what class of pesticides are nerve gases related?

22. Compare chlorinated hydrocarbons with organic phosphates as to their toxicity and biodegradability.

23. What structural feature must be present to identify a carbamate?

24. The epoxy group is $-\overset{\displaystyle\overset{O}{\diagup\!\diagdown}}{\underset{\displaystyle H}{C}}-\overset{}{\underset{\displaystyle H}{C}}-$ and octadecane represents a saturated hydrocarbon with eighteen carbons. Write the structural formula for the gypsy moth's sex attractant pheromone. The correct name is cis-7,8-epoxy-2-methyl-octadecane.

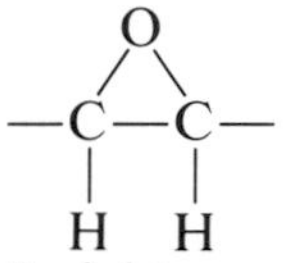

25. Distinguish between pyrethrums and pyrethrins. Why aren't these compounds used as widely as chlorinated hydrocarbons?

Study Questions — Group B

1. Can all pesticides undergo biological magnification?

2. What compounds are used by professionals to rid homes of termites? What precautions are taken to protect the operator and the residents from harm?

3. Two fungicides that are getting attention for their possible environmental effects are captan and folpet. They are chemically classed as phthalimides and are close chemical relatives of thalidomide. Like thalidomide, which was a drug removed from sleeping pills after it was shown to cause birth defects, captan and folpet are also capable of causing deformities, at least in laboratory animal offspring. To read and report about this, try: Shea, Kevin P. "Captan and Folpet." *Environment* 14:1 (Jan.–Feb., 1972): 22–24, 29–32.

4. If you have had some genetics in a biology course, you would find this reference particularly interesting.

> Foster, G. G., et al. "Chromosome Rearrangements for the Control of Insect Pests," *Science* 176 (1972):875–880.

It reviews current theory on the control of insects by genetic manipulation. Read and report on this article.

5. Hexachlorophene has been a pesticide widely used in consumer products. The "pest" that hexachlorophene is effective against is germs. Since its patenting in 1941, the use of hexachlorophene in aerosol deodorants, toothpastes, hair sprays, feminine hygiene sprays, baby powder, and cleaning emulsions has spread to an estimated annual consumption in the U.S. of 4 million pounds or a $250 million industry. In September of 1972, the Food and Drug Administration announced the banning of nonprescription sales of hexachlorophene due to studies linking the chemical with brain damage in infants. Look into the properties of hexachlorophene and the regulatory decision to ban it for consumer use.

6. a. Study the spatial isomers of $C_{12}H_8Cl_6O$ (see Figure 4) by making models of the two compounds. Repeat for aldrin and isodrin.

   b. Dieldrin, endrin, aldrin, and isodrin have identical structures in the highly chlorinated part of the molecule. This can be seen by making space-filling models and looking at a projection of their molecular outlines. Trace their profiles and compare.

7. One of the newest techniques in applying pesticides is encapsulation. A very small amount of pesticide is coated with a layer of plastic of varying strength and porosity, thus releasing its contents over a period of time. The small spheres are suspended in water and dispensed by traditional spraying.

   a. What are the advantages of this technique for a compound such as parathion?

   b. Could encapsulation be useful in the confusion technique used to control gypsy moths?

   c. Encapsulation has been long applied in the pharmaceutical industry. What product(s) do you associate with this technique?

   d. Can you see any potential disadvantages to encapsulation?

8. The objective of this question is for you to find out what pesticides are sold in your area and to evaluate the safety conditions associated with their sale. Visit at least three different stores carrying pesticides in your vicinity.

   a. Check on the variety of pesticides displayed. Which of the many forms are available? Pesticides may be sold as dry powders ready to apply, wettable powders to be diluted, ready-to-apply solutions, "bug bombs," and liquid concentrates for dilution. Pesticides come in a variety of containers, including bags, cartons, bottles, jugs, tubes, and drums.

b. Read the labels and see what information is available. Is only the trade name given or can you tell the active ingredient's chemical name? Are there directions for use together with cautions to be observed? Are there also instructions on the label for disposing of spilled or unused material?

c. Check on the manner of display. Pesticides should be kept away from all articles intended for human and animal use, such as food, clothing, feeds, tobacco, or pet food. All pesticides should be kept apart from insecticides. All containers should be intact and stacking minimized to prevent accidental breakage. (For further regulations, check the pamphlet "Safety Guide for Pesticide Dealers," Publication PA-943, U.S. Government Printing Office, 1970.)

d. If possible, try to evaluate the dealer's extent of knowledge concerning products he is selling. If you ask for something to kill houseflies, for example, what does he recommend? What would he do in the event of pesticide spillage or the explosion of an aerosol can?

Suggested Readings

White-Steven, Robert, ed. *Pesticides in the Environment,* Vol. 1, Part 1. New York: Marcel Dekker, 1971.

Excellent reference for the chemistry and environmental effects of pesticides. Covers all major types of pesticides. Quotes original literature and includes generous references.

Report on 2,4,5-T. A Report of the Panel on Herbicides of the President's Science Advisory Committee. U.S. Government Printing Office, 1971.

Summary report to the President's Science Advisory Committee. Studies the chemistry, use, toxicology, and environmental effects of this herbicide. It is a valuable document as a case study, for it details the scientific considerations that lead to public policy decisions.

Williams, Carroll M. "Third-Generation Pesticides." *Scientific American* 217:1 (1967):13–17.

"New Weapons Against Insects" (#470), and "Moths, Drugs, and Pheromones" (#497). *Men and Molecules*. American Chemical Society cassette tapes (1972).

The first reference presents an overview of our progress through two previous "generations" of pest control methods—inorganics such as lead compounds, and synthetic organics, such as DDT. Biological control represents the third approach. The article includes an interesting account of the author's isolation of juvenile hormone from paper toweling. The two tapes bring the most current research to your attention. Together, the article and tapes would give you an excellent idea of the many approaches to biological control.

Chapter 8
Chemicals in the Internal Environment: Food and Drugs

Steadily increasing numbers of chemicals are being placed into both our external and internal environments. Pesticides are just one component of this picture, and consumers are becoming more aware of the immense variety of food additives and drugs that intentionally or unintentionally have become part of their personal environment.

Public confidence in the safety of foods and drugs has been jolted recently by many events. Senate and House hearings on the effects of chemicals in our environment have focused attention on the possible harm that these agents can cause. Threats such as birth defects, genetic changes, and cancer have been raised for both food additives and drugs. In addition, there are disturbing social and psychological changes that may result from drug abuse.

In the first part of this study, food additives are defined and the general reasons for their usage outlined. The composition of foods necessary for good nutrition is given in Part Two followed by a chemical description of several of the most important classes of additives. We shall also see that even "natural" foods can contain toxins.

The number of drugs in common use today is increasing almost as fast as the list of food additives. Growth in the pharmaceutical industry has unfortunately been paralleled by a sharp rise in the abuse of drugs. In Part Three, we will look at a few of the common drug types, with emphasis on those most in the public eye today.

The main agency charged with assuring the value and safety of our foods and drugs is the Food and Drug Administration, the FDA. It is largely responsible for research, testing, and setting appropriate standards. A discussion of the roles of both the FDA and the public in protecting our internal environment concludes this study.

Part One: FOOD ADDITIVES—WHAT AND WHY?

Food is one of the most basic needs of man. Its quality, together with the purity of the water we drink and the air we breathe, is an important part of our environment. It is essential that we obtain food of sufficient amount, variety, and purity to remain healthy and avoid disease, but in many areas of the world, even these requirements present a severe challenge. The demands of a large population may cause exhaustion of meager supplies in some areas, and proper distribution of available stores can be difficult to achieve even in the most advanced countries. For many Americans, obtaining sufficient food that is nutritious, aesthetically pleasing, and free from contaminants is the goal.

Additives: Accidental or Planned?

The nonfood substances found in our food supply may be added either intentionally or unintentionally. For example, if pesticide residues are found on edible portions of a crop, this is an unintentional additive. This category would also include such biological hazards as salmonella, staphylococcus, and botulism that may come about by chance contamination combined with improper procedures in the preparation of food. Large-scale preparation and distribution now make it possible for an infected batch of food to reach thousands of potential victims. Hormone

Consumer preferences for convenience foods are partly responsible for the increasing use of food additives.

residues in beef and poultry are unintentional food additives; although the hormones were used intentionally to accelerate growth before slaughter, they are not intended to remain in the edible portion that reaches the consumer. Mercury and other heavy metals are also unintentional or accidental additives.

Intentional food additives were first used to extend the usable life of food; they include the use of smoke to treat meat and salt brine to preserve fish. From this modest beginning the number and uses of intentional additives have increased dramatically. The original goal of food preservation remains, but the focus has shifted to such purposes as extended shelf-life, enhancement of nonnutritive characteristics such as color, taste, and texture, and the fortification of food with nutritional supplements. Intentional additives may also provide an essential aid in the processing of food. The World Health Organization of the United Nations has suggested that intentional additives meet the following criteria before being added to the food supply.

A food additive should:

• be safe to use;
• never be used in any amount greater than needed to produce the desired effect;
• be technologically effective;
• never be used with the intent to deceive the consumer about the nature or quality of the food.[1]

In addition, they recommend that the use of nonnutritive additives be kept to the practicable minimum. Naturally, these guidelines are open to considerable interpretation in different countries, but they represent the stated philosophy of using food additives in the United States.

Reasons for Increased Use

There are many factors that have led to an increased reliance on additives in our food supply. The size and geographical distribution of our population has undergone considerable change, leading to the development of large food-processing and distributing centers. The enormous increase in the proportion of meals consumed away from home has also spurred the use of additives; many of these foods depend on automated technology for preparation in quantity, and thus benefit from the use of additives.

Many of the additives now used are important as an economic advantage in competing for the food dollar of the consumer. Eye-catching

---

[1]The use of additives in this deceptive way is called adulteration.

color and ease of preparation have been shown to be important factors in the choices that the average consumer makes in a supermarket today. Mass media advertising has been used to reinforce these preferences or perhaps to even cause them. Over one-thousand new food products are introduced per year and many of these are highly processed "convenience foods" that require the use of additives to be successful. Perhaps only one third of these products survive on the market, showing what one industry spokesman termed "the extreme competition for space in the human stomach." For the first time, in 1969, the sale of processed foods was greater than that of unprocessed, fresh foods. Food additives alone were a 485 million dollar part of the 90 billion dollar food processing industry in 1970. Projections are for this contribution to reach 756 million dollars by 1980. Unfortunately for the consumer, an adequate supply of processed food does not necessarily insure a proper nutritional balance, and furthermore, it is not always possible even to discover exactly what additives are actually present. These "hidden additives" will be discussed in the course of the next section after first looking at what components should be present in a balanced diet.

Part Two: FOODS: PURE AND SIMPLE?

Essential Foods

Carbohydrates. There are several categories of foods that have been recognized as essential for life processes. One of the most important is the carbohydrates—compounds of carbon, hydrogen, and oxygen. Carbohydrates are widely distributed throughout the plant and animal world and help to supply energy for the body. The carbohydrates include such substances as sugars, starch, and cellulose molecules. The majority of carbohydrates fit into the general formula $C_x(H_2O)_y$. The name reflects the original belief that carbohydrates were actually hydrates of carbon, but we now know this is not the case. While useful for simple carbohydrates, the formula does not adequately describe more complex members of the class.

The correct structure of carbohydrates can be illustrated by looking at one of the simplest members of the class, the compound glucose, $C_6H_{12}O_6$. This is a sugar, and since it is composed of only one molecular unit, it is termed a monosaccharide. Glucose is abundant in fruits, plants, and bodily fluids, and serves as the structural building unit for many more complicated carbohydrates. There may be as many as one-hundred thousand glucose units in a polysaccharide such as cellulose. The structure of glucose is shown in Figure 1, together with some other common carbohydrates.

Several totally new breakfast products are now available. The choices range from natural grain and nut cereals to synthetic products such as instant breakfast drinks.

Figure 1. Structure of Common Carbohydrates

Name	Formula	Structure	Comments

Glucose $C_6H_{12}O_6$

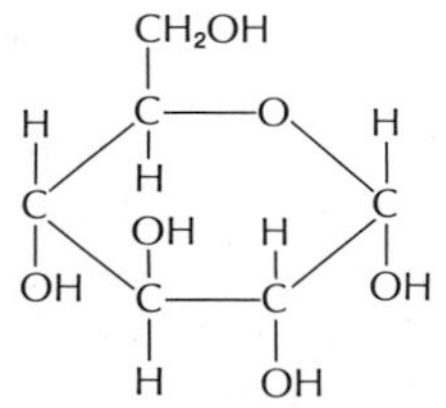

- Relative sweetness (sucrose as 100): 74
- Monosaccharide

Fructose $C_6H_{12}O_6$

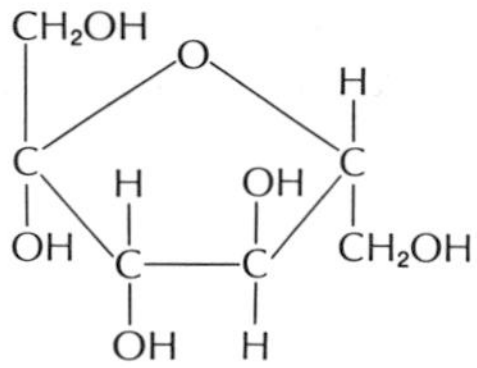

- Relative sweetness: 173
- Monosaccharide

Sucrose $C_{12}H_{22}O_{11}$

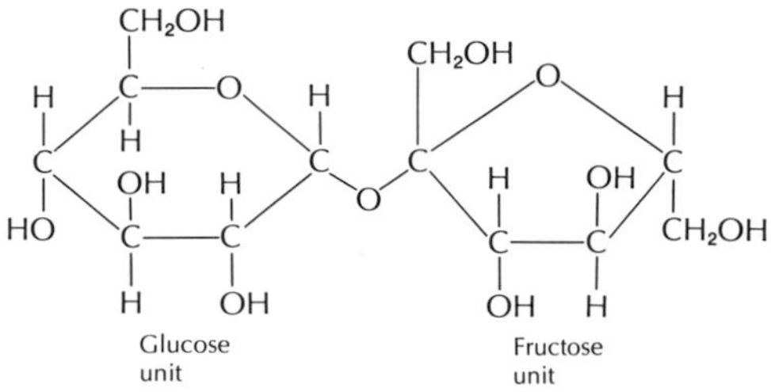

Glucose unit   Fructose unit

- Relative sweetness: 100
- Disaccharide

Lactose $C_{12}H_{22}O_{11}$

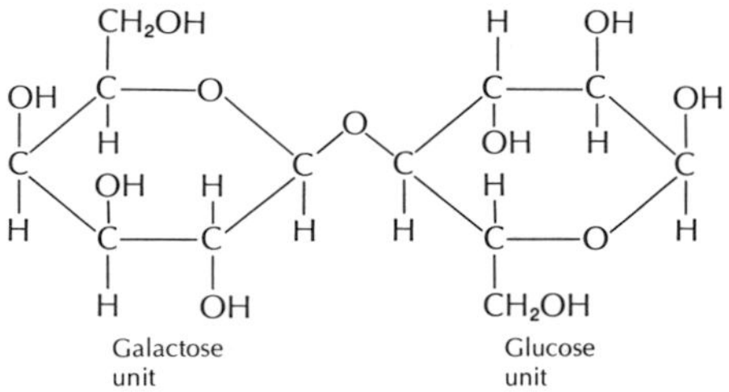

Galactose unit   Glucose unit

- Relative sweetness: 16
- Disaccharide

Starch $(C_6H_{10}O_5)_x$

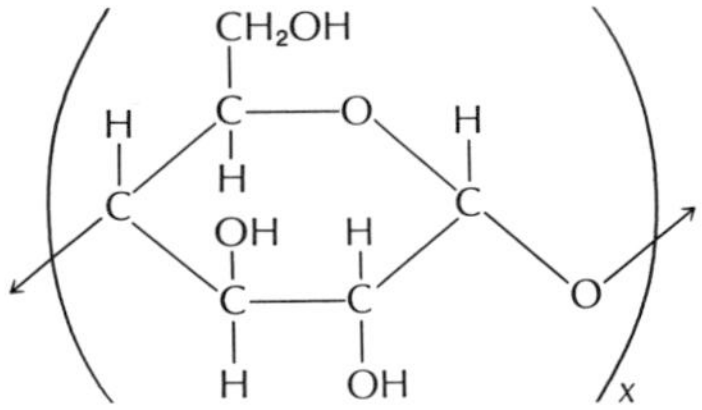

- Glucose unit repeated 200 to 3000 times, majority of units joined in a branched-chain pattern
- α-glycoside linkage between glucose units
- Polysaccharide

Cellulose $(C_6H_{10}O_5)_x$

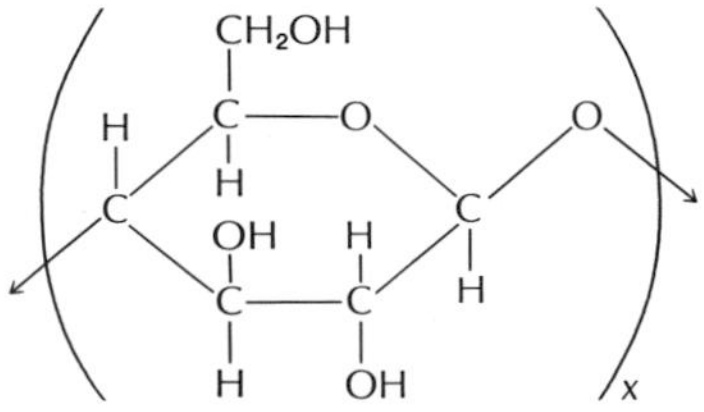

- Majority of units joined in straight end to end pattern; produces filament-like molecules
- Glucose unit repeated several thousand times
- β-glycoside linkage between glucose units
- Polysaccharide

Several important facts about carbohydrates can be seen from Figure 1. These compounds tend to be water soluble due to the presence of so many polar hydroxide (—OH) groups. The possibilities for isomerism should be apparent. The basic formula $C_6H_{12}O_6$ can be achieved structurally in many different ways. In addition to the structural isomers, optical isomers are also important here.

Another important feature of carbohydrates is the subtle difference between the two ways of joining glucose units to form either starch or cellulose. Humans synthesize enzymes that are capable of breaking the α-glycoside linkage; this is the necessary first step for the digestion of starch to sugar. Thus humans can utilize starch and sugar in their diet in order to obtain the glucose units necessary for essential biochemical processes. On the other hand, horses and other herbivorous animals synthesize enzymes that efficiently attack the β-glycocide linkage found in cellulose. Thus the cellulose found in grass can serve as a food source for these animals, but not for humans. This differentiation between starch and cellulose metabolism should be kept in mind when considering the suitability of using sodium carboxymethyl cellulose as a stabilizer and thickening agent in foods.

Optical isomers. If a carbon atom has four different groups attached to it, it is then an asymmetric carbon atom. It is possible to position the attached groups so that two distinct forms are made, with one the mirror image of the other. Since this is a similar situation to your hands, the two forms can be referred to as "right-" and "left-handed" molecules.

For example, lactic acid is formed from the fermentation of lactose in milk. It has four different groups attached to a carbon atom and arranged as in a tetrahedron, the requirements for asymmetry. The groups can be placed in two different ways such that the forms are not superimposable, but rather are the mirror images of each other. They are termed optical isomers.

Optical isomers rotate a beam of polarized light (light that vibrates in only one plane) in opposite directions and on the basis of this may be classed as dextro- (right, clockwise) or levo- (left, counterclockwise) rotators. Although their basic formulas are the same, optical isomers may behave very differently in biochemical systems; enzymes may only "fit," and thus react with, specific shapes. Most simple sugars exist predominantly in the dextro-rotary form.

Dextro-lactic
acid

Levo-lactic
acid

Fats. Fats represent an even more concentrated source of food energy than carbohydrates, although fats usually serve as reserve energy rather than the "quick energy" supplied by sugars. Fats are also compounds of carbon, hydrogen, and oxygen, but they are arranged in a quite different way from the carbohydrates. Chemically, fats are classed as esters of long-chain organic acids. Reaction of the fats with water in the presence of an inorganic acid produces the corresponding fatty acids by hydrolysis. This reaction is actually the first step in the digestion of fats and is carried out by stomach acids. Figure 2 shows the relationship between fats and fatty acids. If this reaction is accomplished with a strong base such as sodium hydroxide, the result is not the free acid but the salt of the fatty acid: soap.

The alkyl groups found in fats are usually long, straight chains with odd numbers of carbon atoms. Therefore, the corresponding fatty acids contain even numbers of carbon atoms. The chains have some degree of unsaturation, meaning that there are double bonds present. The presence of unsaturated bonds generally lowers the melting point, and thus many of the vegetable fats which are highly unsaturated are liquids rather than solid at room temperature. They may be called oils to emphasize their liquid state, but the term fat, once reserved for solids, now encompasses the liquid form as well.

Saturated and Unsaturated Fats. For many years the solid fats were considered to be a superior product and the cheaper, more plentiful vegetable oils underwent the process of hydrogenation to be changed from liquids to solids. This was accomplished in the presence of powdered nickel or another catalyst. For example:

$$\left(CH_3-(CH_2)_7-\boxed{CH=CH}-(CH_2)_7COO\right)_3 C_3H_5 + 3H_2 \xrightarrow{\text{metallic}}_{\text{catalyst}}$$

Unsaturated
Glyceryl trioleate

$$\left(CH_3-(CH_2)_7-\boxed{CH_2-CH_2}-(CH_2)_7COO\right)_3 C_3H_5$$

Saturated
Glyceryl tristearate

The essential reaction occurs at any available carbon-carbon double bond locations in the unsaturated fat.

$$\underset{\overset{|}{H}}{\overset{\overset{H}{|}}{-C}}=\underset{\overset{|}{H}}{\overset{\overset{H}{|}}{C}}- \ + \ H_2 \longrightarrow -\underset{\overset{|}{H}}{\overset{\overset{H}{|}}{C}}-\underset{\overset{|}{H}}{\overset{\overset{H}{|}}{C}}-$$

Since medical evidence now points up the association between a diet high in saturated fats and the accumulation of cholesterol (a fatlike substance that deposits in the blood vessels and causes them to stiffen,

Figure 2. Fats and Fatty Acids

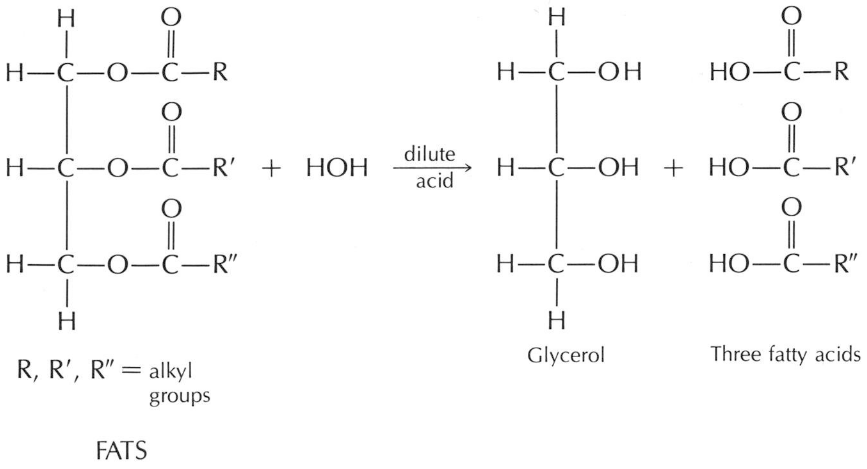

```
     H    O                          H              O
     |    ||                         |              ||
  H—C—O—C—R                      H—C—OH      HO—C—R
     |                               |              O
     |    O                          |              ||
     |    ||                         |         HO—C—R'
  H—C—O—C—R'    +  HOH  —dilute→  H—C—OH   +    O
     |                acid           |              ||
     |    O                          |         HO—C—R''
     |    ||                         |
  H—C—O—C—R''                     H—C—OH
     |                               |
     H                               H

R, R', R'' = alkyl                Glycerol      Three fatty acids
            groups

        FATS
```

thus reducing the flow of blood), it is desirable to both measure and regulate the amount of saturated fats in the diet. This is particularly true for those people with a known tendency to synthesize too much cholesterol in their systems.

To measure unsaturation, a simple iodine test can be carried out and "iodine values" determined. The iodine adds to the double bond as the hydrogen did, but no catalyst is needed. The iodine values are defined by the number of grams of iodine that will add to 100 g of fats. Thus a high iodine value would mean many double bonds present or a highly unsaturated fat; the advertisements would hail this as a "polyunsaturated fat." Low iodine values would indicate a more saturated fat. Some comparative values are given in Table 1.

On the basis of such tests, many new products have appeared on the market replacing the older formulations of margarine that were typically 80 percent hydrogenated fats. The newer "soft" margarines contain a higher percentage of lower melting point polyunsaturates. The more highly unsaturated oils have one disadvantage over fats–the presence of the double bonds makes the molecules more susceptible to reaction with oxygen. Reaction with atmospheric oxygen is usually detrimental because the lower molecular weight fragments produced are more volatile and in extreme may produce offensive odors and tastes associated with rancidity. Therefore antioxidants may be necessary additives to control this process. Certain vegetable oils naturally possess antioxidants that help to stabilize them.

Table 1. Iodine Values for Determining Degree of Unsaturation of Fats

Butter	30–40
Lard	46–70
Olive oil	79–90
Castor oil	81–90
Peanut oil	84–102
Cottonseed oil	105–114
Corn oil	109–133
Soybean oil	127–138
Safflower oil	140–156

Figure 3. Amino Acids

General Formula

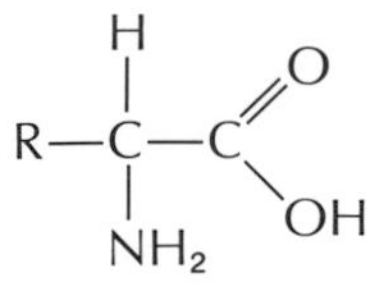

$$R-\underset{\underset{NH_2}{|}}{\overset{\overset{H}{|}}{C}}-C\overset{\displaystyle O}{\underset{\displaystyle OH}{}}$$

Examples:
Glycine

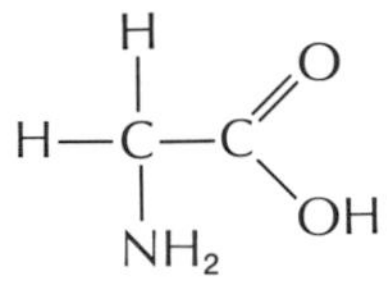

$$H-\underset{\underset{NH_2}{|}}{\overset{\overset{H}{|}}{C}}-C\overset{\displaystyle O}{\underset{\displaystyle OH}{}}$$

Phenylalanine

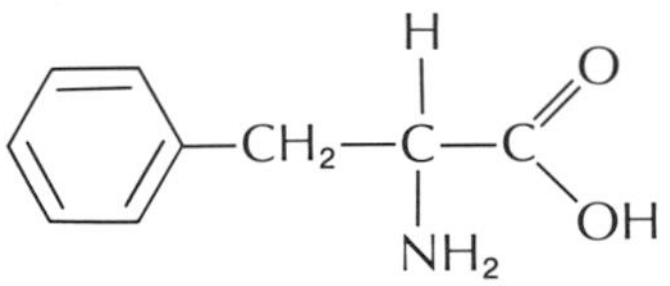

$$\text{(benzene ring)}-CH_2-\underset{\underset{NH_2}{|}}{\overset{\overset{H}{|}}{C}}-C\overset{\displaystyle O}{\underset{\displaystyle OH}{}}$$

Lysine

$$\underset{\underset{NH_2}{|}}{CH_2}-(CH_2)_3-\underset{\underset{NH_2}{|}}{\overset{\overset{H}{|}}{C}}-C\overset{\displaystyle O}{\underset{\displaystyle OH}{}}$$

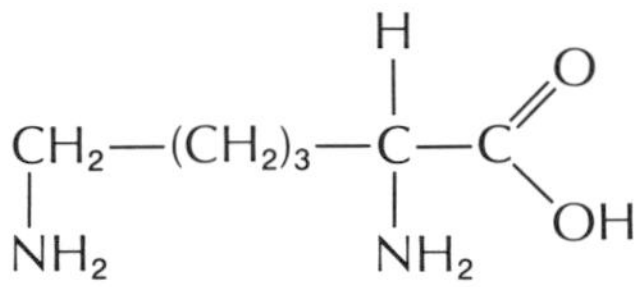

Proteins. Proteins are very large molecules containing carbon, hydrogen, oxygen, and nitrogen, usually sulfur, and often phosphorus. They are exceedingly diverse in their properties and functions and are found in all living organisms. The protein is not used primarily to provide energy but rather to form the necessary structural material for life. Enzymes, so essential for biochemical reactions, are also proteins, as are hormones and antibodies.

Like cellulose and starch, proteins are polymers or macromolecules made up of many basic building structures joined together. The simplest unit is one of the many amino acids. Altogether about twenty amino acids have been identified in natural systems. (The general formula, as well as some examples, are given in Figure 3.)

The protein polymer is formed by tens of thousands of amino acids linking together. This amazing polymer may contain up to hundreds of thousands of units, all held together by an amide linkage. Such a linkage is the result of an elimination of a water molecule from the two important features of adjacent molecules, as shown in Figure 4.

Figure 4. Protein Formation

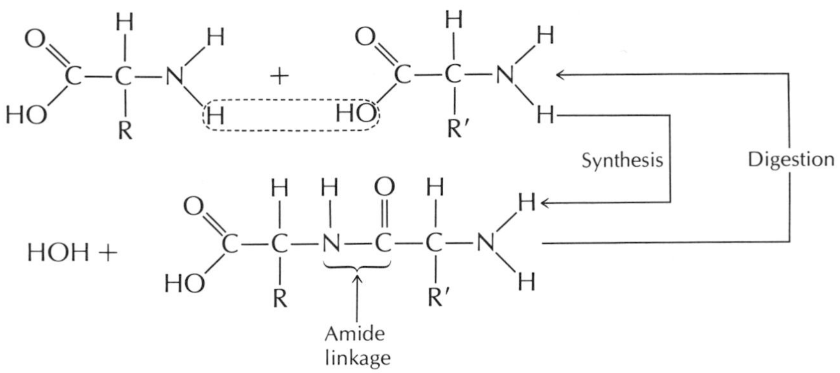

Since the —COOH and —NH$_2$ groups are still available on the resulting molecule, the polymerization process is free to continue. Most proteins have molecular weights over 10,000, but weights up to 40,000,000 are possible. In this way an amazing array of different polymers can be formed from the 20 amino acids. The polymer can often be found in coiled or folded forms, and hydrogen bonding between —C=O and —NH groups serve to hold the molecule in shape.

Several amino acids are deemed essential to our diet, for they cannot be synthesized by the animal system in sufficient quantity to meet the need. Therefore, these essential compounds must be included in food to avoid characteristic physical changes and eventually death. The essential amino acids, together with their recommended daily intakes, are given in Table 2. The minimum daily requirement is half the recommended daily intake in each case. All of these essential amino acids are found naturally in the levo-rotary form. The amount of light rotation is commonly used to identify the purified acids.

Most sources of animal protein have a balanced supply of amino acids, but protein products derived from cereal grains may be deficient in one or more of the amino acids. Therefore wheat protein may have to be supplemented with lysine, rice with lysine and theonine, corn with lysine and tryptophan, and soy protein with methionine. Some natural protein sources are given in Table 3 for comparison of the amount of their over-all protein content.

A promising source of protein is whey, the watery part of milk left over from cheese manufacturing. New applications of processes such as membrane dialysis can produce a protein concentrate from what has traditionally been a severe water-pollution problem, due to the high biological oxygen demand of the previously discarded whey. (Some of the inedible whey solids are finding use as stabilizers for foams used to apply herbicides or fungicides or as covers for the soil after using gaseous fumigants.)

Table 2. Essential Amino Acids

Amino acid	Recommended daily intake (grams)
Tryptophan	0.5
Phenylalanine	2.2
Lysine	1.6
Threonine	1.0
Valine	1.6
Methionine	2.2
Leucine	2.2
Isoleucine	1.4

Table 3. Natural Protein Content

Food	% Protein in edible portions
Human milk	1.1
Cow's milk	3.3
Rice, polished	7.0
Corn meal (86% extract)	9.5
Wheat flour (70% extract)	10.0
Whole egg	12.9
Lean meat	18.0
Lean fish	19.0
Peanuts (roasted)	26.0
Soybean flour	36.7

The search for low-cost, high-protein foods has been actively pursued by several government agencies and private companies in an effort to improve the nutritional standards of the world's rapidly growing population. Although such protein products will never be an answer to the problem of an adequate food supply without a satisfactory population policy, the new protein sources can improve the health and physical development of millions of people.

One long-range approach is to develop new strains of grain crops that are higher in protein. This is another example of the "gene infusion technique." For now, the approach is to use available protein vegetable sources. The cheapest and most abundant source of vegetable protein is the soybean, and various types of products using soybean extracts have been marketed in different parts of the world. Wheat flour, peanut flour, corn flour, and rice derivatives are also used, often fortified with vitamins, minerals, and amino acids. To gain market acceptance for these new products, it is desirable to have them in a form such that they can be used together with natural products for that culture. Thus Incaparina, a cereal-type blend of cottonseed or soybean flour, corn flour, vitamins, minerals, and yeast has had acceptance in Guatemala and Colombia. Vita Bean is a milklike soybean drink that has been sold for several years now in Hong Kong. One of the best sources of soy protein is still tofu, oriental soy curd.

The Indian government has experimented with several fortified foods, including Bal Ahar, a cereal blend of wheat and peanut flours together with nonfat milk solids, vitamins, and minerals, that supplies 22 percent protein. Fortified Atta is a similarly enriched flour containing 13.5 percent protein. "Modern Bread" now produced by commercial bakeries in India is fortified with lysine, vitamins, and minerals and has been widely accepted in India, although it probably does not reach the people who are in most serious need.

Modern protein foods have made an impact in the United States, for many of the soybean extracts can be spun into fibers and used to produce textured meatlike products such as small baconlike bits or simulated ground beef. Many more products such as macaroni, rice, and flours, could easily be enriched with protein as well as fortified with vitamins and minerals, and mandatory enrichment laws are now on the books in many states.

Soy protein has been extracted from soy meal and then spun into these fibers; each ribbon contains 16,000 monofilaments. Coloring and flavoring can be added during the process. The spun protein fiber is dried and then fabricated to resemble natural animal products. (*General Mills Photo*)

Minerals and Vitamins. In addition to the three main classes of proteins, fats, and carbohydrates, the human body must also have minerals and vitamins for proper nutrition. (It is always understood that water is essential for life processes as well.) The important sources of minerals in order of decreasing importance are milk, meat, eggs, cereals, vegetables, and fruit and nuts. Some essential mineral elements are calcium, cobalt, copper, iron, magnesium, manganese, potassium, sodium, molybdenum, zinc, chlorine, iodine, and phosphate ions. While too much of a specific mineral can be toxic, too little can cause specific physiological response as well.

Proper amounts of vitamins are also essential nutritional factors, an observation which led to the discovery of these organic substances. A great deal of information still needs to be worked out on the nature and methods of action for the vitamins. Not all scientists even agree about the identity of all the essential vitamins. It is clear that lack of niacin causes pellagra and lack of Vitamin C (ascorbic acid) causes scurvy, to cite two well-documented cases, but the evidence is not clear for all other vitamins. Some vitamins originally identified as a single substance have turned out to be a group of related naturally occurring substances, all active in preventing the characteristic deficiency disease. Vitamin A is such a compound substance, as are vitamins D, E, and K.

All of these groups are fat soluble. The water-soluble vitamins are those that consist essentially of only one active substance such as vitamin C, niacin, thiamine (B_1), riboflavin, (B_2), pyridoxine (B_6), vitamin B_{12}, folic acid, pantothenic acid, and biotin.

A proper vitamin intake is usually achieved simply by maintaining a diversity in diet, including milk, raw foods, yellow and green vegetables, and protein sources. Highly processed foods are usually lower than the original foodstuff in vitamin content, unless fortification has replaced some or all of the removed vitamins. Taking additional vitamin tablets may be a necessary treatment for some diseases, but a great deal of money is wasted by taking excess vitamins. Excess amounts of water-soluble vitamins are eliminated by the body. Excess amounts of the fat-soluble vitamins are most likely to cause physiological damage, for they are stored in fat tissue. Fortunately in most cases there is a large margin between therapeutic and toxic doses.

Recommended dietary intakes for vitamins and minerals have been established by the Food and Nutrition Board, part of the National Research Council, National Academy of Sciences. Daily levels needed to maintain good nutrition have been suggested for the water-soluble vitamins (ascorbic acid, folacin, niacin, riboflavin, thiamine, B6, and B12), fat-soluble vitamins (A, D, and E), and minerals (calcium, phosphorus, iodine, iron, and magnesium). There also are suggested levels for total caloric intake and protein. All recommended daily allowances depend on the individual's age and sex. A complete table appears in *Recommended Dietary Allowances,* Publication #1694 (1968) of the National Academy of Sciences. The same table appears in Goodman, Louis S., and Gilman, Alfred, eds. *The Pharmacological Basis of Therapeutics,* 4th edition, New York: The Macmillan Company, 1970, p. 1644.

Additives: Natural and Synthetic

All of these essential components of our food supply—carbohydrates, fats, proteins, minerals, and vitamins—are now regularly supplemented with a wide variety of additives. Some of the additives are themselves derived from foods; lecithin is a natural product of corn and soybeans that is used as an emulsifier and an antioxidant. Some of the additives have been synthesized in the laboratory to duplicate natural products in short or seasonal supply. Such synthetics can provide a more uniform product at a lower cost. Citric acid, for example, is widely used as an acidulant and flavoring agent, but the natural compound, which used to be isolated from lemons and limes for commercial use, has largely been replaced by citric acid made by fermentation of sucrose or dextrose. Some of the total number of food additives have been created by food chemists to answer a specific need. This type of additive may be tailor made to improve some aspect of the wholesomeness, appearance, or taste of the food itself. The additive may also help in some stage of production, processing, or storage but not appear in the final product. We will now look at some of the major classes of intentional additives, both of natural and synthetic origin.

Antioxidants. Antioxidants were one of the first additives to be used; they prevent deterioration due to oxidation in fats and oils. These compounds are also referred to as "freshness stabilizers" or "oxygen interceptors." This last term is most descriptive of their method of operation, for the compounds preferentially react with oxygen, thus protecting the fats from oxidation which would turn them rancid. Antioxidants can also terminate any polymerization reactions that depend on the presence of free radicals, which may turn out to be an important function. In living systems, free radical oxidation of tissues can lead to incorrect synthesis of proteins and eventually to the death of cells. This is one mechanism involved both in aging processes and also in smog damage to lung tissue. It may be that antioxidants, including vitamin E, can serve a useful role as "free radical scavengers" in slowing down these processes.

The first commercial antioxidants were the natural compounds lecithin and gum guaiac, but their rather poor heat stability has lead to their partial replacement by synthetics. Some commercial antioxidants are given in Figure 5.

Antioxidants are often used in combination with each other in order to take advantage of unique properties. Very small amounts are effective, some in concentrations as low as 0.0025 percent. The maximum concentration allowed by the Food and Drug Administration in foodstuffs is 0.02 percent. Synergists combined with the antioxidants are common for such compounds; ascorbic acid, citric acid, and phosphoric acid act to remove small amounts of metallic ions which might promote more rapid oxidation. Today antioxidants are found not only in fats and oils but in many other products such as potato chips, cereals, nuts, soups, crackers, cake mixes, pet food, and processed meat. Antioxidants are also used in food-packaging papers such as ice cream cartons or potato chip wrappers. This indirect use of BHA/BHT has led to problems for individuals sensitive to these antioxidants, for their presence in the packaging cannot be detected by reading the label.

Colors. Colors are added to foods to make them more attractive and eye-appealing. This is not an unimportant function, for numerous studies have shown the necessity for foods to look attractive in order for a person to maintain an adequate diet. Again, the original additives were natural in origin, such as the use of turmeric, a yellow dye from the root of an

Figure 5. Antioxidants

Name	Structure	Comments

Lecithin

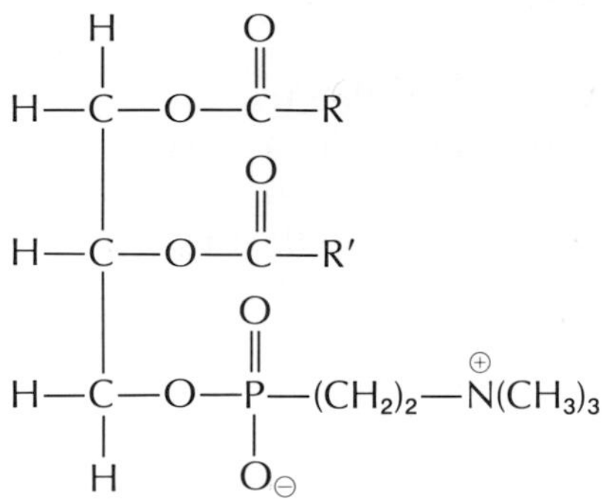

- Naturally occurring substance
- Also useful as an emulsifier

BHA (butylated hydroxyanisole)

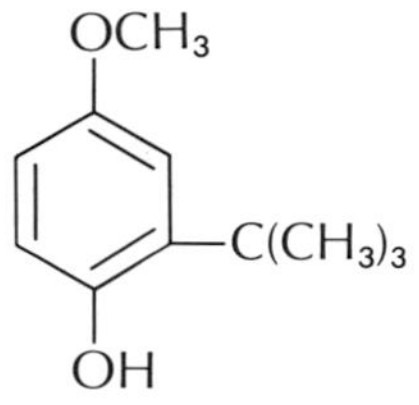

- Synthetic
- Most widely used
- Stable even under high-temperature processing
- Effective in low concentrations and also in combination with other antioxidants

BHT (butylated hydroxytoluene)

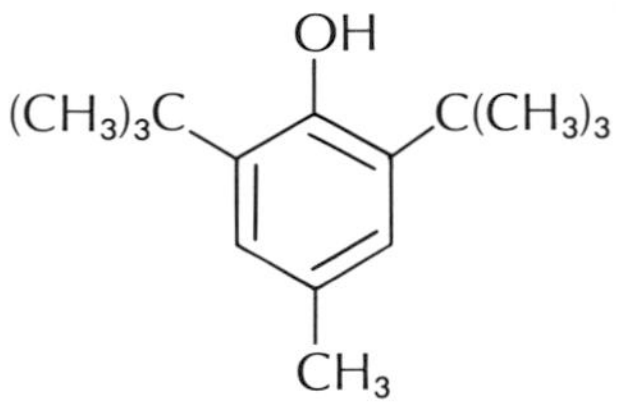

- Synthetic
- Not quite as stable as BHA
- Cheaper than BHA due to other nonfood antioxidant uses in rubber, gasoline, lubricating oil

Propyl gallate

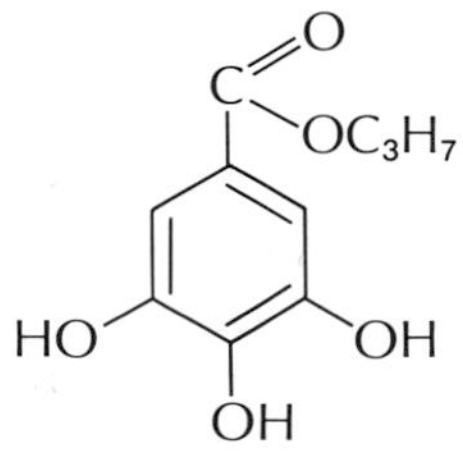

- Synthetic
- Greatest antioxidant ability but less stable in processing
- Can give a blue or green color in the presence of small amounts of iron or copper

East Indian herb. Even inorganic substances have been used to color food, but the results were not always satisfactory to the consumer. Several people in the nineteenth century undoubtedly (perhaps fatally) regretted eating pickles colored green with copper sulfate, red cheese colored with vermillion (HgS) or red lead (Pb_3O_4), or green Christmas pudding created by a clever caterer from copper arsenite. Today about 90 percent of the colors used in foods are synthetics which have advantages of being uniform, stable, and usually cheaper.

Many of the artificial colors are developed from coal tar extracts. Since this class of compounds is suspected of being carcinogenic, the safety of coloring agents has come under attack, and in several cases the compounds have been removed from the market. When the Federal Food and Drug Act was originally passed in 1906, seven synthetic colors were approved; by 1950, the number had grown to nineteen. As the result of investigations in the next decade, several colors were banned altogether or for all but very specific uses (see Table 5).

Currently there are twelve colors approved for food uses including the very new (1971) Allura Red AC (Red #40) which was introduced after six years and 500,000 dollars worth of testing by Allied Chemical Corporation. Its approval helps to fill the color void left by the banning in 1964 of Red #4 for all uses except maraschino cherries. Red #4 was shown to cause damage to the bladder and adrenal glands, but the total ban first imposed was relaxed enough to allow its continued use in cherries, since it was deemed that this foodstuff did not constitute a major component of the diet. The other approved colors are Food, Drug, and Cosmetic Blues #1 and #2, Green #3, Red #2 and #3, Violet #1 (used mainly on meats for inspection and grading stamps), Yellows #5 and #6, Orange #13 and Citrus Red #2. These approved colors are often mixed to create a desired shade. For example "black raspberry" results from a mix of Red #2, Blue #1, Yellow #5 and Yellow #6. Lime green is created by the mixture of Yellow #5 and Blue #1. "Chocolate" is the result of Red #2, Yellows #5 and #6, and Blue #1.

At present, all artificially colored foodstuffs, whether prepared in the United States or imported into this country, must contain no coloring other than the twelve certified colors, and the presence of the artificial color must be declared. In practice, the declaration of color is poorly enforced, particularly in items such as oranges, red potatoes, and sweet potatoes that are sold loose in produce bins. The shipping cartons may contain the required "color added" label, but the consumer does not see this. Regulations concerning colors vary widely in other countries, so that import-export of colored foodstuffs becomes complicated. Japan allows twenty-two synthetic food colors and Denmark thirty-three, but only ten are certified in Canada, three in the Soviet Union, and none at all in Greece.

Figure 6. Common Organic Acids.

Name	Structure	Natural sources
Citric acid	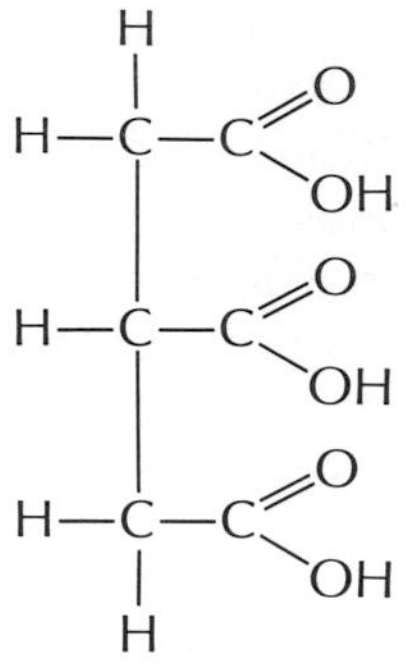	• Citrus fruits
Tartaric acid	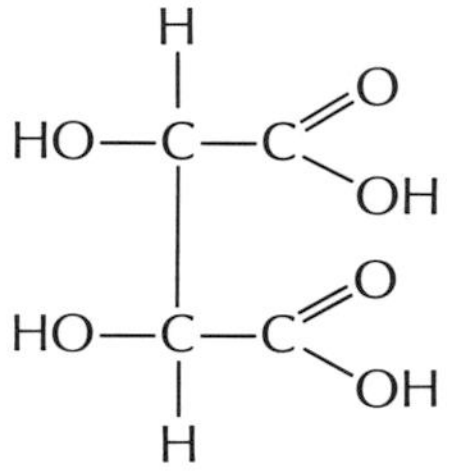	• Grapes, wine
Lactic acid	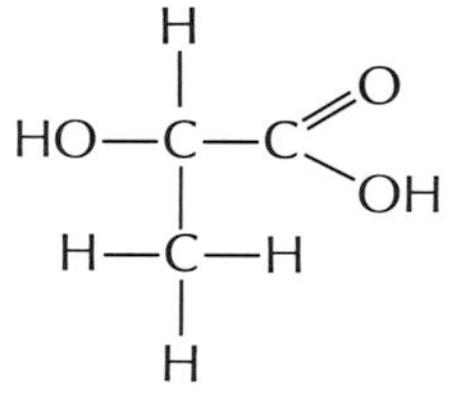	• Milk, especially sour milk
Malic acid	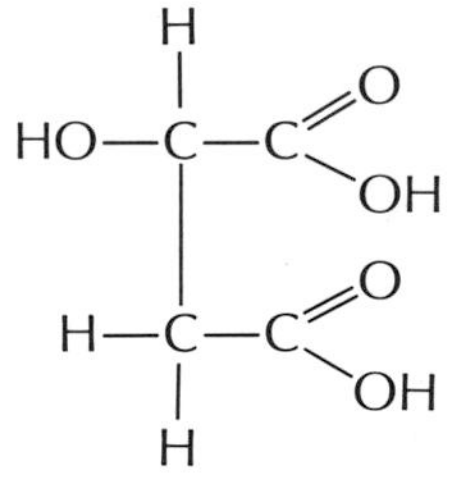	• Apples
Acetic acid	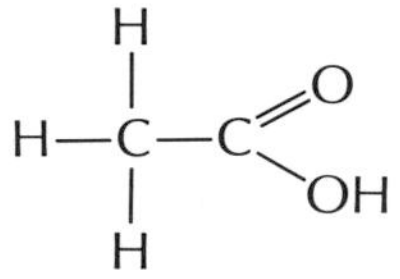	• Vinegar

Acidulants and Alkalies.   Acidulants are acids added to foods in order to provide a tartness in the taste. The degree of sourness is proportional to the hydrogen ion concentration (pH) in solution. Since both mineral (inorganic) and organic acids produce hydrogen ions in solution, both categories can be used as acidulants. The acids also may serve to prevent decomposition of the food by keeping the pH low and thus are useful in processing.

Phosphoric acid (H_3PO_4) is the most widely used inorganic acid. It provides tartness in cola soft drinks and is added to beer and cheese. The most commonly used organic acid is citric acid. It is usually prepared synthetically to be added to foods, although it does occur widely in nature. Citric acid accounts for 60 percent of all acidulants added to foods. There are several other organic acids that are responsible for the natural or artificial taste of common foods. Some of these are shown in Figure 6.

In some cases it may be necessary to adjust the pH by reducing the natural acidity of the food, and then alkalies are needed. Several of the carbonate (CO_3^{-2}) and bicarbonate (HCO_3^-) salts are useful for this purpose. Buffering agents, which control the over-all range of pH values, include such chemicals as sodium phosphate, sodium acetate, and sodium citrate. They may be found in many foods, particularly dessert mixes and whipped toppings.

Flavors.   Flavors are the largest single category of food additives. Of the more than 1100 approved chemical flavors, at least 750 are synthetic substances. The actual mechanism by which we perceive flavors has been the subject of much research, and it is now generally agreed that we can recognize four basic tastes — sweet, salty, bitter, and sour. Correlations between chemical structure and taste qualities have been established for sour and salty tastes but have been less successful with the sweet and bitter taste qualities. The taste receptors located on the tongue and soft palate are sensitive in different regions to the basic tastes, such that sweet is perceived at the tip of the tongue, for example, and sour at the edge.

Very slight structural changes produce markedly different taste sensations. As an example, consider this set of closely related compounds.

These are all related to the same basic structure, but the first one is judged to be four thousand times sweeter than sucrose, the second one tasteless, and the last one bitter!

A similar relationship exists between saccharin and a closely structured compound.

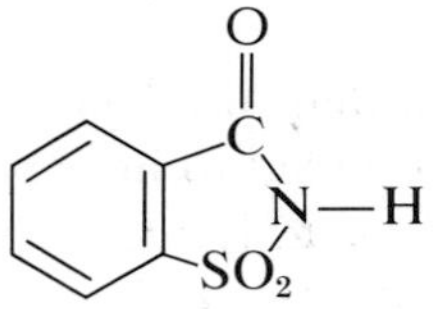

Saccharin—very sweet

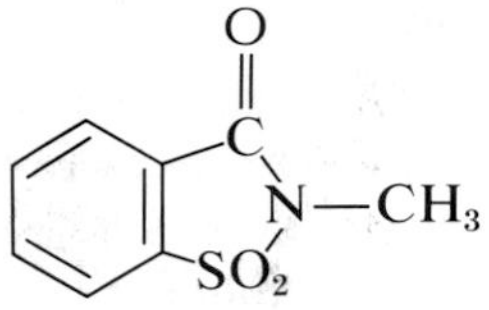

n-methyl saccharin—tasteless

Recently a new substance called Monellin has excited the interest of food chemists. This sweet, white extract has been isolated from a West African wild red berry, also known as the serendipity berry. Unlike sugar and artificial sweeteners, monellin is a protein and is the first known protein to cause a sweet sensation on the tongue. It can produce a lingering sensation of sweetness for at least an hour after eating and studies are under way to determine what causes its effect to be different from other sweeteners. The food industry is very interested in testing this and other substances for use in order to help replace cyclamate sweeteners banned by the Food and Drug Administration in 1969–70.

Many of the natural and commercially successful synthetic fruit flavors are chemically related, in that they belong to the class of compounds known as esters. Esters are the product of acid and alcohol reaction, and the process of forming esters can be compared with the inorganic process of neutralization.

Inorganic neutralization reaction

$$\underset{\text{acid}}{HCl} + \underset{\text{base}}{NaOH} \longrightarrow \underset{\text{water}}{HOH} + \underset{\text{salt}}{NaCl}$$

Organic esterification reaction

$$\underset{\text{acid}}{R{-}C{\overset{O}{\underset{OH}{\lessgtr}}}} + \underset{\text{alcohol}}{R'{-}OH} \longrightarrow \underset{\text{water}}{HOH} + \underset{\text{ester}}{R{-}C{\overset{O}{\underset{O-R'}{\lessgtr}}}}$$

Some esters and their characteristic flavors are given in Figure 7.

Mixtures of flavors are common, as is "encapsulating" the food flavors by combining them with gum arabic. This minimizes the deterioration of the sometimes delicate flavor, particularly for very volatile components of fruit flavors.

Flavor Enhancers. The growing emphasis on flavor additives has at the same time spurred the use of flavor enhancers. The commercially successful synthetics of this class are MSG (monosodium glutamate), IMP (disodium 5'-inosinate) and DMP (disodium 5'-guanylate). Mixtures of flavor enhancers have a synergistic effect. These compounds

Figure 7. Esters Used as Flavors

Name	Structure	Flavor
Pentyl acetate	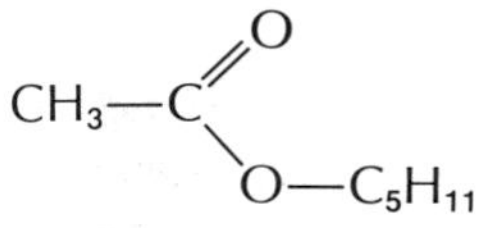 $CH_3-C(=O)O-C_5H_{11}$	• If C_5H_{11} is straight chain, flavor is of pears • If C_5H_{11} is branched, flavor is of bananas
Butyl acetate	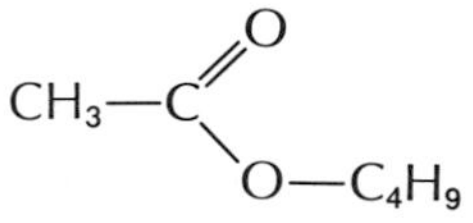 $CH_3-C(=O)O-C_4H_9$	• Raspberries, if C_4H_9 is straight chain • Strawberries, if C_4H_9 is branched chain
Octyl acetate	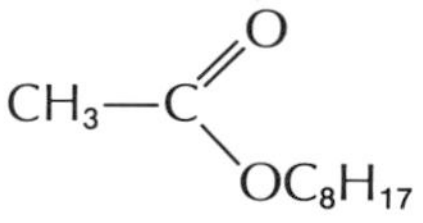 $CH_3-C(=O)OC_8H_{17}$	• Orange
Ethyl butyrate	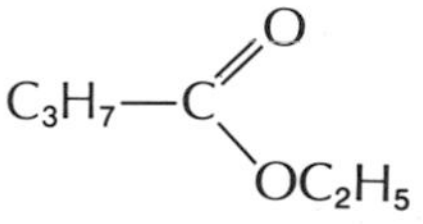 $C_3H_7-C(=O)OC_2H_5$	• Strawberries
Pentyl valerate	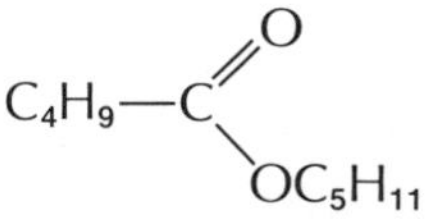 $C_4H_9-C(=O)OC_5H_{11}$	• Apple
Methyl salicylate	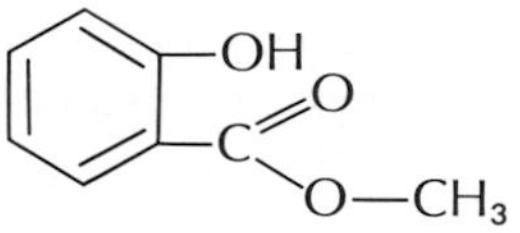 (benzene ring)-OH, $C(=O)O-CH_3$	• Wintergreen

add no flavor of their own to food but serve to heighten the flavor already present. The mechanism that causes the increased flavor sensation is not clearly established. One theory is that flavor enhancers work by increasing the sensitivity of certain taste buds. They may be effective by stimulating greater saliva flow or by acting to combine with trace metals present, thus freeing more taste-bud receptors to react to the taste-stimulating compounds present. Flavor enhancers are generally used to intensify the flavor of high-protein foods such as meat, fish, eggs, and cheese. They are not useful for foods rich in sugar or other carbohydrates.

The most widespread member of this class of additives is monosodium glutamate. MSG is a salt of a naturally occurring amino acid, glutamic acid. MSG has this structure:

$$\underset{HO}{\overset{O}{\diagdown}}C-(CH_2)_2-\underset{NH_2}{\overset{H}{\underset{|}{\overset{|}{C}}}}-\underset{O^{\ominus}Na^{\oplus}}{\overset{O}{C}}$$

Although glutamate is present in all proteins in the body, an excess amount can become toxic and destroy nerve cells. It is estimated that MSG is now added to more than 10,000 different processed foods in the United States. Convenience foods particularly benefit from addition of MSG, and there may even be some preservative qualities associated with its use. Restaurant food is often liberally laced with MSG.

Oriental cooking in particular has long used MSG to increase meaty flavor; MSG is a main ingredient of soy sauce. Reports of a condition dubbed "Chinese Restaurant Syndrome" led to medical research which links ingestion of MSG in susceptible people with headaches and temporary weakness and numbness. The symptoms may also include loss of breath, fainting, and chest pains that resemble heart disease. Continuing research has shown other effects of MSG in experimental animals; parts of the brain are numbed and temporarily inhibited; there are also demonstrated teratogenic effects in mice. Pending a review by the Food and Drug Administration, manufacturers in late 1969 voluntarily withdrew this additive from baby food, where it probably did more to convince mother that the food was tasty than it did for the child. A report in July 1970 by the National Research Council of the National Academy of Sciences concluded that "reasonable use" of MSG by older children or adults is not hazardous except to sensitive individuals. Adults wishing to avoid MSG will have a difficult time, for even a careful reading of all labels will not uncover the products to which MSG may be legally added. Many categories of food, such as mayonnaise, French dressing, and salad dressings, for example, do not have to list MSG if it is used.

Other Classes of Additives. We have hardly dented the list of additives approved for use in our foods. The ingenuity of the food industry in finding chemicals for solving specific problems is truly amazing. A few more of the categories are given in Table 4 for your reference in trying to decide what function is served by the myriad of ingredients you find listed on the packages in your store.

Bread is an example of a major food item that reflects the shift towards highly processed foods. The soft white bread that can be found in every store motivated one writer to this thought:

> To the Editor of the [Albany, New York] *Times-Union*: Give us this day our daily calcium propionate (spoilage retarder); sodium diacetate (mold inhibitor), monoglyceride (emulsifier), potassium bromate (maturing agent), calcium phosphate monobasic (dough conditioner), chloramine T (flour bleach), aluminum potassium sulfate (acid baking powder ingredient), sodium benzoate (preservative), butylated hydroxyanisole (anti-oxidant), mono-isopropyl citrate (sequestrant); plus synthetic vitamins A and D. Forgive us, O Lord, for calling this stuff BREAD.
>
> Averill Park   J. H. Reed
> *(Courtesy, Albany (N.Y.) Times Union)*

The lack of nutritional value in white bread has been pointed out by many researchers, particularly the loss of important minerals and vitamins during the milling and bleaching processes. White bleached flour by itself has so little nutritional value that insects cannot live in it, leading to a long shelf life for the flour. Altogether 93 different additives may be placed in bread, including some nutrients to replace a part of those lost; this is the meaning of "enriched" bread. As an alternative, many smaller bakeries are now producing high-quality breads with a minimum of processed flours and additives.

Each natural or synthetic food has to be judged on the same criteria of nutrition, appeal, and safety. Just as the presence of synthetic additives does not necessarily mean a food is harmful, the fact that a food is entirely "natural" is no guarantee of its safety for man. Nature's own additives include a rather impressive array of plant, animal, and marine toxins that cause obvious symptoms when eaten. Furthermore, there are many other substances that contain small amounts of naturally occurring chemicals capable of interfering with normal body functions.

CHEESE FLAVORED **BURGER** For DOGS

INGREDIENTS: Beef by-products, sucrose, soy grits, soy flour, soy protein concentrate, food starch-modified, propylene glycol, animal fat (preserved with citric acid, BHT, BHA, monoglyceride citrate, and propyl gallate), flaked soybean hulls (1.95%), dicalcium phosphate, dehydrated pasteurized process cheddar cheese, dried skimmed milk, iodized salt, monocalcium phosphate, dried whey, calcium carbonate, phosphoric acid, dehydrated pasteurized process blue cheese, potassium chloride, sodium carboxymethylcellulose, potassium sorbate, choline chloride, calcium carbonate, vitamin E supplement, vitamin A supplement, ferrous fumarate, riboflavin supplement, ethoxyquin a preservative, artificial color, vitamin B_{12} supplement, irradiated dried yeast, zinc oxide, thiamine mononitrate, niacin, cupric oxide, manganous oxide, cobalt carbonate, potassium iodide, folic acid supplement, water sufficient for processing. (Pat. 3,202,514)

SEMI-MOIST MAINTENANCE DOG FOOD

GUARANTEED ANALYSIS

Crude Protein...18.5% min.
Crude Fat....... 7.0% min.
Crude Fiber..... 3.0% max.
Ash............ 7.5% max.
Moisture........27.0% max.

How many of these ingredients can you identify? The use of additives is not limited to food for human consumption.

What does the label tell you? The Fair Packaging and Labeling Act of 1966, enacted as an amendment to the basic Federal Food, Drug, and Cosmetic Act of 1938, seeks to insure that the customer is provided with adequate information about the product's quantity and composition. The essential information found on most labels for food products includes the weight or volume, the ingredients, and the manufacturer. In some cases the label does not list all ingredients present. For example, any "cola" or "pepper" beverage may contain up to 0.02 percent by weight caffeine although this ingredient need not appear on the label. All other soft drinks must label added caffeine. How is this possible?

The Commissioner of FDA can establish food definitions and standards if such action will "promote honesty and fair dealing in the interest of consumers." Standards have been set for many items, such as eggs and egg products, oleomargarine, nut products, canned fruit and fruit juices, fruit jellies and preserves, mayonnaise and salad dressings, cheese and cheese products, and nonalcoholic beverages. Each food class consists of mandatory ingredients, often specified as to the amount that must be present. The class also has defined permissible and optional ingredients. Ingredients that are either mandatory or permissible do not have to be named on the label. Thus emulsifying agents do not have to be identified on the labels of pasteurized process cheese. Monosodium glutamate is a permissible ingredient in salad dressings, French dressings, and mayonnaise. People wishing to avoid particular additives cannot always do this successfully as there are some 223 permissible ingredients not necessarily found on the label. The present confusion over hidden additives could be lessened either by requiring listing of all ingredients or at least listing of all but mandatory ingredients.

Table 4. Other Classes of Food Additives

Type	Use	Examples
Emulsifiers	•Disperse one liquid into another quickly and uniformly •Common in nondairy creamers, ice cream, margarine, candy, cake icings, desert toppings, mayonnaise	•Lecithin (also serves as antioxidant) •Propylene glycol •Mono- and diglycerides •"Polysorbates" such as polyoxyethylene, sorbitan monooleate or tristearate
Stabilizers and thickeners	•Produce smooth texture by binding up one ingredient to prevent separation •Adjust consistency of icings, cheese spreads, salad dressings, gelatin, pie fillings, ice cream, chocolate drinks, diet drinks, instant breakfasts, etc. •Prolong life of "head" on beer	•Vegetable gums such as gum arabic, gum ghatti, gum tragacanth, carob bean gum •Sodium carboxymethyl cellulose •Seaweed extracts, such as agar, algin, (and carageenan until recently banned)
Firming, anticaking, moisture-retaining	•Improve physical properties of foods •Retain moisture in coconut, marshmallows, candies •Prevent moisture retention in baking powder, dried milk, nondairy creamers •Keep canned fruits and vegetables firm, pickles crisp	•To retain moisture; sorbitol, glycerol, propylene glycol •To prevent moisture absorption; calcium silicate, sodium silico aluminate •For firming; calcium salts, including chloride, phosphate
Leavening agents	•Used to release CO_2 from sodium bicarbonate in baked products	•Calcium, sodium, aluminum phosphate •Cream of tartar (potassium hydrogen tartrate)
Preservatives (other than antioxidants)	•Preserve by reducing or eliminating bacteria, molds, etc. •Useful for bread, baked products, acid foods, uncooked meat and poultry, fish	•Calcium or sodium propionate •Sorbic acid •Sodium benzoate •Propylene oxide •Antibiotics •Nitrates and nitrites (curing meats and adding color)
Artificial sweeteners	•"Low-calorie" foods •Necessary for those who cannot properly metabolize sugar	•Saccharin •Cyclamates (now restricted use)
Sequesterants	•Also known as chelating agents or metal scavengers •Tie up trace metal ions that catalyze oxidation or other reactions in foods •Prevents clouding of soft drinks due to reaction between water minerals and coloring agents •Important for color, flavor, and texture control in cheese, margarine, canned frozen foods, beer, soft drinks	•EDTA (ethylenediaminetetraacetic acid) or its salts •Citric acid •Sodium phosphate •Chlorophyll—natural green plant pigment

Natural Food Toxins

One classic case in which natural food toxins produce obvious symptoms is ergotism. This set of symptoms has been known since 600 BC and flourished from the Middle Ages almost to the present. Ergotism results from eating a mold (*claviceps purpurea*) which grows on rye and other cereal grains. Resulting symptoms are itching and tingling skin, mental disturbance, physical deformity, circulatory problems, and abortion. This unfortunate disease is also referred to as St. Anthony's Fire, Holy Fire, or Hell's Fire due to the accompanying burning sensation. Ergot mold was pinpointed as the cause by 1670, but it was not until 1950 that components had been identified. The complex nature of ergot led one researcher to call it "a veritable treasure house of pharmacological constituents."

One of the pharmacologically active components is known to us as LSD. The related compound ergotamine is a very powerful drug used therapeutically to bring about muscle contractions for abortion or for checking hemorrhaging after childbirth. They are both types of alkaloids. The structures are given in Figure 8 for these two representative compounds.

Figure 8. Examples of Ergot Alkaloids

Basic structure	R =	Compound
	—OH	Lysergic acid
	—N(C$_2$H$_5$)$_2$	Lysergic acid diethylamide (LSD)
		Ergotamine

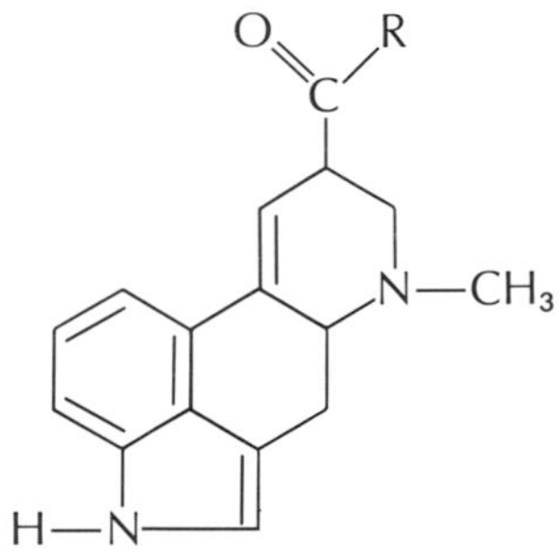

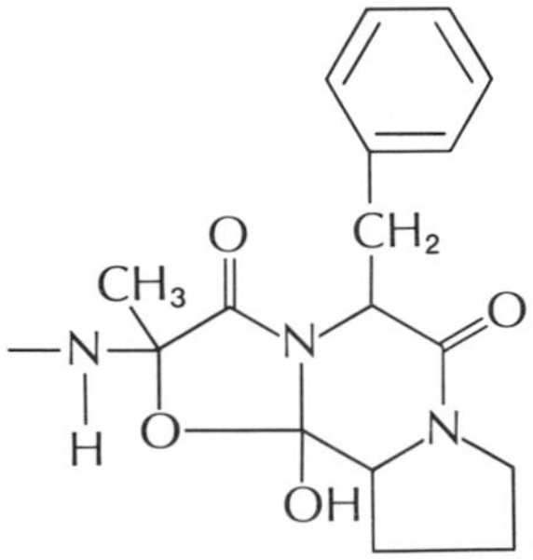

Outbreaks of ergotism in Russia (1926), Ireland (1929), and France (1953) are isolated cases in this century, for now grains are checked carefully for the presence of ergot mold in order to prevent this disease.

Other less spectacular natural food toxins have been eaten by man for thousands of years with little apparent effect. One reason is that man has learned to minimize the ingestion of the toxins by several means. One method is to remove the portions most likely to contain the offending substance such as discarding the leaves of rhubarb, which contains oxalic acid. Proper harvesting practices such as avoiding shellfish in certain seasons or allowing grapefruit to mature can also minimize the danger from natural toxins. The heat used to prepare food also may be beneficial, for example in breaking down hydrogen-cyanide-producing glycosides in dark lima beans.

The presence of natural food toxins is not in any way a rationalization for the unjustifiable use of food additives but instead points out the truth in saying that all foods are chemicals. All chemicals for consumption must be found to meet the three standards of nutrition, appeal, and safety. The amount of a possible toxicant that is safe to consume is a very difficult judgment. This decision depends on such factors as the consumer's age, physical state, possible allergic reactions, and synergistic effects with other chemicals. Many common substances can become toxic when consumed in large enough amounts. Perhaps this is what is meant by saying:

> There are no harmless substances; there are only harmless ways of using substances.

Part Three: DRUGS OF USE AND ABUSE

If the patterns of modern living have led to the introduction of food additives into our food supply, surely some of the same patterns have produced our drug-conscious culture. The pressure of our living styles has created a ready market for headache remedies and tranquilizers. Others turn to antifatigue agents (pep pills) to help themselves cope. Advertising again plays a part in assuring us that some real or imagined advantage will be gained by taking a few pills. Even the medical profession itself is often criticized for overprescribing drugs. Some people elect to abuse drugs as an avenue of escape altogether.

These criticisms must be balanced against the real victories that have been achieved by developing drug formulations remarkably effective in the treatment of specific diseases or symptoms. Drugs have a wide variety of functions—pain relievers, sedatives, antacids, central nervous system stimulators, fever reducers, hormones for regulation of fertility, and antibiotics, to name just a few. The different types and

Figure 9. Some Important Types of Drugs

Class	Example	Structure of Example	Comments
Pain Relievers	Aspirin (acetylsalicylic acid)	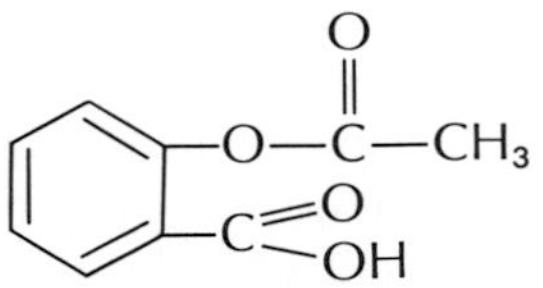	• Acts as an analgesic (pain reliever) and as an antipyretic (fever reducer) • Some people cannot tolerate aspirin; may be able to take phenacetin or acetaminophen as a substitute • Little evidence to support increased effectiveness for buffered or combination products
Stimulant	Caffeine	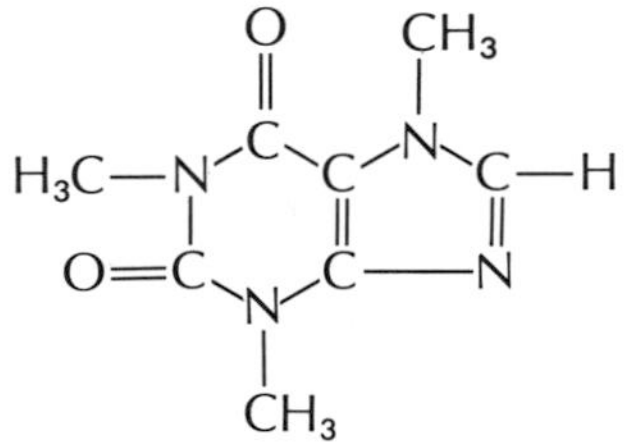	• Mild stimulant • Found in coffee, tea, cocoa, cola, some combination pain relievers, antisleep agents
Hormones	Progesterone	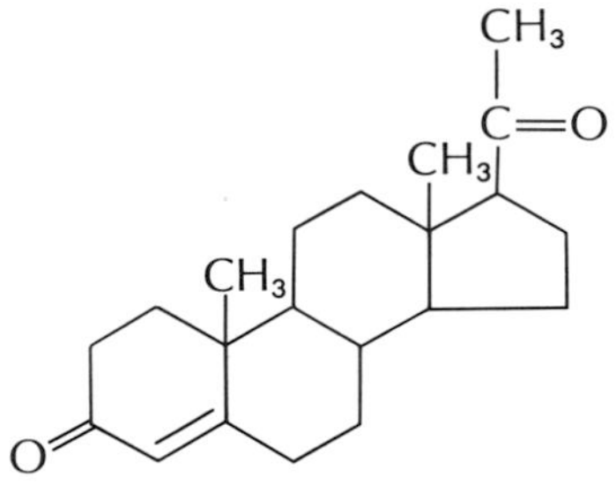	• Many hormones have the same four-ring carbon skeleton: called steroids • Progesterone is one of the naturally occurring female hormones • When prepared synthetically for use in birth control pills, the $-\overset{\|}{\underset{O}{C}}-CH_3$ group may be replaced by a group such as $-\overset{\|}{\underset{O}{\underset{\|}{H}}}C\equiv CH$ to facilitate absorption into the system
Narcotic	Morphine	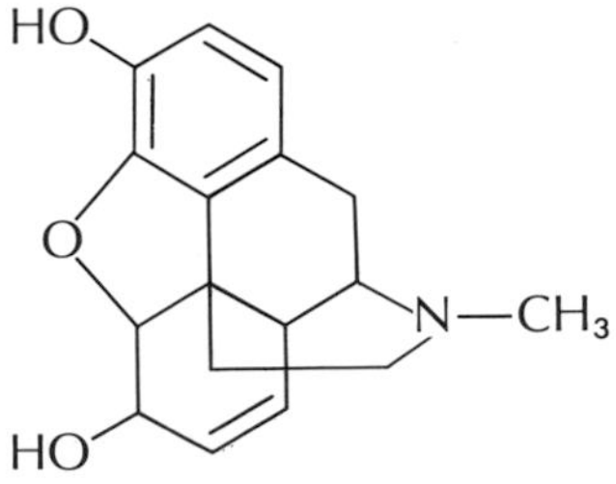	• Produces sedation and pain relief • Addictive drug; controlled by federal regulation • Replacement of one $-OH$ group by $-OCH_3$ group produces codeine. If both $-OH$ groups are replaced by $-O-\overset{\|}{\underset{O}{C}}-H_3$ groups, the result is heroin

Figure 9. (continued)

Class	Example	Structure of Example	Comments
Antihistamine	Promethazine	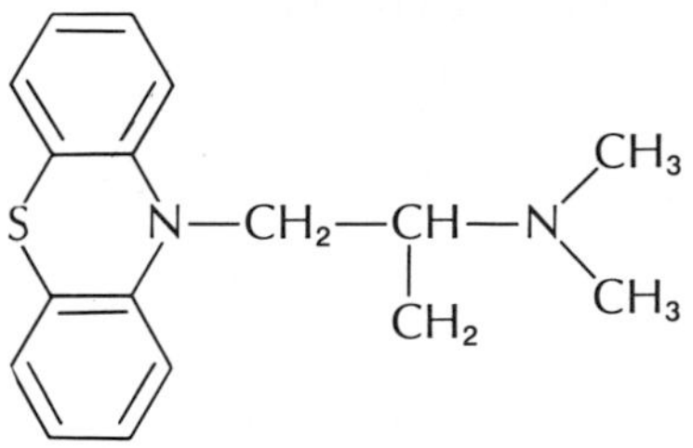	• Used to reduce the intensity of allergic reactions
Antibiotic	Penicillin-G	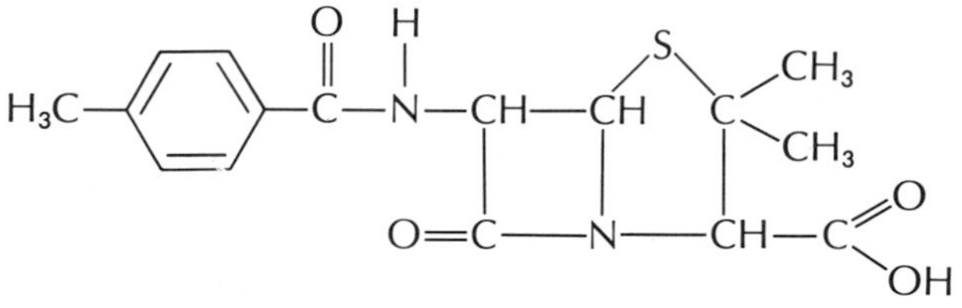	• Penicillin-G is the most effective of the group of compounds known as penicillins • Treatment of infections
	Sulfanilamide	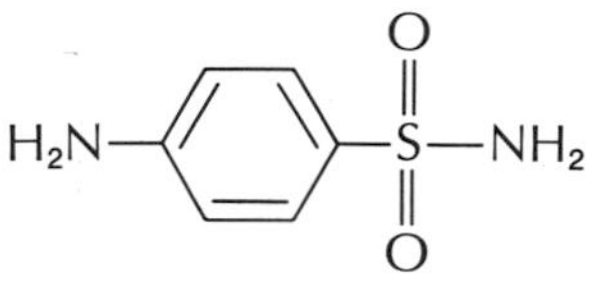	• Over 5000 compounds of this type have been studied; about 20 are effective • First important chemicals used for the control of infection • Often referred to as "sulfa drugs"

formulations of drugs available is truly fantastic, and therefore, in the following sections, our attention will focus on drugs of current concern. Figure 9 will give you a brief glimpse of some of the other types of drugs with which you may be familiar.

Important Types of Drugs

Amphetamines and barbiturates are among the most widely used drugs in the United States. Unfortunately, they are also widely misused. It is estimated that 50 percent of all the amphetamines and barbiturates produced in the United States are diverted to illegal uses. What are these compounds that have valid medical applications as well as the potential for such widespread illicit usage?

Figure 10. Amphetamine Structures

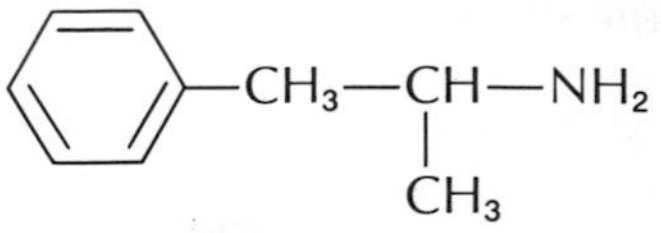

Amphetamine

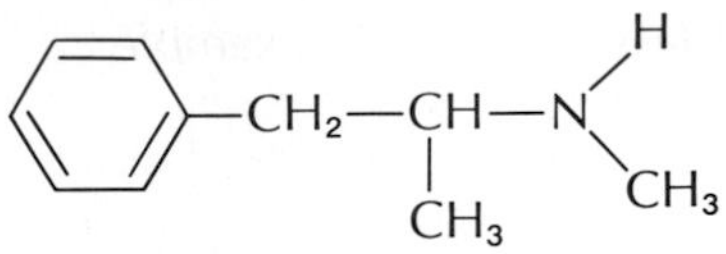

Methamphetamine

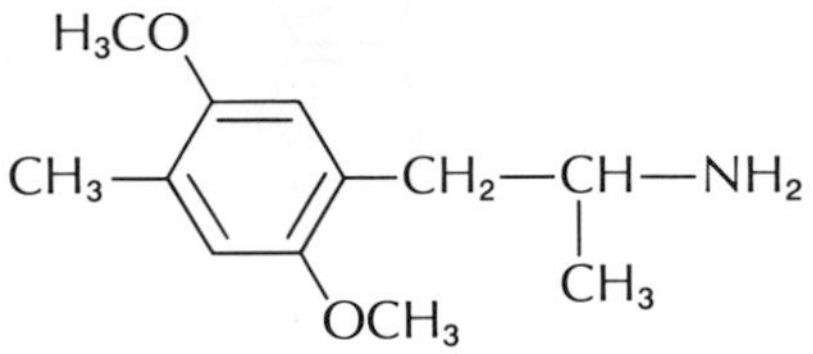

STP (a methoxyamphetamine)

Amphetamines

Amphetamines are known to be effective as appetite depressants, as antifatigue agents, and as mild mood-elevating drugs. They can also be used for the treatment of narcolepsy, which is the uncontrollable tendency to fall asleep at inappropriate times. Clinical observations show that amphetamines can cause restlessness, nervousness, talkativeness, irritation, and in extreme cases, amphetamine psychosis. In illicit usage, this class of drugs is known for their stimulant action by such names as uppers, bennies, pep pills, or speed. A controversial use of amphetamines involves the treatment of hyperkinetic children. Paradoxically, the amphetamines seem to calm some of these children rather than to induce the usual stimulating reaction.

Chemically, amphetamines are characterized by the presence of a benzene ring, a three carbon chain, and an amino group. The basic amphetamine structure and related compounds are shown in Figure 10. Amphetamines have optical isomers. (Compare with lactic acid described earlier.) The dextro-isomer is about four times as potent as the levo-isomer and about twice as potent as a mixture of the isomers.

Any substitution other than small alkyl or alkoxy groups on the benzene ring will abolish or radically alter the nature of the effects. Even shifting the methyl group from the carbon next to the amino group to the carbon next to the ring will destroy the effects of amphetamines. The distance from the amino group to the benzene ring is very important, too. All of these structural requirements serve to point out once again the great difference in properties that can result from minor structural changes.

Amphetamines seem to act on the nervous system by blocking the uptake and release of naturally occurring chemicals that transmit nerve impulses. Structurally, amphetamines resemble natural neurotransmitters such as norepinephrine, serotonin, or dopamine. It is thought that the similarity of the drug to the natural agents allows the drug to take up positions usually occupied by the neurotransmitters and thus short circuit the nervous system. There is a great deal more to know about such processes; further studies of molecular biology will help us to clarify and expand our present knowledge. Since amphetamine psychosis resembles classic schizophrenia in some ways, it may be that biochemical research into the action of amphetamines will also help lead to effective treatment for this mental illness.

Barbiturates

Barbiturates are referred to as "downers" since they act to depress the central nervous system. Dangerous depressions can occur if too high a dose of barbiturates is taken. This is because, in large doses, barbiturates act not only on the central nervous system but also as general depressants on a wide range of biological functions. Oxygen consumption by tissue is reduced, and the activity of important muscles such as the heart is depressed. Alcohol and barbiturates together have a synergistic depressant effect and should never be taken together. Under controlled conditions, the synergistic effects of barbiturates can be used advantageously by combination with anesthetics, creating a greater sedative-hypnotic effect for medical treatment.

Barbiturates are used for inducing sleep or as sedatives. Some forms are used as anticonvulsants in the treatment of epilepsy. Experimentally they have been used in connection with psychotherapy and in the treatment of alcoholism; all such uses involve strict controls.

Figure 11. Barbiturate Structures

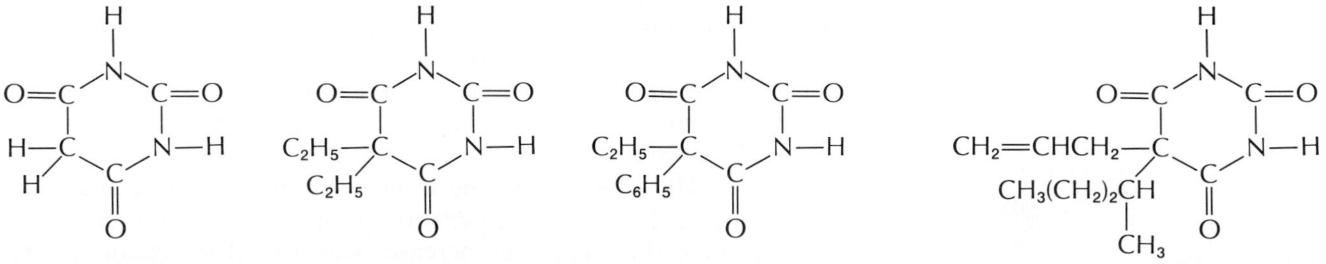

Barbituric acid (inactive)

Barbital (Veronal)

Phenobarbital (Luminal)

Secobarbital (Seconal)

The parent compound for all barbiturates is barbituric acid. This compound is not itself pharmacologically active. Over 2000 derivatives of this acid have been prepared, but only six are medically useful. The six active compounds are formed by replacement of two hydrogen atoms on the same carbon atom by various alkyl or aromatic groups. Figure 11 shows some of these compounds.

Once again, minor changes in structure can drastically affect the nature of the drug. Simply by altering the length of a side hydrocarbon chain, the drug can be altered from an anticonvulsant to a convulsant.

Both barbiturates and amphetamines create a tolerance in the user; continued use requires larger and larger doses to produce the same effect. Physical dependence on these drugs is not established, and there is either a mild or nonexistent abstinence syndrome.

Marijuana

Marijuana has had a long history of use in many cultures. The variable properties of marijuana grown in different regions can be related to the proportion of active compounds present. Since these active compounds are not very soluble, the common exposure is by smoking. The concentrated resin collected from the cannabis plants can be eaten in as many forms as the imagination and taste allow—cookies, tea, scrambled eggs and other combinations have been reported.

The molecules now believed to be responsible for the euphoric "high" experienced by marijuana smokers are shown in Figure 12.

The compounds in Figure 11 show that a feature as subtle as the number and location of double bonds creates a distinct difference in properties. There may be some conversion from one form to another during storage, processing, and smoking. These changes could be partially responsible for the variable effects demonstrated when different people smoke the same amount of marijuana, although psychological expectations and history of usage have been shown to be influencing factors as well.

It is interesting to note the absence of nitrogen in the marijuana structure, an element present in the great majority of drugs acting on the nervous system. Experiments in which nitrogen is synthetically introduced into the molecule have produced a whole series of THC-related compounds, most of which are biologically active. Similar results have occurred by adding sulfur to the ring.

Active THC compounds tend to increase the pulse rate and result in reddening of the eyes due to dilation of the blood vessels. It is commonly reported that pupil size increases with use of marijuana, but recent controlled experiments tend to contradict that idea. This is but one example of the conflicting nature of the evidence connected with the

The characteristic leaves of a marijuana plant make identification rather easy. *(National Institute of Mental Health)*

basic question: Is marijuana harmful to man? Researchers have reported effects of smoking marijuana on blood sugar levels, but some have concluded the result is hypoglycemia and some the opposite effect, hyperglycemia. The meaning of experiments on brain wave changes are similarly confused. What can be seen is the need for better clinical research. The use of pure synthetic preparations of active THC compounds helps dispel some of the uncontrolled variables in experimental work. This has only been possible since 1967 when the first synthesis specific for the active forms of THC was accomplished.

Despite widespread use, there have been few cases of serious health effects resulting from marijuana usage. There never has been a documented case of lethal overdosage. Hallucinations have resulted from

Figure 12. Compounds Isolated from Marijuana Plants

Two pharmacologically active forms

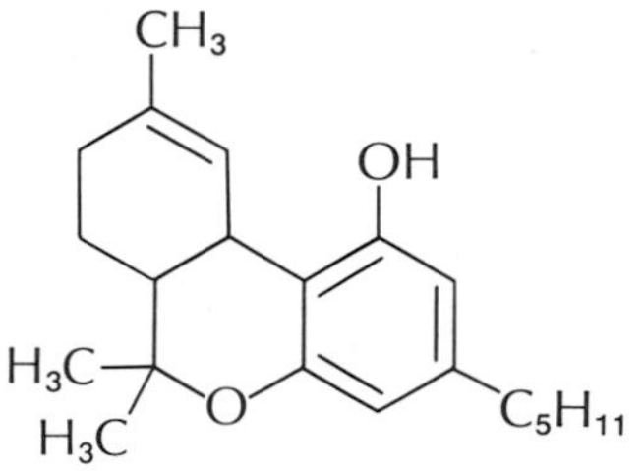

Δ^1 — tetrahydrocannabinol[a]
Δ^1 — THC

or

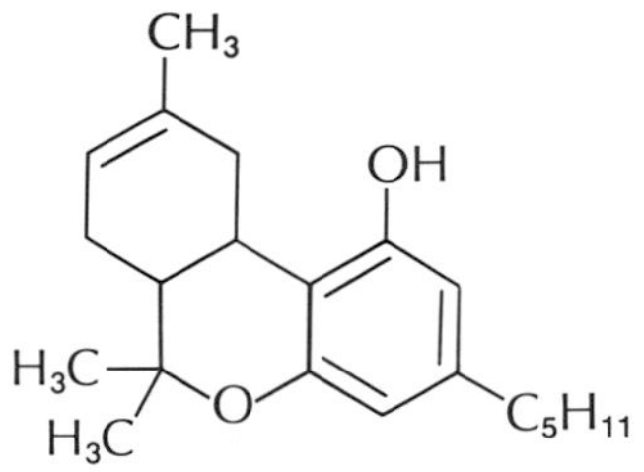

Δ^6 — tetrahydrocannabinol
Δ^6 — THC

Two pharmacologically inactive forms

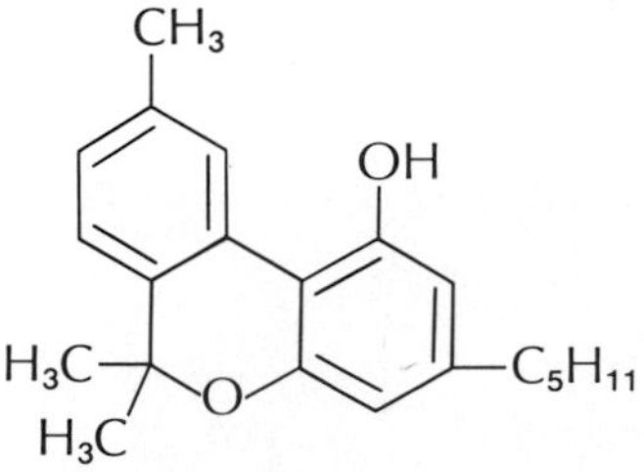

Cannabinol

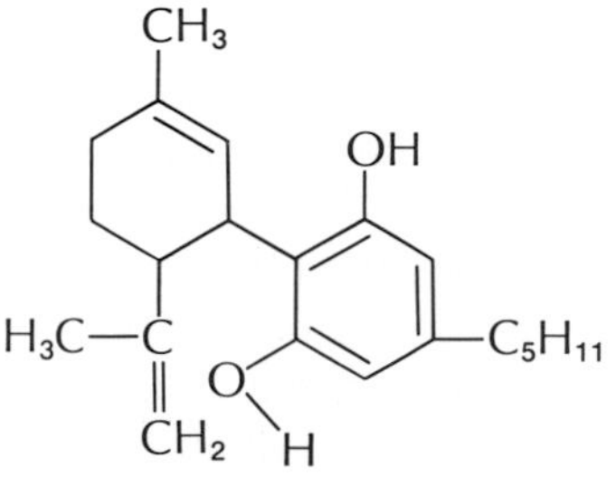

Cannabidiol

[a]There are two systems commonly used for identifying cannabinol compounds. The numbering is slightly different in the two systems, so you may find Δ^1-THC identified as Δ^9-THC; Δ^6-THC referred to as Δ^8-THC.

Over-the-counter drugs are available in an impressive variety which parallels the large number and types of food products. The safety of these drugs is regulated by the Food and Drug Administration. Recently the FDA has begun to also monitor their effectiveness. This move stirred considerable apprehension in the seven billion dollar per year over-the-counter drug industry in the United States. Most of these drugs are intended to help the user with temporary and minor problems. As with any drug, there may be side effects or allergies produced in a specific user. Some people, for example, cannot tolerate aspirin but may be able to use acetaminophen for minor pain relief.

The pictures at right illustrate some types of over-the-counter drugs. Twenty million pounds of aspirin, in many formulations, are consumed per year. Does aspirin help relieve stomach acidity? Antacids, also consumed in great quantity, relieve "excess stomach acidity" by the following type of reaction.

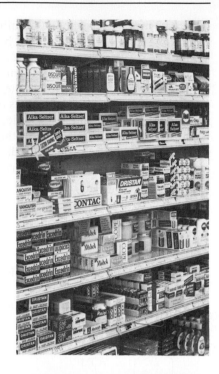

$$2 \text{ HCl} + \text{MgCO}_3 \longrightarrow \text{MgCl}_2 + \text{H}_2\text{O} + \text{CO}_2$$

| Stomach acid | One common ingredient of antacids | Dissolved salt | Water | Carbon dioxide gas |

Aspirin

Ethyl Alcohol

Alcohol is a potent drug, yet purchase and self-administration are legal for adults. Despite the well-known effects of ethyl alcohol, our society generally disapproves of use only if a dependence develops. Ethyl alcohol as a food contains seven calories per gram but contains no nutrients. As a drug, it alters behavior by action on the brain. The National Institute of Mental Health estimates that nine million people in the United States are alcoholics, at least four million of whom are part of the labor force. Costs associated with this group are estimated to be from six to eight billion dollars per year in lost work time, medical care, crime, and accidents. Yet this figure does not represent the real personal tragedy of these people and their families. How can society deal with alcoholism successfully? Is it a different problem than drug abuse?

high doses as have unpleasant gastrointestinal discomforts. There has been no scientific evidence of any carcinogenic or teratogenic effects. A physical addiction does not result from use.

The present drive for legalization, or at least decriminalization, of marijuana is largely a social and political phenomenon. It can be compared to the process of setting standards in any field of pollution, for it becomes a question of how we perceive benefits versus risks. Unfortunately, the question is further complicated because the underlying criteria in this case are not clear cut; the scientific evidence is both conflicting and incomplete.

Part Four: WHO'S IN CHARGE?

The Food and Drug Administration, FDA, is the federal agency charged with assuring the safety of foods, drugs, and cosmetics. The first legislation giving FDA its authority was the Food and Drug Act of 1906. The Food, Drug, and Cosmetic Act of 1938 substantially added to this power. The background for the enactment of these far-reaching pieces of legislation makes interesting reading for those curious about the relationships between industry and governmental regulation.

Legislation: Food Additives

Many additional food-regulating provisions were established in 1958 with the passage of the Food Additive Amendments and in 1960 with the Food Color Amendments. Prior to 1958, no evidence of safety was required for the use of additives, although hundreds of chemicals were in common use. In seeking to regulate the use of these compounds as well as the introduction of new chemicals into the food supply, it was necessary to reach a compromise between giving blanket approvals to all additives in use before 1958 and requiring expensive and time-consuming laboratory tests for each substance. Therefore a list of common substances such as spices, sugars, vinegar, and baking powder, was drawn up and circulated to 900 experts in the fields of toxicology, food technology, and related fields. They were asked to give their professional opinions on the safety of these substances, based on their knowledge of use and toxicology testing. Less than half of these experts replied to this survey, and more than half of those made no specific comment other than approving the list. A few substances were deleted from the list, and in 1959 a two-part list of approximately 600 substances was published and became known as the GRAS (generally recognized as safe) list. Spokesmen for both the food industry and the FDA agree that the actual number of GRAS items is now considerably larger than this

Table 5. Food Additives Banned by FDA

Additive	Use	Action
Monochloroacetic acid	•Preserve wine, carbonated beverages, salad dressings, pickles	•Banned in early 1940's—caused illness
Sulfites	•Make stale meat appear red	•Use for adulteration is illegal since FD&C Act of 1938
Nitrogen trichloride	•Bleach and age flour	•Banned in 1949; caused fits and convulsions in animals
Dulcin (4-ethoxyphenylurea)	•Artificial sweetener (250 × sucrose)	•Banned in 1950; caused cancer in rat livers
Coumarin (extract from tonka bean)	•Synthetic vanilla flavors, chocolate, candies	•Both extract and beans banned in 1954 after 75 years of use; liver damage in rats and dogs
Food colors FD&C Orange #1, 2, Red #32 FD&C Yellow #1, 2, 3, 4, Red #1 FD&C Red #4		•Banned in: 1956 1960 1965 (except for cherries) •Showed a variety of harmful effects on laboratory animals
DES (diethylstilbestrol)	•Synthetic female sex hormone: enhances growth of poultry, cattle (used since 1954)	•Banned in poultry—1959; shown to be carcinogenic •Banned in cattle feed as of January, 1973. Still allowed in the form of a pellet implanted in the animal's ear if no residues are present at time of slaughter.
Safrole	•Chief flavoring in root beer	•Banned in 1960, caused liver cancer in rats (sassafras leaves and bark can still be used if shown to be safrole-free)
Carrageenan	•Emulsify, stabilize, and thicken chocolate and evaporated milk, ice cream, instant breakfasts, puddings, desert toppings, baby formulas	•Removed from GRAS List in 1972; caused birth defects in laboratory animals
Cobaltous salts (acetate, chloride, sulfate)	•Improve stability of beer foam	•Withdrawn by industry in 1966 after unexplained deaths of heavy beer drinkers in U.S. and Canadian studies •Banned as a beer additive by FDA in August, 1966
NDGA (nordihydroguiaretic acid)	•Natural antioxidant used to inhibit rancidity in fats	•Banned by Canada in 1967 •Removed from GRAS list in 1968 •Now banned by USDA except in lard or shortening
Cyclamates	•Artificial sweetener for soft drinks, diet foods used since 1950	•Removed from GRAS list and banned from soft drinks in 1969, from foods in 1970; caused bladder and other cancer in rats

initial list but no one single compilation seems to exist. New GRAS items appear from time to time in the *Federal Register.*

Substances on this list do not have to be proven safe. If a chemical does not appear on the GRAS list, it is not an automatic exclusion from the food supply but rather means that extensive proof of safety must be furnished before the substance is allowed in foods. Thus the GRAS list is not a compilation of all allowable food additives but simply those that were exempt from the requirements of laboratory proof of safety in 1958.

Regulation of Carcinogens: The Delaney Clause

Another important feature of the 1958 Food Additives Amendments was the Delaney clause. This states that:

> No additive shall be deemed safe if it is found to induce cancer when ingested by man or animals, or if it is found, after tests which are appropriate for the evaluation of the safety of food additives, to induce cancer in man or animals.

This clause gives the FDA specific power to remove an additive even from the GRAS list if subsequent tests show it can produce cancer. It also reinforces the requirements for the testing of potential new additives. The authority of the Delaney clause enabled the FDA to remove cyclamates from the market in 1969–1970 after a great deal of evidence had accumulated showing that cyclamates caused cancer in laboratory animals. Birth defects and other genetic damage were also noted in the case of cyclamates and constitute a serious danger, although the authority of the Delaney clause relates specifically to cancer-causing properties. This restriction seems to place too narrow an interpretation on the intent of the Delaney clause.

Another problem with a strict interpretation of the Delaney clause is that it does not cover those agents that are not themselves carcinogenic but rather are metabolized into cancer-causing substances. This is the situation with nitrites, widely used compounds that serve both a cosmetic and a preservative function for meat and fish. Nitrites may also help develop the characteristic flavor of "cured" meats. Of these three functions, only the cosmetic reaction is understood at this time. In meats for example, the nitrites change the red component of meat (myoglobin) to another red but less reactive compound (nitrosomyglobin). This retards the formation of brown metmyoglobin which is still edible but a color not preferred by the consumer. Virtually all hot dogs, sausages, and packaged luncheon meats contain sodium nitrite ($NaNO_2$) together with sodium nitrate ($NaNO_3$) to serve the dual purposes of coloring and preserving.

The problem occurs in that the nitrites (but not the nitrates unless they are first reduced to nitrites) have been found to react with amines from proteins to form a class of substances known as nitrosoamines. An example of this reaction is:

$$(C_2H_5)_2\text{---}N\text{---}H + Na^{\oplus\ominus}O\text{---}N{=}O$$

Diethyl   Sodium
amine   nitrite

$$\longrightarrow (C_2H_5)_2\text{---}N\text{---}N{=}O + Na^{\oplus\ominus}OH$$

Diethyl   Sodium
nitrosoamine   hydroxide

The nitrosoamines have been identified in fish treated with currently allowable levels of nitrites (200 ppm). The nitrosoamines are known carcinogens, although all evidence of tumor production has been gathered at concentrations higher than current allowed usage. Still, it is estimated that a 90 percent reduction in the use of nitrites would be accomplished if the purely cosmetic uses were discontinued. Other preservatives are known that could serve the curing function of nitrites if it becomes necessary, after all the evidence is evaluated, to ban nitrites from our food supply.

Even before the Delaney clause, the responsibility of the FDA to insure the safety of food for human consumption led to banning hazardous chemicals. In some cases the offending substance had been used for several years, but the increased ability of scientists to measure the effects of exceedingly small amounts led to the discovery of previously overlooked effects. Also, large-scale use and increased scientific communication can make the cause of minor problems or isolated phenomena more obvious. Examples of banned substances are given in Table 5.

Legislation: Drugs

A similar situation to the GRAS list exists in the case of regulating drugs. The Kefauver-Harris Drug Efficacy Amendments of 1962 are the drug industry equivalent of the 1958 Food Additives Amendments. These drug amendments established two classes of drugs. New drugs were required to undergo stricter independent testing for safety and efficacy. Drugs currently in use were judged safe by virtue of their use, clinical evidence, and prior testing, forming the GRAS list for drugs. In 1964, a study was proposed to specifically evaluate the effectiveness of these accepted drugs. This study was started at least partially in response to consumer criticism over pricing practices. By 1969, over 4000 formulations had been studied and 11 percent were rejected as being ineffective. Only 15 percent were classed as effective, while 27 percent were rated "probably effective" and 47 percent as "possibly effective."

A related plan to review the effectiveness of over-the-counter drugs was announced in early 1972. It is the intent of FDA to write standards of safety, efficacy, therapeutic limits, and directions for use. Categories to be considered include antacids, cough and cold remedies, mood drugs, pain killers, laxatives, mouth washes, and mineral-vitamin products.

The Drug Abuse Control Amendments to the Federal Food, Drug, and Cosmetic Act were passed in 1965 in response to the abuse of drugs that act on the central nervous system. This regulatory law supplements the Harrison Narcotic Act and the Federal Marijuana Regulations, and all are enforced by the Bureau of Narcotics and Dangerous Drugs in the United States Department of Justice. Many states and cities have passed additional legislation dealing with the control of drugs likely to be abused.

Standards for Safety

The current review of over-the-counter drugs illustrates one of the most important responsibilities of FDA, for it is charged with setting appropriate guidelines for testing the safety of food additives and drugs. In the case of food additives, this task has been largely assumed in the past by the National Research Council of the National Academy of Sciences (NAS-NRC). This organization of academic, research, and industry scientists serves as an official advisor to the United States Government. To further standardize and improve the testing carried out, the FDA itself now plans to issue criteria for all future testing procedures.

At present, a new food additive has to undergo two-year rat and dog

This mature miniature sow weighs only about 150 pounds. An idea of her small size can be gained from comparison with the 12 by 23 inch swing door in the background. Such miniature swine are proving extremely useful in biomedical research. *(DHEW/FDA/Bureau of Foods/Division of Toxicology)*

feeding studies and a two-to-three generation reproduction study in rats. Additional tests in rabbits may be required as well. The particular additive is administered at several different dose levels and by different methods of delivery. Blood analysis and enzyme activities are studied as are kidney and liver functions. As many as thirty different tissues from sacrificed animals are studied for abnormal changes, and evidence of deformed offspring is scrutinized. Similar extensive tests are carried out for evaluation of new drugs. Once these scientific experiments are completed, criteria are established for the substance in question. After evaluation, appropriate standards for use are set. The ever-present difficulty of extending animal data to humans may be somewhat alleviated by the development of the "minipig," a specifically bred pig that is about 30 percent smaller than other pigs and is thought to be closer to man in bone density and in other important ways. Still to be devised are reliable experimental methods for detecting subtle changes or synergistic effects of different additives. Appropriate computer analysis of experimental data may be very important in this regard in future studies. Computer programs are also being devised to help determine priorities so that drugs and additives most in question can be tested first, for it is clearly not a real possibility to simultaneously test all the chemicals being added to our internal environment.

Inspection and Recall

Another activity of FDA is inspection and, if necessary, the recall of contaminated foods, drugs, or cosmetics. Inactive ingredients in drugs have been reported as well as mistakes in composition. Bacterial contamination of pizza, candy, soups, and other products have all received widespread attention in the press. Rodent and insect fragments, oil or petroleum residues, glass, and pesticides also have been the cause of food recalls. Since food recalls are never 100 percent successful, the consumer is left with some lingering doubts about a product and at least a temporary drop in sales for that product is the result. In the case of a small firm, the publicity surrounding a food recall can mean the end of business altogether. Even though the vast majority of foods and drugs sold are free from contamination and error, the public is becoming more concerned about the quality of their food and drug products.

Consumer Reaction

There is one particularly interesting way in which consumers are showing their increased interest in the safety and purity of the food supply. This is the growth of the "organic" or natural foods stores. Foods sold in these outlets are grown without the use of synthetic fertilizers or pesticides and processed without the use of artificial additives.

There is increasing demand for products such as organically grown fruits and nutritious grains.

The meats are hormone free. These stores may or may not be incorporated into a more traditional "health foods store" and each one has to be looked at individually to determine the types of products found there. In 1971, sales from the natural foods industry amounted to about 200 million dollars or only about 0.16 percent of the entire foods market, but accelerated growth is predicted in the next few years. Even large distributors and producers have now seen fit to add some "natural" products to their lines, such as cereal grains, unbleached flours, and organic fruits in localities where they are available. Advertising is also taking a new turn; where formerly color and convenience were stressed, nutritional values and lack of additives are now made a major point for some products. In fact, an observable backlash against additives is now surfacing in ads such as that for a "natural" ice cream that is "made by the hand of nature and not the mind of man." One example, taken from a large circulation newspaper, is shown in Figure 13.

The Future Outlook

Federal regulations promoting truth in labeling and preventing unsubstantiated advertising claims will certainly help the consumer in the future. If this is coupled with nutritional education, the chances of making intelligent decisions concerning food are increased. After all, the food producers will only make what the consumer will buy. An educated public will have the best chance of finding a proper balance between nutrition and convenience. It would be just as irresponsible to reject all food additives as it would be to unnecessarily add chemicals that have not been reasonably shown to be safe to our food supply.

It may take much more than an educational campaign to influence current patterns of drug usage. Legislation may be useful in controlling the manufacture and distribution of illicit drugs, but it surely does not provide a sufficient answer for reducing drug abuse. Additional research will help to solve some of the scientific problems, but complicated areas of politics, psychology, and sociology remain before inappropriate self-medication can be reduced and drug abuse stopped.

If you wish to make your voice heard on the topic of food additives and drugs, be sure to write to the agency most directly responsible.

• For questions of safety, labeling, adulteration, and the general philosophy of food additives and drugs: Food and Drug Administration, Washington, D.C. 20852.

• For meat, poultry, and egg inspection, labeling and grading, pesticide residues on food crops: U.S. Department of Agriculture, Washington, D.C. 20250.

•For false or exaggerated advertising: Federal Trade Commission, Washington, D.C. 20580.

•For questions of enforcement of federal drug regulations: Bureau of Narcotic and Dangerous Drugs, Department of Justice, Washington, D.C. 20537

•For pressure for united consumer action: Special Assistant to the President for Consumer Affairs, White House, Washington, D.C. 20500.

Study Questions — Group A

1. Glucose and fructose have the same molecular formula, $C_6H_{12}O_6$. How do their structures differ?

2. If a sugar has formula $C_{12}H_{22}O_{11}$, must it be sucrose? Explain.

3. Compare the general structures of starch and cellulose. Why can man digest starch but not cellulose?

4. In order for a molecule to display optical activity, what structural requirement must be met? Use this to explain why phenylalanine will have optical isomers but glycine will not. (Glycine is the only amino acid that does not exist in optical isomers.)

5. Show how oleic acid can be found in two structural isomers, cis and trans.

6. Unsaturated fatty acids occur more commonly in vegetable oils than in animal fats. One common fatty acid of vegetable origin is linoleic acid. Its formula is:

$$CH_3(CH_2)_4CH{=}CHCH_2CH{=}CH(CH_2)_4COOH$$

Compare its degree of unsaturation with that of oleic acid.

7. Corn oil is 46 percent oleic and 42 percent linoleic acid. Cottonseed oil is 33 percent oleic and 44 percent linoleic. Can you determine from this which oil will be more unsaturated?

8. "Bromine values" are given as one way of analyzing and comparing gasolines. By analogy with the "iodine values" for fats, what particular aspect of the gasoline is measured by the bromine value? Why is that important in the performance of the gasoline?

9. Is stearic acid a saturated or an unsaturated fatty acid? How can you tell from the formula?

10. In Chapter 6, soap was identified as the sodium salts of long-chain organic acids. Show how sodium stearate, a typical soap, can be formed by the reaction of stearic acid, $CH_3(CH_2)_{16}COOH$, with sodium hydroxide, NaOH.

11. What structural features can be used to recognize amino acids?

12. Amino acids usually do not exist in the free form, but rather there is a transfer of a proton from the acid (—COOH) group to the more basic (—NH$_2$) group. Write the structural formula for alanine, CH$_3$CH(NH$_2$)COOH, first as the free amino acid and then in the changed form that results from proton transfer.

13. Organic acids are not as "strong" as most inorganic acids. This is another way of saying that the organic acids do not free as many hydrogen ions in solution. For example, in water solution:

$$\text{Hydrochloric acid} \quad HCl \longrightarrow H^+ + Cl^-$$

$$\text{Acetic acid} \quad CH_3COOH \rightleftharpoons CH_3COO^- + H^+$$

What differences in bonding does this suggest for the two acids? Assuming identical concentrations, which acid would have a lower pH?

14. Write first a word equation and then a chemical equation for the reaction of butyl alcohol and acetic acid to produce butyl acetate, the ester responsible for the odor of raspberries.

15. What alcohol and acid would have to be combined to produce the ester associated with wintergreen flavor?

16. Monsodium glutamate is the sodium salt of glutamic acid. Write the structure for glutamic acid. Is this an amino acid?

17. Be able to describe and give an example of each of the essential food types: carbohydrates, fats, proteins, vitamins, and minerals.

18. Soaps act as emulsifying agents in promoting the mixture of grease and water. Using the natural substance lecithin as an example, explain how emulsifying agents can be useful in foods. Which part of the lecithin do you expect to be lipophilic? Lipophobic?

19. a. Properly diluted frozen orange juice contains 45 mg of ascorbic acid (vitamin C) per 100 g of juice. A "juice drink" has to be 50 percent juice, an "–ade" has to be 25 percent juice and a "drink" has to be 10 percent juice. Assuming each starts with juice containing 45 mg/100 g, how much vitamin C would you get from drinking an equal amount (100 g) of each of these types of orange-based liquids?

    b. If a "drink" has been fortified with 10 mg of vitamin C per 100 g of drink and sells for half as much as frozen juice, which is a better buy based on the vitamin C content only?

    c. If people want a diluted orange drink, why don't they just buy orange juice (fresh or frozen) and simply add water?

20. Salicylic acid is $C_6H_5(OH)COOH$. Its structure is:

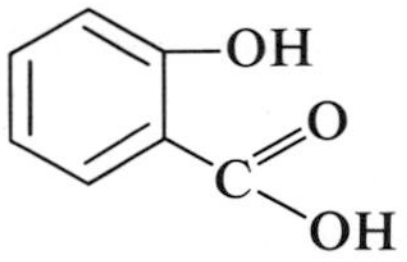

What are the structural differences between aspirin, methyl salicylate, and the basic salicylic acid? (Figures 7 and 9 might be helpful to you.)

21. Which of the following substances would you expect to stimulate the central nervous system? Which would have a depressant action?

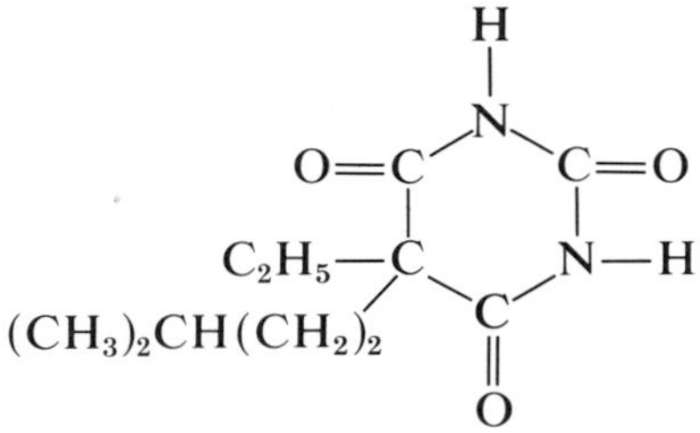

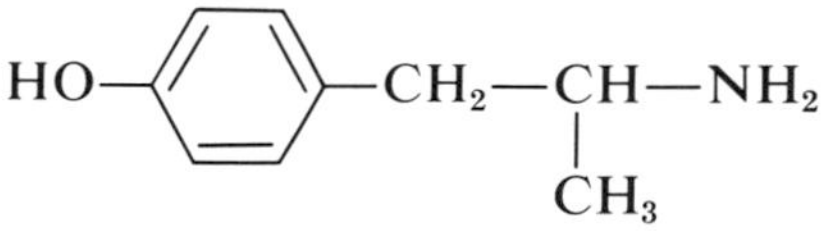

22. Amphetamine is an optically active molecule with the d-form being pharmacologically active. Where is the center of symmetry for this molecule? Draw structures showing the two possible optical isomers. How would you tell which form was actually the dextro- form?

23. After consulting Figure 9, write the structures for codeine and heroin.

24. Barbituric acid results from the reaction of urea, 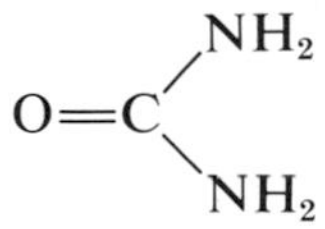 , with malonic acid, 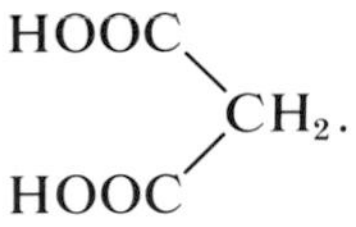 . Write an equation showing the reaction.

What simple molecules are eliminated in this reaction? (For this reason, the reaction is termed a condensation reaction.)

25. Check the growth of your environmental chemistry vocabulary. What do each of these abbreviations literally stand for? Explain why each is significant in the study of food additives.
    a. FDA b. BHA c. MSG d. IMP
    e. THC f. DES g. GRAS h. NAS-NRC

Study Questions — Group B

1. The diversity of food products available in a large supermarket is truly amazing. One food industry executive has predicted that by 1980 around 12,000 food items will be available, over half of these being different from those sold today. As one measure of this diversity of products, visit a large supermarket and make a list of the different rice products available. (Do not include different sizes of the same product.) If you don't find over thirty, try again! Compare this number with the sale of plain white and brown rice thirty years ago. How many of the rice products also contain additives?

2. To gain more familiarity with food additives, pick at least ten food products and list the ingredients found in each one. Try to identify the materials present as to being a basic part of the foodstuff or one of the types of additives. Handbooks and other references may be necessary for identification in some cases; consult the instructor for help too. Here is one example:

   General Foods' *Awake* (frozen concentrate for imitation orange juice). Ingredients as of June, 1972.

   > Citric acid; (acidulant, flavor)
   > Gum arabic; (thickener)
   > Carrageenan; (stabilizer)
   > Vitamins A, B$_1$, C; (nutrient supplements)
   > Calcium phosphate; (anticaking compound)

   Which of these ingredients will have to be replaced due to recent FDA action?

3. Consult the *FDA Papers* (renamed *FDA Consumer* in January 1973) for both seizure actions and notices of judgment. See if the current cases involve any foods in your area and if so, follow up on the background and outcome of the case.

4. There are many ways in which the food and drug industries can be compared. What parallels do you see? You might consider such points as reasons for growth, the role of advertising, consumer acceptance, controversy over safety and effectiveness, and increasing federal regulations.

5. Two opposing views of the controversy over food additives can be summarized in these representative quotes.

   > Some additives are clearly hazardous to humans, others are suspect, and most are needless additions designed to deceive the food purchaser. (Ralph Nader)

   > I think consumers are being unduly concerned by a lot of chemical names they don't understand. It is almost impossible for me

to conceive of meeting the demands of a country like ours without food additives. (A. S. Clausi, Vice President of General Foods)

a. What factors in American life have led to the common usage of additives in our food supply? Are any of these factors subject to change that would significantly affect the use of additives in the future?

b. Which additive(s) do you feel qualify as "needless additions designed to deceive the food purchaser"?

c. Which additive(s) do you feel are necessary in meeting the food "demands of a country like ours"?

d. Some industry spokesmen argue that complete labeling of food with all ingredients and additives only serves to unduly alarm the consumer with long "chemical names they don't understand." How do you feel about this statement?

6. a. The use of the synthetic estrogen DES (diethylstilbestrol) to enhance the growth of cattle is still being hotly debated. For background, you might start with "The Price of Beef," *Environment* 13:6 (1971):44–51. New regulations were proposed by FDA and USDA in late 1971 to allow at least seven days of feeding without DES before slaughter as the previous standard of a 48-hour period did not appear adequate to prevent some hormone residues from reaching the market place. Hearings were held in July of 1972, leading to a ban of DES in beef feed. The later stages of the regulatory action are detailed in *Science* (July 28, 1972): 335–337, and *Science* (August 11, 1972):503. Report on the DES controversy, including the most recent developments.

b. DES has recently been tested as a "morning-after" pill to prevent pregnancy. In the short run, it has appeared to be both safe and effective when used in controlled dosages although its use is projected only for "emergencies" and not as a routine contraceptive practice. What potential problems are there in this use of DES?

7. Synthetic estrogens and the progesterone hormones are also widely used in birth control pills. The pill is one of the most significant developments of this century and yet its action is not at all well understood. For background on the chemistry and action of the pill, try these references: *Science* 153 (1966): 493–500. *Chemical and Engineering News* (March 27, 1967):44–49. (Both of these are reprinted in *Chemicals and Life* by Kenneth E. Maxwell (Dickenson, 1970).) Organize a class presentation summarizing your findings.

8. a. One alternative to the use of synthetic estrogens and progesterone is a new class of compounds now under development. These compounds are called prostaglandins. What is the nature of these compounds and what is the current outlook for widespread testing and marketing?

   b. What other methods of birth control are presently available? What are the advantages and disadvantages of each method?

9. What special programs exist in the schools in your area to educate students on the use and abuse of drugs? How successful have these programs been in curbing the use of illicit drugs?

10. Set up a panel discussion on the question of the legalization of marijuana. After the discussion, sample opinion of those present by conducting a poll. Do you think the outcome of your poll would be mirrored in a city-wide poll in your area? Why or why not?

Suggested Readings

Food Additives

Kermode, G. O., "Food Additives." *Scientific American* 226 (March 1972): 15–21.

> Review article on the types of food additives and the reasons for use. Contains an extensive table of GRAS items.

National Research Council. *Evaluating the Safety of Food Chemicals.* National Academy of Sciences, 1970.

> Gives a valuable discussion of the methods used to establish the safety of an additive. It is soon clear that the extensive nature of the procedures precludes testing all GRAS items.

Turner, James S. *The Chemical Feast.* New York: Grossman Publishers, 1970.

> Hard-hitting, thoroughly documented analysis of the Food and Drug Administration.

Drugs

Grinspoon, Lester. *Marihuana Reconsidered.* Cambridge, Mass.: Harvard University Press, 1971.

> Written for the nonspecialist reader by an eminent psychiatrist. It

includes the history, chemistry, psychology, physiology and social effects of marijuana and discusses in a rational fashion the pros and cons of legalization.

Goodman, Louis S. and Gilman, Alfred. *The Pharmacological Basis of Therapeutics, Fourth Edition.* New York: Macmillan, 1970.

Despite its rather imposing title, this is the place to go for complete information on drugs. This book is known as the "blue bible" of pharmacology and has the most current information as well as a new emphasis on drugs and society.

Chapter 9
Chemistry Creates the Age of Polymers and Plastics

The plastics industry can be traced back to the late eighteen hundreds when the manufacture of celluloid modestly started a revolution in synthetic materials. The tremendous growth of the plastics industry in the last twenty years is a tribute both to advancing chemical knowledge about the nature of polymers and to engineering ingenuity in producing materials with specific, desirable properties. As with many "modern miracles," there have been some new problems created along with the new products. The improper disposal of plastics may create an unsightly mess and thus contribute to the general litter problem as do all nondegradable substances. Completely new hazards have been created as is the case of giant sea turtles dying from a mistaken attempt to eat jellyfish that in actuality were polyethylene bags! The safe incineration of plastics has been questioned, and even newer concerns center on the possible hazards associated with the chemicals used in producing plastics, including phthalate and PCB plasticizers.

In this chapter some basic chemistry of polymers and plastics will be examined with special emphasis on the more important commercial products such as vinyl plastics, natural and synthetic rubber, nylon, and polyesters. This information will then be used as the basis for examining some of the problems and prospects of the "Plastics Age."

Part One: POLYMERS, MACROMOLECULES, AND PLASTICS

Polymers are giant molecules of almost unimaginable variety. Nature has always known the secrets of putting together many (*poly*) small units (*meros*) and creating a polymer or, as it is sometimes called, a macromolecule, but the complexity of giant molecules created a great challenge to chemists in the past. Within the last decade, research on both natural and synthetic polymers has produced a vast array of new products as well as an increased understanding of the natural polymers. Cellulose and proteins have previously been cited as examples of natural polymers. Silk, natural rubber, resins, and silicates also are macromolecules. If the giant molecules are made synthetically they may be referred to as plastics.

The process of repeatedly joining the individual units resulting in the formation of a large molecule is called polymerization. The molecule so produced typically has a characteristic molecular weight of several thousand, and its properties can be almost tailor made for a desired application. Such things as the polymer's melting point, degree of elasticity, strength, shape retention, clarity, sensitivity to light or electricity, and rate of oxidation can largely be controlled by choosing suitable starting materials and conditions of polymerization.

Classification of Polymers

There are several ways to classify polymers. Their structure, physical properties, technological uses, or the types of reactions by which they are prepared are all commonly used systems. When classified by physical properties, polymers may be divided into the large categories of elastomer, thermoplastic, and thermosetting. Elastomers are natural or synthetic rubbers or rubberlike elastic substances with the property of returning to their original shape after the release of a distorting force. Thermoplastic polymers soften or melt when heated and harden again upon cooling. They are able to do this if the long chains of the polymers are held to other chains by rather weak bonds that are easily broken. Generally if a linear chain fits poorly into another chain and is composed of nonpolar units, the interchain bonds will not be very strong. Examples of this are some forms of polyethylene, polypropylene, polyvinyl chloride, and several acrylics such as plexiglas and lucite. This class may also be soluble in some organic solvents. Thermosetting plastics have highly interconnected chains that lend rigidity and thermal resistance to the plastic. Usually this type of plastic will burn before it will melt. They are not soluble in organic solvents. Examples of this type of plastic are Bakelite, polyester fabrics, and epoxy resins.

These three categories are not mutually exclusive, for several elastomers are thermoplastics, and some thermosetting plastics are elastomers in some stage of their production. Furthermore, thermoplastics can be made to closely resemble thermosetting plastics by altering the condition of polymerization. For our purposes, the system of classification based on the type of reaction used to form polymers will be the most useful. In Parts Two and Three we will examine the important reactions of addition and condensation polymerization.

Part Two: ADDITION POLYMERS

An addition polymer is one in which the recurring units have the same composition as the monomer or monomers from which they were formed. The simplest molecule that will undergo addition polymerization is ethylene, C_2H_4. The resulting polyethylene is the leading plastic in terms of tons produced and also has had the highest growth rate over the last twenty years.

Mechanism of Addition

For any addition polymer to form, there must be double bonds present so that the monomer unit, ethylene in this case, can join to itself repeatedly. This process is illustrated in its simplest form by this reaction:

$$n\left(\begin{array}{c} H \quad H \\ | \quad\ | \\ C=C \\ | \quad\ | \\ H \quad H \end{array}\right) \longrightarrow \left(\begin{array}{c} H \quad H \\ | \quad\ | \\ C-C \\ | \quad\ | \\ H \quad H \end{array}\right)_n$$

The n refers to the number of repeated monomer units. It may be called the degree of polymerization.

The double bond in ethylene is no longer present in the polymer, for two of the electrons that were once used to join the two carbons are now helping to bond adjacent carbon atoms.

This reaction does not occur spontaneously; it is necessary to initiate the opening of the double bond. Commonly a peroxide catalyst is used for this purpose; being somewhat unstable, it will break down to release a reactive free radical containing an unpaired electron.

$$R—O—O—R \longrightarrow 2(R—O \cdot)$$

The electron-deficient peroxide fragment is then attracted to the most electron-rich part of the ethylene molecule, the double bond. This is the key step, for a free radical forms on an ethylene molecule by this reaction.

$$R—O\cdot + \overset{\overset{\displaystyle H}{|}}{\underset{\underset{\displaystyle H}{|}}{C}}=\overset{\overset{\displaystyle H}{|}}{\underset{\underset{\displaystyle H}{|}}{C} } \longrightarrow R—O—\overset{\overset{\displaystyle H}{|}}{\underset{\underset{\displaystyle H}{|}}{C}}—\overset{\overset{\displaystyle H}{|}}{\underset{\underset{\displaystyle H}{|}}{C}}\cdot$$

Once this happens, the possibilities for further reaction become exceedingly complex. The simplest step at this point would be if the free radical ethylene species met with another similar species. They would join, resulting in a termination of the polymerization process.

$$R—O—\overset{\overset{\displaystyle H}{|}}{\underset{\underset{\displaystyle H}{|}}{C}}—\overset{\overset{\displaystyle H}{|}}{\underset{\underset{\displaystyle H}{|}}{C}}\cdot + R—O—\overset{\overset{\displaystyle H}{|}}{\underset{\underset{\displaystyle H}{|}}{C}}—\overset{\overset{\displaystyle H}{|}}{\underset{\underset{\displaystyle H}{|}}{C}}\cdot \longrightarrow R—O—\overset{\overset{\displaystyle H}{|}}{\underset{\underset{\displaystyle H}{|}}{C}}—\overset{\overset{\displaystyle H}{|}}{\underset{\underset{\displaystyle H}{|}}{C}}—\overset{\overset{\displaystyle H}{|}}{\underset{\underset{\displaystyle H}{|}}{C}}—\overset{\overset{\displaystyle H}{|}}{\underset{\underset{\displaystyle H}{|}}{C}}—O—R$$

This reaction will not predominate if the concentration of the peroxide is kept low relative to the number of ethylene molecules. Rather, the free radical ethylene is more likely to find another ethylene molecule and form a longer free radical.

$$R—O—\overset{\overset{\displaystyle H}{|}}{\underset{\underset{\displaystyle H}{|}}{C}}—\overset{\overset{\displaystyle H}{|}}{\underset{\underset{\displaystyle H}{|}}{C}}\cdot + \overset{\overset{\displaystyle H}{|}}{\underset{\underset{\displaystyle H}{|}}{C}}=\overset{\overset{\displaystyle H}{|}}{\underset{\underset{\displaystyle H}{|}}{C}} \longrightarrow R—O—\overset{\overset{\displaystyle H}{|}}{\underset{\underset{\displaystyle H}{|}}{C}}—\overset{\overset{\displaystyle H}{|}}{\underset{\underset{\displaystyle H}{|}}{C}}—\overset{\overset{\displaystyle H}{|}}{\underset{\underset{\displaystyle H}{|}}{C}}—\overset{\overset{\displaystyle H}{|}}{\underset{\underset{\displaystyle H}{|}}{C}}\cdot$$

Formation of long-chain free radicals can continue almost indefinitely as long as the original ethylene supply remains. This chain mechanism involving active sites on the growing molecule is typical of the mechanism that produces addition polymers. The bonds joining the monomer units are simple covalent bonds with a pair of electrons being shared. The stability of the single covalent carbon-carbon bond accounts for the observed lack of biodegradability for most plastics.

Engineering the Properties of Polyethylene

The properties of the polymer can be controlled by adjusting the temperature and pressure of the reaction as well as the relative concentrations of catalyst and monomer. Under high temperature and pressure, the free radical chain has a greater tendency to loop back on itself and pull off a hydrogen atom from somewhere on the body of the chain. This would leave an unpaired electron along the chain that would then serve as a site for the addition of another ethylene molecule. The result would be a branched polymer rather than a straight-chain molecule. If branches from adjacent chains join together, the result is a cross-linked polymer. The three types of polyethylene polymers and the general properties are given in Figure 1.

Figure 1. Different Forms of Polyethylene

Type	Representation[a]	Comments
Straight chain		• Can line up in closely packed rows • May have some crystalline properties • High melting point for crystalline structure • Dense, rigid, and tough
Branched	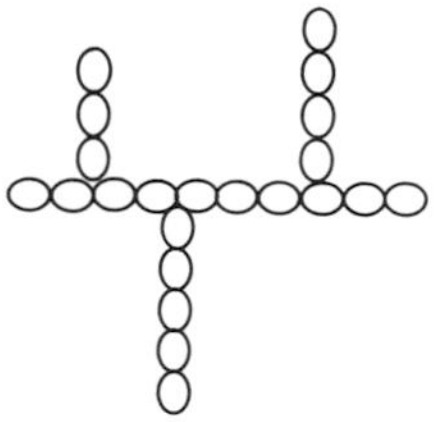	• Branches prevent close alignment of chains • Less dense but more flexible than straight chain • Squeeze bottles are made from moderately branched plastics • More susceptible to heat — lower melting points than straight chained
Cross-linked	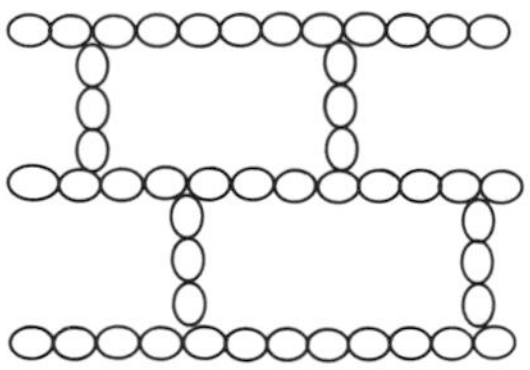	• Harder but less flexible than branched • Rigid plastics such as containers, dishes are highly cross-linked

[a] Each circle represents one ethylene monomer unit, not one atom.

Cross-linking polymer chains is the essential step in creating "durable-press" cotton fabrics. Schematically the cross-linking of cellulose chains looks like this:

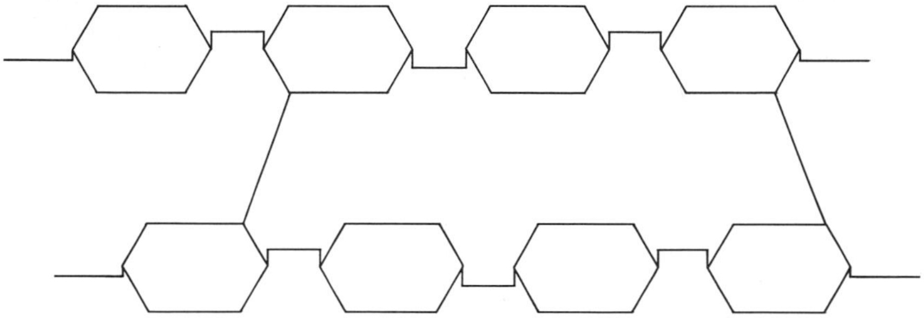

Cross-linking increases the resiliency of the fiber and thus the fabric has a greater tendency to return to its original shape after wearing or washing.

Typical compounds used to make the cross-link are dimethylol urea,

$$HOCH_2NHCNHCH_2OH,$$
$$\overset{\|}{O}$$

or dimethylol ethyleneurea. This compound is shown as it cross-links two cellulose units.

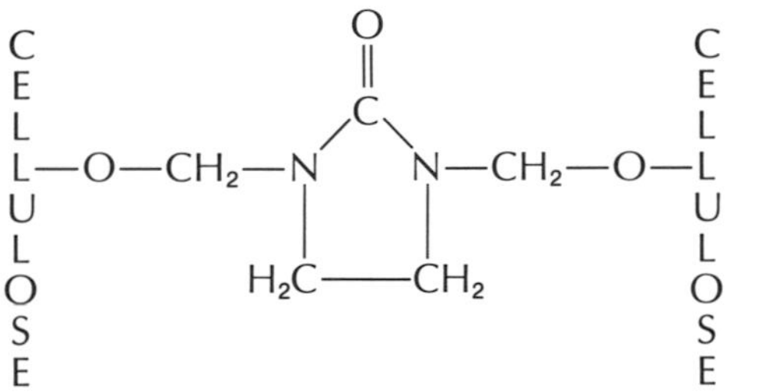

One side effect of cross-linking a fiber is that a decrease in strength and resistance to abrasion is also usually noted. These problems are thought to be caused by the restrictions that the cross-linking places on the movement of the cellulose units. If a stress occurs on the linked fiber, the cellulose units cannot move about freely to distribute the stress and therefore ruptures of the fibers result. Introduction of synthetic blends with cotton helps to overcome this problem but does not eliminate it completely.

Two Pressure Processes for Polyethylene

The differences in properties caused by structural arrangement are reflected in the characteristics of high-pressure polyethylene as compared with low-pressure polyethylene. High-pressure polyethylene processes were first developed in 1933. Iron reaction vessels are sealed at a pressure of 1500 atmospheres. A temperature of 190 to 210°C is maintained and the oxygen content is kept from 0.03 to 0.10 percent. The oxygen reacts with the ethylene to form a peroxide which acts as the initiator. Large molecules with considerable branching are created by this process (200,000 to 500,000 in molecular weight). The branching of the polymer prevents close alignment of the molecule chains. As a result the product is typically 60 percent crystalline, melts at 111°C, and has a density of 0.92 g/cm^3.

Despite the commercial success of this process, two factors led to the development of the low-pressure processes. One was the sometimes unpredictable side reactions which altered the final properties of high-pressure polyethylene. Very small amounts of impurities or variations in the oxygen content significantly altered the degree of branching and therefore the product. The second factor was the safety of the reaction. The workers called the reaction vessels "cannons" for their tendency to explode at the necessary high pressures. Excess oxygen or impurities could cause spontaneous decomposition of the polymer mixture to carbon, methane, and hydrogen which then exploded. One engineer remarked that in the early days of commercial operations, a ton of scrap metal was produced for every ton of polyethylene!

Low-pressure polyethylene was developed during World War II and in the late forties. The key to this process lies in using catalysts other than peroxides to initiate the polymerization. Useful substances include a mixture of aluminum triethyl ($Al(C_2H_5)_3$) and titanium tetrachloride ($TiCl_4$), which is now known as the Ziegler catalyst. Other metallic chlorides are just as effective as the titanium compound; nickel, zirconium, cobalt, and platinum can be used. Standard Oil developed a molybdenum oxide (MoO_3) catalyst suspended on a silica-alumina support system. Phillips Petroleum uses a chromium oxide catalyst on the same type of support system. All of these systems allowed the polymerization to occur without extraordinarily high pressures. Typically a pressure of 10 to 30 atmospheres and a temperature of 60 to 70°C is enough to create the desired polymer. The reaction may be carried out by bubbling the ethylene over the catalyst in an inert solvent such as diesel oil, a saturated hydrocarbon. The polymer is removed from solution by filtration. The yield gives long straight-chain hydrocarbons rather than the highly branched structures of high-pressure polyethylene, and this is reflected in the properties. The product is usually 90 to 95 percent cystalline, has a density of 0.95 to 0.97 g/cm³, and melts at 124 to 134°C. Molecular weights up to 3,000,000 have been produced by low-pressure polymerization of ethylene.

Vinyl Plastics

The mechanism for the formation of different types of polyethylene serves as a model for closely related addition polymerization reactions which use substituted ethylene as the monomer unit. The wide variety of resulting plastics form the group known as vinyl plastics.

```
H   H
|   |
C = C
|   |
H   X  ←——— Replacement of one or more hydrogens by
             another atom or group of atoms
```

In many cases the chemical nature of the substituted group is responsible for the undesirable products when the plastic is incinerated. Some examples of vinyl plastics are given in Figure 2.

The Importance of Plasticizers

One of the major advantages of vinyl-type plastics is that they lend themselves particularly well to modification by the use of plasticizers. Plasticizers are chemicals used to soften a plastic to facilitate processing or to increase the flexibility of the final product. The compounds do this by replacing some of the monomer-to-monomer bonds with weaker plasticizer-to-monomer bonds. This allows a freer movement of the polymer segments, which produces the flexibility. Roughly 75 percent of all plasticizers in use in the plastics industry today find their way into vinyl plastics. The final product may contain as much as 30 to 50 percent plasticizers by weight.

Phthalate Plasticizers. One type of plasticizer is PCBs, discussed in Chapter 7. Another important group is the phthalates. These compounds have provided the best properties for a low cost and thus have been widely accepted by industry. The structures of common phthalate plasticizers are given in Figure 3.

One of the most important properties of a good plasticizer is low volatility. If the material were to evaporate easily from the finished plastic, the properties of the plastic would change, and the vaporizing material could react with nearby materials or possibly cause a health effect. In addition, the plasticizer should not easily migrate out of the plastic by contact with nearby material and should be resistant to com-

Figure 2. Vinyl Plastics

Monomer unit	Polymer formula	Uses

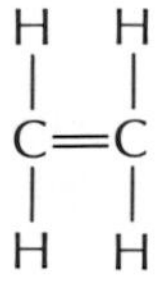

Ethylene

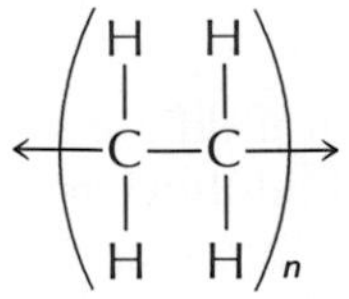

$$\begin{array}{ccc} H & & H \\ | & & | \\ C & = & C \\ | & & | \\ H & & H \end{array}$$

Ethylene

Polyethylene

$$\left(\begin{array}{ccc} H & & H \\ | & & | \\ C & - & C \\ | & & | \\ H & & H \end{array}\right)_n$$

Polyethylene

- Films
- Tubing
- Containers
- Molded objects
- Electrical insulation

$$\begin{array}{ccc} H & & H \\ | & & | \\ C & = & C \\ | & & | \\ H & & Cl \end{array}$$

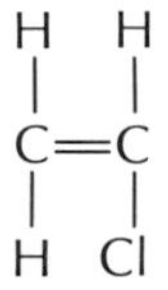

Ethylene chloride
or vinyl chloride

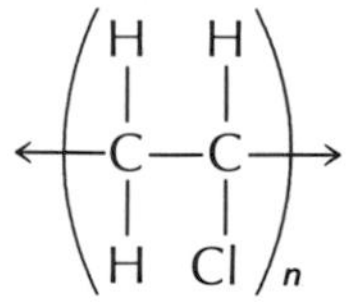

$$\left(\begin{array}{ccc} H & & H \\ | & & | \\ C & - & C \\ | & & | \\ H & & Cl \end{array}\right)_n$$

Polyvinyl chloride
(PVC)

- Phonograph records
- Sheet plastic wrap
  (if monomer is $C_2H_2Cl_2$,
  result is Saran Wrap)
- Incineration may
  produce HCl or
  phosgene ($COCl_2$)

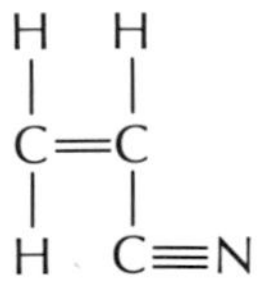

$$\begin{array}{ccc} H & & H \\ | & & | \\ C & = & C \\ | & & | \\ H & & C \equiv N \end{array}$$

acrylonitrile

$$\left(\begin{array}{ccc} H & & H \\ | & & | \\ C & - & C \\ | & & | \\ H & & C \equiv N \end{array}\right)_n$$

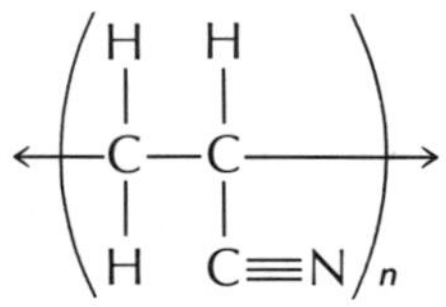

Polyacrylonitrile

- Fiber production,
  esp. orlon, acrilan

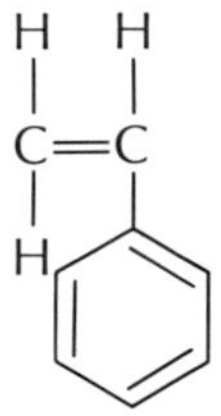

$$\begin{array}{ccc} H & & H \\ | & & | \\ C & = & C \\ | & & | \\ H & & \end{array}$$

Styrene

$$\left(\begin{array}{ccc} H & & H \\ | & & | \\ C & - & C \\ | & & | \\ H & & \end{array}\right)_n$$

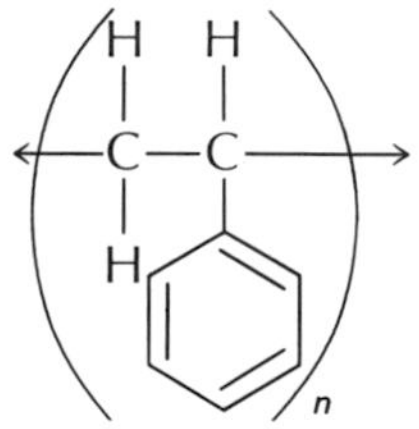

Polystyrene

- Molded objects
- Electrical insulation
- Makes styrofoam if a
  gas-producing chemical
  is added during
  polymerization

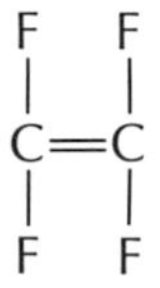

$$\begin{array}{ccc} F & & F \\ | & & | \\ C & = & C \\ | & & | \\ F & & F \end{array}$$

Tetrafluoro-
ethylene

$$\left(\begin{array}{ccc} F & & F \\ | & & | \\ C & - & C \\ | & & | \\ F & & F \end{array}\right)_n$$

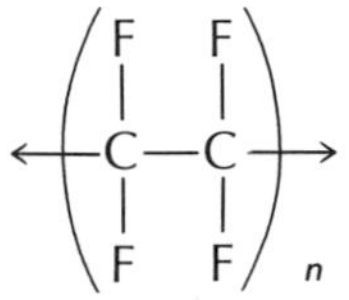

Polytetrafluoro-
ethylene

- Chemically resistant
  films or molded objects
- Electrical insulation
- Teflon

mon solvents such as water and organic fluids. Concern over the use of phthalates has centered on just these points. The National Aeronautics and Space Administration does not allow polyvinyl chloride to be used in space capsules, since the plasticizers will evaporate at reduced pressures and then condense on optical equipment. Reports have been made of phthalates leaching out of PVC bags used for storing blood and of phthalates vaporizing from plastics used in the interiors of cars. Phthalates have been identified in the heart muscles of various animals and also in fish tissue by several researchers.

Phthalate plasticizers are generally considered to have low toxicity, but recent animal studies have turned up evidence of neurological and teratogenic effects of phthalates at low concentrations. It may be as in the case of herbicides that small amounts of related compounds present as impurities are actually responsible for observed medical symptoms. Phthalates are now approved by the FDA for use in plastic food wrapping, although this permission could be lifted if further experimentation verifies new data showing that phthalates are stored in human organs. Since this class of compounds is known to have teratogenic effects at higher concentrations, further work will be necessary to determine the safety risk. The possible natural occurrence or synthesis of these compounds cannot be overlooked either.

Figure 3. Phthalate Plasticizers

Basic phthalate Structure:

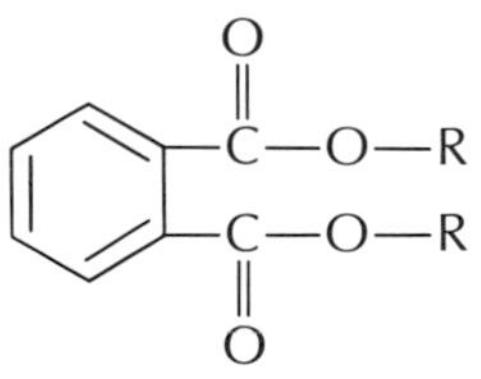

Name

Nature of R

DOP (di-octyl phthalate which is di-2-ethylhexyl phthalate)

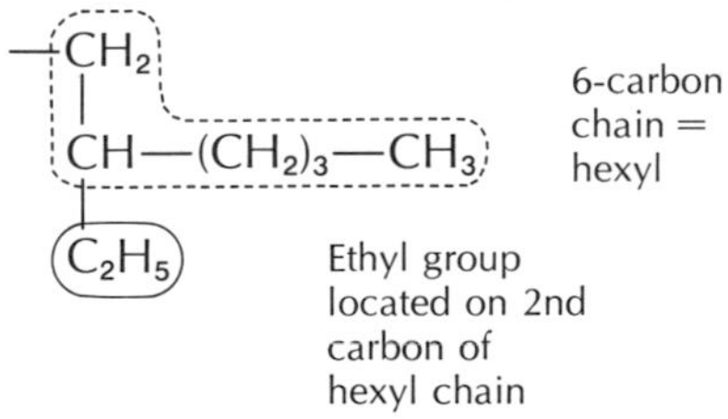

6-carbon chain = hexyl

Ethyl group located on 2nd carbon of hexyl chain

DIOP (di-isooctyl phthalate, which is di-2-methylheptyl phthalate)

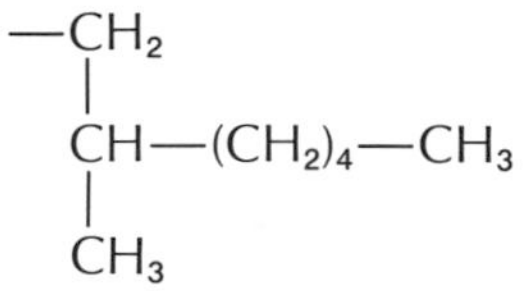

DIDP (di-isodecyl phthalate which is di-2-methylnonyl phthalate)

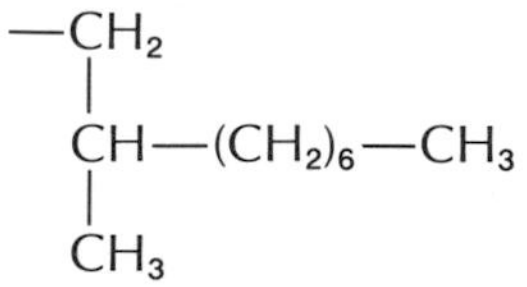

Just as in the manufacturing of detergents, several other classes of compounds can be added to plastics to alter the final properties.

Class	Use	Examples
Fillers	•To give specific mechanical and electrical properties	•For bulk and reinforcement: asbestos, marble flour, wood-pulp, walnut-shell flour, hemp •For hardness: metallic carbides, quartz, mica
Stabilizers	•Increase resistance to heat, water, ultraviolet light, chemicals	•Graphite, sand, powdered metals, asbestos •Organic metal compounds of tin, cadmium, zinc, barium (1–3 % by weight)
Mold lubricants	•Facilitate release of molded objects from forms	•Metallic soaps, such as sodium stearate
Dyes and pigments	•To add color	•Metallic and organic pigments, powdered metals, phosphorescent calcium sulfide •Some pigments may also act as fillers or stabilizers
Plasticizers	•Increase flexibility; resistance to moisture, chemicals, weathering	•Phthalates, phosphates, esters of dibasic acids and fatty acids, PCBs

Rubber: Natural and Synthetic

Rubber is another important type of addition polymer. As a natural product from certain trees, it was shown to be a polymer composed of C_5H_8 units as early as 1826. By 1860, the structure was identified as being that of isoprene, a compound containing two double bonds. The polymerization process proceeds by the opening of both double bonds followed by the re-formation of one bond in a new location.

$$
\begin{array}{c}
\text{H} \quad \text{CH}_3 \quad \text{H} \quad \text{H} \\
| \qquad | \qquad | \quad | \\
\text{C}=\text{C}-\text{C}=\text{C} \\
| \qquad\qquad\qquad | \\
\text{H} \qquad\qquad \text{H}
\end{array}
\longrightarrow
\left(\!\!
\begin{array}{c}
\text{H} \quad \text{CH}_3 \quad \text{H} \quad \text{H} \\
| \qquad | \qquad | \quad | \\
\text{C}-\text{C}=\text{C}-\text{C} \\
| \qquad\qquad\qquad | \\
\text{H} \qquad\qquad \text{H}
\end{array}
\!\!\right)_n
$$

Isoprene
(2-methyl-1, 3-butadiene)

$n = 5000–8000$ units

The highly bonded structure of rubber polymers is responsible for their chemical stability. It also means that they do not readily biodegrade. Discarded tires create litter on land and in waterways. In landfill disposal sites, tires present a unique problem, for they trap air pockets and slowly rise to the top of the landfill rather than decomposing. *(Earl Dotter)*

Although the structure of isoprene was known, man was unable to duplicate natural rubber until 1954. The problem lay in the fact that nature produces only the "cis" form in creating the polymer, a feat that proved difficult to imitate synthetically. Eventually a specific catalyst was found that would produce only the stereo-specific form rather than the mixtures of "cis" and "trans" isomers formed by man previously. The question of duplicating nature's processes had become less important by 1954 as the impetus of World War II had already resulted in several successful synthetic rubbers. Less than one-fourth of all rubber used in the United States today is natural rubber.

Synthetic rubber is commonly a copolymer system. Such an addition polymer is the result of two basic units adding to each other rather than the repetition of a single monomer unit. Some important synthetic rubbers are shown in Figure 4. If double bonds remain in the polymerized form, these rubbers can also be vulcanized. The usual assortment of other additives can be used to further tailor make the rubber.

Figure 4. Synthetic Rubbers

Monomers   *Polymer*   *Comments*

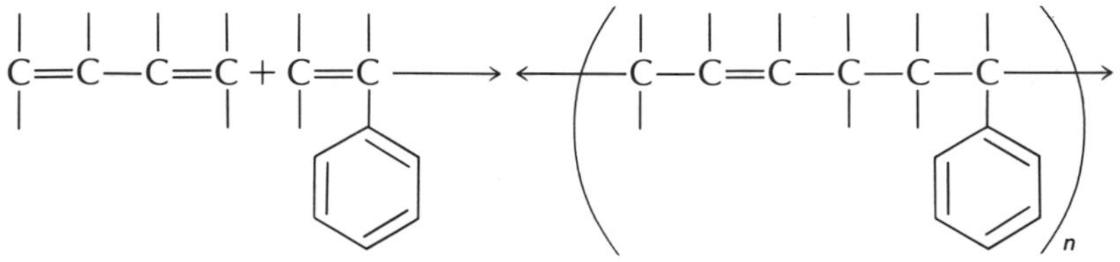

Butadiene   Styrene   SBR (styrene-butadiene rubber)

- Now accounts for over half of all synthetic rubber produced
- Usually start with 75% butadiene and 25% styrene

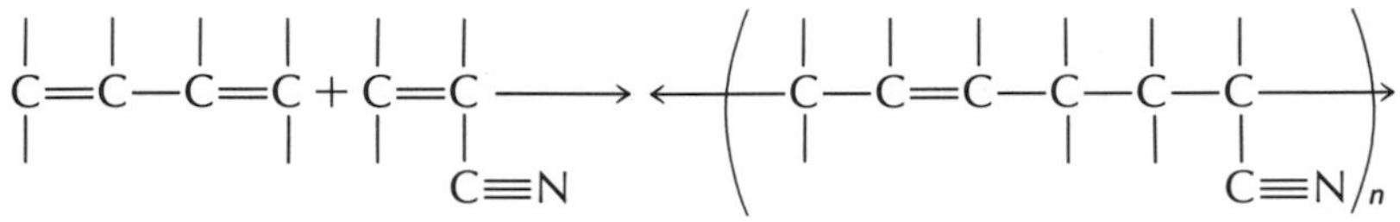

Butadiene   Acrylonitrile   Nitrile rubber

- Resistant to gasoline, oils, fats
- With SBR, one of the earliest synthetic rubbers

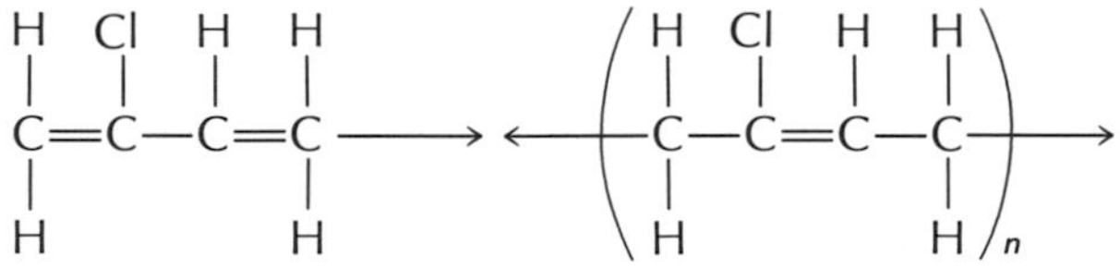

Chloroprene   Neoprene

- Also resistant to gasoline, oil, fats
- Used in hoses, gloves, shoe soles, etc.

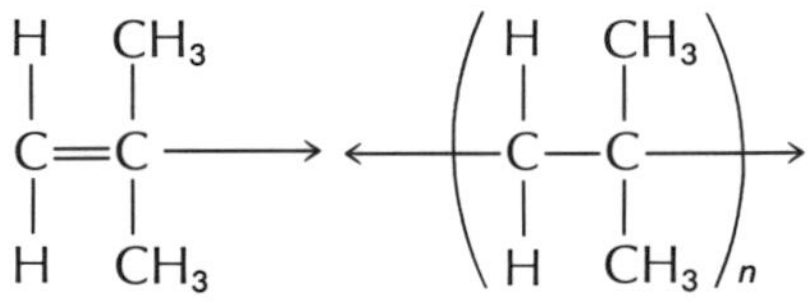

Isobutene   Butyl rubber

- Often copolymerized with butadiene
- Used for inner tubes as gases cannot pass through

The presence of the double bond in natural and certain synthetic rubbers makes it possible to carry out vulcanization. This is a process of treating the rubber with sulfur. The sulfur adds to the double bond and allows cross-linking to occur between chains, thereby increasing the strength and resilience of the rubber. The function of the S is illustrated by these diagrams:

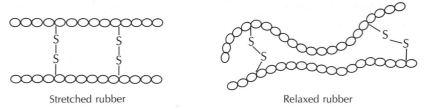

Stretched rubber   Relaxed rubber

The undesirable stickiness of the rubber is also reduced by the vulcanization process.

Part Three: CONDENSATION POLYMERS

Formation of Polyesters

A condensation polymer results from the repeated combination of two types of molecules, usually with the elimination of a small molecule such as water in the process. The composition of the polymer is not exactly that of the monomers of which it is composed. For example, in the formation of a "polyester," the process of esterification takes place in the usual way (see Chapter 8). To enable this reaction to continue in order to create the polymers, a difunctional acid and alcohol are used. This process is illustrated in Figure 5. The exact nature of the difunctional acid and alcohol determines the type of polyester produced (see Figure 6 for Dacron, for example).

Figure 5. Formation of a Condensation Polymer

Difunctional acid   Difunctional alcohol   Difunctional acid   Difunctional alcohol

$+ n \cdot H_2O$

Several ester linkages = polyester

Other Condensation Polymers

Other difunctional molecules will also undergo condensation. The formation of protein is an example of a condensation polymer in which an amino acid reacts with itself to form protein polymers with the elimination of water molecules. They are able to do this since the amino acid is a difunctional molecule containing both an acid group $\left(-C\diagdown_{OH}^{O}\right)$ and an amine group ($-NH_2$). This same type of reaction is responsible for the formation of nylon, for a difunctional acid reacts with a difunctional amine with the elimination of water. This and other condensation polymers are shown in Figure 6.

Figure 6. Condensation Polymers

Monomers — Polymers

Adipic acid + Hexamethyl amine → Amide linkage

Terephthalic acid + Ethylene glycol → Ester linkage

Maleic acid + Ethylene glycol → Ester linkage

Bisphenol A + Diphenyl carbonate → Ester linkage

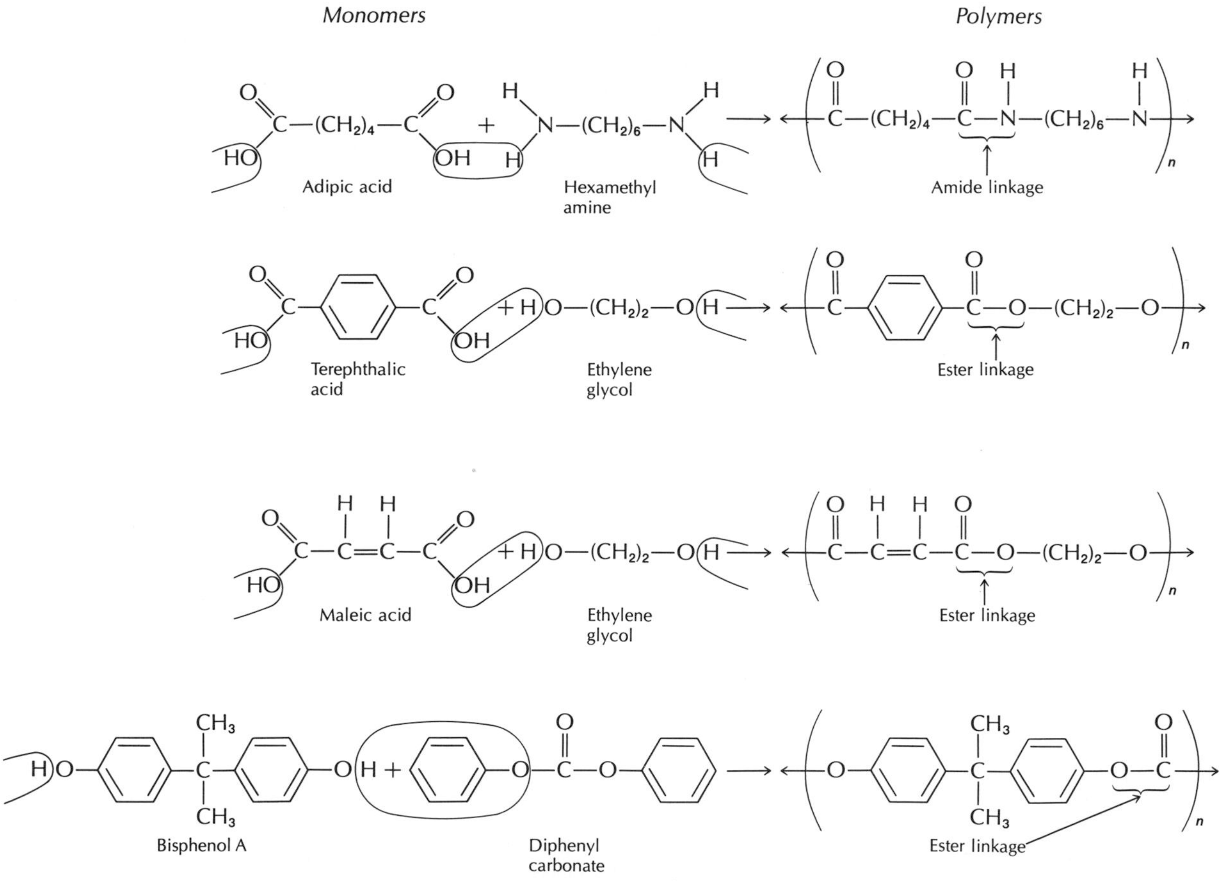

Although most synthetic rubbers are addition polymers, an important exception is silicone rubber. This is made by the condensation of dimethylsilanediol.

$$HO-\overset{\overset{\displaystyle CH_3}{|}}{\underset{\underset{\displaystyle CH_3}{|}}{Si}}-OH \longrightarrow \left(\overset{\overset{\displaystyle CH_3}{|}}{\underset{\underset{\displaystyle CH_3}{|}}{Si}}-O\right)_n + H_2O$$

$$n \approx 10{,}000\text{--}40{,}000$$

One popular form of this synthetic is "Silly Putty" which bounces, breaks when snapped, and yet loses its shape when allowed to stand.

Comments

- Polyamide type of condensation polymer
- Since each of the monomers has 6 carbons, this particular type of nylon is called Nylon 66
- Hydrogen bonding between chains helps to give fiber strength

- Polyester type of condensation polymer
- Dacron if processed into fibers
- Mylar if processed into sheets, very flexible, yet strong
- Commercial starting material may be phthalate in which case CH_3OH is the molecule eliminated. A metallic oxide catalyst is required.

- Polyester type of polymer
- Alkyd resin—used for coatings, paints, plasticizers
- May use trifunctional alcohol such as glycerol $(C_3H_5(OH)_3)$ to give increased possibility for growth of polymer in three directions

- Polyester-type; Lexan
- Phenol (C_6H_5OH) is the molecule eliminated
- Clear as glass but extremely tough— nearly as strong as steel
- Used on visors of astronauts' helmets; breakproof windowpanes

A more serious use of this polymer is for medical applications. Very pure silicone rubber for medical use is manufactured under the trade name Silastic (Dow Corning trademark). For medical purposes the polymer is made without most of the additives commonly used. This precaution minimizes possible undesirable side effects of the rubber on body tissue and blood.

Medical grade silicone rubber is now preferred to many other implantable synthetics for its unique combination of properties. It is very flexible due to the presence of the silicon-oxygen backbone of the polymer. It is nontoxic and can even be sterilized by heat due to its favorable thermal stability. It can easily be molded into the intricate shapes needed for various applications. For these reasons, Silastic has been used successfully for devices implanted in the body to repair the heart, middle ear, trachea, fallopian tubes, and even detached retinas. Tubing made from this nonwetting polymer is preferred in draining fluid from the brain, chest cavity, and other areas of the body. Silastic can be used as a building material in plastic surgery. Perhaps you first heard of silicone rubber from the widespread publicity it received after its use in enlarging women's breasts. (This operation has fallen into disfavor from reputable plastic surgeons.)

Despite all the excellent properties of silicone rubber, it has been found to promote blood clotting if the blood is moving very slowly through Silastic tubing. The main disadvantage is the lack of strength in situations where the rubber must be continually flexed. Continuing research is aimed at developing alternative materials (such as Dacron-coated heart valves) as well as improving the properties of silicone rubber.

Part Four: THE AGE OF PLASTICS: PROBLEMS AND PROSPECTS

Industrial Use of Plastics

The widespread impact of plastics technology is evident in many areas of American life. Plastics are now competing with more traditional materials, as well as expanding into new types of uses. Construction and automobiles are two examples of well-established industries that have been changed by the introduction of suitable plastic products. The Society of the Plastics Industry (SPI) estimates that about 4.5 billion pounds of plastics or one fourth of all plastics produced in this country in 1971 went into the construction industry. Despite considerable opposition from unions, builders, and code authorities, the use of plastics is expected to grow. Currently the main uses of plastics in construction are for individual components such as PVC for paneling, molding, flooring, or polypropylene for pipes. Epoxy resins find use as adhesives for exterior finishes such as stucco and molded concrete. If modular home construction becomes more popular then the use of reinforced structural materials such as glass-reinforced polyester and rigid vinyl with molded polyurethane foam cores will grow proportionally.

Reinforced plastics also are useful in the aerospace industry, for appliances and equipment, consumer goods, marine accessories, and other areas where their combination of high strength, light weight, and good chemical resistance make them attractive. Automobile manufacturers have used such materials to make hoods and front ends that would absorb impact with less damage than metal. The use of reinforced plastics for the entire body of the car has not been generally accepted by the industry but again, individual components account for a large share of the plastics produced in the U.S. today. About 10 percent of all PVC produced in 1970 went into mats, convertible tops, and upholstery for automobiles. Bucket seats are molded from polypropylene and steering columns from polyacetal. Acrylonitrile-butadiene rubber is used for grills and instrument panels. The generally accepted industry figure is that by 1980, each car manufactured in the United States will contain 200 pounds of plastics. Already, the average use is over 100 pounds per car.

Plastic blister packs are used to display and yet protect the product inside. These racing car kits are enclosed in Tenite butyrate plastic, a plastic with high clarity, easy formability, and toughness. *(Eastman Chemical Products)*

Plastics for Packaging

Perhaps the most significant area of growth for plastics has been in packaging. Here new plastics have taken their place with paper, cellophane, and aluminum wraps to the extent that 20 percent of the 19.5 billion pounds of all plastics produced in 1970 went into packaging materials. Polyethylene garbage bags are a good example of the growth of consumer usage of plastics. From a distribution of one billion bags in 1968 the market grew to four billion in 1971 and is expected to reach 10 billion by 1975. Unlike plastics used in automobiles or construction, packaging materials are disposed of almost immediately, and therefore the spectacular growth of the plastics industry in this field has focused attention on the disposal problem. Discarded plastics create a visible littering problem and potentially contribute to air pollution if the wastes are burned. Just how serious are these problems?

Packaging plastics account for the majority of plastics found in municipal refuse. Typically the waste contains vinyl plastics such as polypropylene, polyvinyl chloride, and polystyrene. Of the 190 million tons of solid waste produced in the United States per year, about 2 percent is plastic at the present time. Even though the percentage is small, that means over two and one-half million tons of plastic waste must be discarded in a safe and convenient way. By 1980 it is estimated that plastics will account for almost 3 percent of all collectable wastes, and thus the problem will continue to grow. The environmental effects of the plastic component of wastes are related to the method chosen for disposal. To evaluate the possible effects, we will look at some of the techniques currently utilized to cope with solid waste disposal.

Plastics and Solid Waste Disposal

Landfill. Landfill disposal accounts for over 90 percent of all solid wastes at the present time. In its simplest form, this means just dumping wastes into available canyons. Abandoned mines, sand pits, and worked-out quarries make disposal sites in many areas. If land for landfill is unavailable, ocean dumping is seen by some to be an alternative in coastal areas.

In its most sophisticated form, sanitary landfill disposal implies that a bulldozer compacts the refuse and covers it with earth which is again compacted. Alternate layers of refuse and dirt prevent blowing litter and fires, and discourage vermin. This procedure only occurs in about 6 percent of landfill operations in the United States. Oxygen inside both types of landfill is soon exhausted, and therefore the majority

Privately delivered solid wastes are covered immediately with a layer of dirt in this sanitary landfill area. (*Michael D. Erikson*)

of decay takes place anaerobically. Methane is released as well as hydrogen sulfide, ammonia, and other gases.

Most plastics are not readily biodegradable either aerobically or anaerobically and thus are stable components of the landfill. Some observers feel that the remarkable increase in the use of polyethylene bags will slow down the settling process which occurs in landfill, for the plastic will prevent decomposition of its contents. This will postpone the use of the land for any other purposes such as parks, parking areas, or especially for building as accumulations of methane trapped by structures can easily become explosive.

Incineration. Disposal of wastes by incineration is widely practiced by municipal, private, and industrial concerns. In some European countries, the heat derived from the incineration of trash is used for municipal heating purposes, but in the United States this has not been the case up to now because of the availability of other fuels. Certainly attitudes are due to change, and several schemes have been recently publicized involving the burning of dried and compacted wastes.

Most of the criticism aimed at the incineration of plastic centers on the resulting air pollution caused by the plastics burned. Possible products of combustion are hydrogen chloride, sulfur oxides, organic acids, aldehydes, and large amounts of particulate matter. Another concern is possible harm to the incinerator itself, due to excessive corrosion and clogging of the system by melting plastics.

Attempting to answer these charges, the Society of the Plastics Industry sponsored a research project at New York University's Department of Chemical Engineering. These tests showed that in a conventional modern incinerator, solid wastes containing up to 6 percent or more plastic can be safely handled without adversely affecting the incinerator's operation. Since plastics are essentially hydrocarbons, their burning gives appreciable heat value and the higher temperature does increase NO_x emission to some degree. However, the higher temperature also increases the completeness of combustion, an important factor in reducing visible smoke when burning damp material. Even polystyrene, which gives a high proportion of unburned hydrocarbons when burned by itself, will burn efficiently in a municipal incinerator under favorable oxygen and temperature conditions. Hydrogen chloride produced can be 85 to 95 percent removed by equipping the incinerator with a wet scrubber. The scrubber water will also serve to dissolve many of the other air pollutants as well. Hydrogen chloride is also produced by the incineration of other components of solid waste such as paper, grass, and wood, so it is hard to evaluate the role of plastics themselves in producing HCl. No free chlorine gas (Cl_2) or toxic phosgene ($COCl_2$) were detected in the tests.

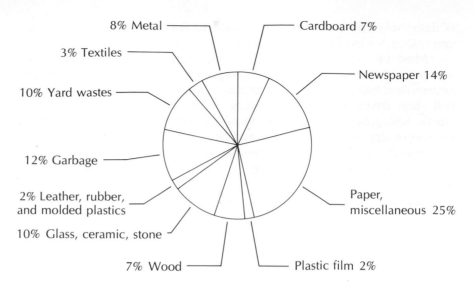

8% Metal

3% Textiles

10% Yard wastes

12% Garbage

2% Leather, rubber, and molded plastics

10% Glass, ceramic, stone

7% Wood

Cardboard 7%

Newspaper 14%

Paper, miscellaneous 25%

Plastic film 2%

Solid waste disposal presents many challenges, particularly in large cities. Amounts of solid wastes are increasing faster than the growth of our population predicts. This means that per capita waste is increasing, a reflection of greater affluence and our use-once-and-throw-away attitude. Such an approach is limited by available natural resources and by the troublesome question—exactly where is "away"?

The recycling of wastes presents an opportunity to ease the disposal problem and to reutilize materials. In certain industries, recycling has long been practiced; recycled copper accounts for 42 percent of the total copper consumed in the United States. Municipal refuse has not been a good candidate for recycling in the past, because the complexity of materials that make up the waste makes separation difficult and economically unattractive.

New technology makes it possible to separate and reuse more components of municipal refuse. This modern solid waste recycling plant in Franklin, Ohio, is seeking to demonstrate the feasibility of many new ideas in separation. It is also planned to show the relationships between solid waste and other environmental controls. For example, purified effluent water from a waste water treatment plant on the same site will be used in the recycling plant.

Several new plastics are being developed that are said to be completely nontoxic when incinerated. Extensive tests of Barex-210, an acrylonitrile plastic, and Lopac, a nitrile-based plastic, have shown no harmful combustion products. Major soft-drink companies are now experimentally marketing nonreturnable bottles based on these plastics.

If heat is applied in the absence of oxygen, then pyrolysis rather than incineration occurs. Municipal wastes could yield a mixture of organic acids, oils, gases, tars, and charcoal at temperatures from 600 to 1000°C. Plastics and rubber wastes would be efficiently decomposed in this process. The products would have to be separated and then could be sold as raw materials or used for fuel. At present, no municipal pyrolysis units are operating, but several successful industrial demonstration plants have been built.

Separation and Recycling of Plastics

There are no practical techniques known for separating plastic from the other components of solid wastes. This limits the possibilities for recycling plastics from municipal wastes. Direct reuse of plastic containers is possible, but generally the plastic cannot again be used for food due to problems of adequate sterilization. Plastic waste recycling has therefore consisted largely of the reuse of industrial waste plastic. Scraps of any thermoplastic polymers can be melted and reformed into other useful products. The plastic can also be pulverized and mixed with traditional materials to form heating fuels or building materials. New processes have been developed to reclaim the polyurethane materials used in automobile and polyethylene terephthalate wastes from injection molding and fabric production. This latter process would also be suitable for use with packaging materials. The recovery of raw materials, together with possible recycling ordinances and packaging taxes, may provide sufficient economic incentive; in the past, there has been little economic reason for recycling since the raw materials for manufacturing new plastics are relatively cheap and abundant.

Biodegradable Plastics

Efforts to reduce the contribution of plastics to the solid waste problem as well as to eliminate the unsightly littering of plastics have centered on altering the plastic so that it becomes biodegradable. It is ironic that polymer chemists have put a good deal of effort into finding stabilizers that helped stop degradation reactions due to ultraviolet light, heat, or bacteria; now the research effort is turned towards modification of the polymer so that it will break down in a predictable way under the same conditions.

The desired reaction can be brought about by chemically modifying

1

2

3

4

5

6

Bio-Degradable Plastics, Inc., of Boise, Idaho, has developed a light-sensitive additive for polystyrene. Finished products commonly made from this plastic are foam egg cartons, meat trays, drinking cups, and nonfoamed objects such as picnic dinnerware, dairy cartons, and bags. Many of these items are associated with litter, and the production of biodegradable polystyrene will help to eliminate this problem. Once the product is exposed to sunlight, the degradation is initiated and continues, with the help of several common soil and air organisms, until the product is totally biodegraded. This series of photographs documents the decomposition.

1. 0 days, no litter in the environment.
2. 1–5 days, cup lid made with light-sensitive additive is discarded.
3. 30–90 days, product begins to break apart; decomposition is under way. In a sunny location, there is a faster reaction.
4. 60–120 days, continued decomposition and total fragmentation of lid.
5. 90–150 days, decomposition is almost complete.
6. 6–12 months, no evidence of discarded lid; total time depends on local sun and microorganism environment.

Research is continuing by this same company to produce a biodegradable concentrate for polyethylene.

the polymer itself or by the addition of suitable compounds. Canadian chemists have recently developed a series of photosensitizing "activator groups" that can be chemically incorporated into the polymer chain. These areas of the polymer then become subject to bond-breakage due to ultraviolet light; the degradation time can be controlled by careful modification of the polymer or by mixing the light-sensitive polymer with conventional material. This system has been successfully tested on polyethylene, polypropylene, polystyrene, polyamides, polyesters, and PVC. A photodegradable polystyrene foam is being test marketed in Japan. A potential drawback of this scheme is that the degradation does not continue in the absence of ultraviolet light. However, whatever absorption has occurred tends to make the polymer brittle which may allow wind, rain, and other forces to succeed in breaking the plastic into fragments that are small enough for attack by soil microorganisms.

English scientists have approached the problem by employing an additive system. The additive, like the activator group, would absorb ultraviolet light. This reaction typically creates free hydroperoxy radicals that attract hydrogen atoms from the polymer molecule. A continuation of this process would result in an eventual breakdown of the polymer backbone. Once initiated by light, this process could continue even in the dark and so degrade composted or buried plastics.

Both the additives and modifiers of the polymer chain can be picked so they are sensitive to light of 280 to 330 mu in wavelength. This is useful, since window glass cuts off light with wavelength shorter than 330 mu, and therefore the containers would be stable in stores. One experimental system makes use of a dye included in the polymer so that the plastic would change color when free radical reactions started to occur, providing further safety. All such additives or modifications of the polymer chain must meet toxicity tests and also must not interfere with the plastic's fabrication.

One promising approach to producing a biodegradable plastic container is to make a "sandwich" of an easily degraded plastic between two ultra thin layers of conventional plastics. Such a three-layer bottle has been made by Ilikon Corporation and was expected to be marketed in mid-1972. The middle of the sandwich is Klucel, a water soluble hydroxypropyl cellulose plastic. This accounts for 90 percent of the bottle. The outside layer would be cheap, tough polystyrene, and the innermost layer, in contact with the product, would be chosen from approved plastics. The degradation of the bottle is triggered by peeling off the polystyrene and is complete in two hours if it is totally immersed in water. The thin innermost and outermost layers remain to be disposed of in traditional ways, but the problem has been reduced by 90 percent. Klucel is already approved by the FDA since it is used as a food stabilizer and binder, so its use should not present any toxicity problems.

A completely new idea for the disposal of plastics and all solid wastes is the *fusion torch*. A nuclear fusion reactor would be capable of producing temperatures up to 100 million degrees centigrade but solid wastes need only to be heated to 10,000°C before the compounds present will be vaporized and totally decomposed into elements. The rest of the heat could then be used to heat water to generate electricity.

The elements produced in the fusion torch at high temperature would then need to be separated. Engineers feel this is possible by existing electromagnetic methods, since only about twelve elements occur in solid wastes in significant quantities. Elements such as carbon, oxygen, hydrogen, sulfur, and iron are common. Another option would be to allow the elements to selectively recombine into useful compounds such as hydrocarbons for fuel. This could be accomplished by controlling temperature and pressure conditions.

If the fusion torch becomes reality, then two problems can be solved simultaneously—the disposal of solid wastes and the diminishing supply of raw materials. This type of total recycling may prove in the long run to be more feasible and desirable than working out recycling technology for each type of material. This would particularly be true in cases where the recycling process itself consumes a significant amount of energy such as in the case of aluminum. The fusion torch for solid waste disposal would be an important benefit from the development of fusion power to generate electricity.

The Future

Plastics will certainly be an important technological component of our future. Thermoplastics in particular have shown strong growth during 1972, and demand from manufacturers of automobiles, packaging materials, and other consumer-related products will probably continue. The prospects are bright for the industry and for the creative uses of these man-made materials, but can all the potential environmental problems be overcome?

We have looked at disposal and incineration as methods of ending the useful life of a plastic. The continued research into biodegradable plastics is another aspect of the future. However, one other factor may become the limiting constraint placed on the growth of plastics. This is the fact that the raw materials of plastics come, at the present time, from resources that cannot be renewed in our earth—coal and petroleum. Until effective recycling is possible, the scale of use of these resources for plastics production might well be the subject of debate by all components of our society.

Study Questions—Group A

1. How "big" is a polymer? It is referred to as a large molecule, but what molecular weight range is implied? How does the molecular weight compare with that of a familiar molecule such as water?

2. What is a vinyl plastic? List several examples and their uses.

3. Redraw the diagram on page 328, but replace the dashes with the proper number of electrons.

4. What free radical species would be produced from dimethyl peroxide, $(CH_3)_2O_2$? What use could this free radical have?

5. Polypropylene is formed from the propylene monomer:

$$\begin{array}{cc} H & H \\ | & | \\ C\!=\!C \\ | & | \\ H & CH_3 \end{array}$$

   Write equations showing how two propylene units join together in the presence of a peroxide catalyst.

6. Compare the structures of polypropylene and polystyrene. Which polymer would you expect to be more flexible? Remember that in a flexible polymer the chains must have freedom to move over each other.

7. Effect of catalyst composition on molecular weight of ethylene polymers.
   a. Graph the information, placing molar ratio on the x axis and average molecular weight on the y axis.
   b. Use the graph to predict the molecular weight of the product if an 8:1 molar ratio of $AlR_3/TiCl_4$ were used. What other molar ratio would give the same molecular weight? What ratio would be needed to produce a weight of 200,000?
   c. What would be the expected result if pure $TiCl_4$ were used? If pure AlR_3 were used?

8. Why did it take so long to synthetically produce rubber with the same chemical construction as natural rubber?

9. Draw two bonded isoprene units as they would appear in the "cis" form. This is also referred to as an isotatic polymer. (The "trans" form is referred to as a syndiotactic polymer, and an atactic polymer has random spatial positions for the $-CH_3$ group.) Which form would you expect to have the most pronounced crystalline properties?

10. Compare the chain mechanism for the formation of an addition polymer such as polyethylene to a chain reaction such as the controlled fission of uranium.

Molar ratio $AlR_3/TiCl_4$	Average Molecular Weight (in grams)
12	272,000
6	292,000
3	298,000
1	284,000
0.63	160,000
0.53	40,000
0.50	21,000
0.20	31,000

From: *PETROCHEMICALS: THE NEW WORLD OF SYNTHETICS,* copyright 1969 by Ray T. Wendland. Reprinted by permission of Doubleday and Company.

11. What causes the differences in properties observed for high-pressure and low-pressure polyethylene?

Use these data for questions 12–16.

Production of Plastics

| | Production, millions of pounds | | | |
	1966	1967	1968	1969
Polyester	470	513	615	667
Polyethylene				
Low density	2648	2716	3306	3831
High density	910	1082	1261	1610
Polypropylene	554	662	878	1084
Polyvinyl chloride	2164	2142	2635	3032

Source: Chemical and Engineering News, September 7, 1970, p. 77A.

12. Present these data graphically.

13. Which type of plastic showed the largest pound increase over the period 1966–1969?

14. Which type had the largest percent increase in the same period?

15. Which type showed the steadiest rate of growth?

16. Low-density polyethylene has a predicted growth rate of 7.9 percent per year for the decade 1970–80. Does this represent an increase or a decrease as compared with the growth rate for the period 1966–69?

17. Polyvinyl chloride production was 3.44 billion pounds in 1971 and 4.13 billion pounds in 1972. (Chemical and Engineering News, August 28, 1972, p. 8.) Compare the amount of growth for the period 1971–72 with the growth for the period 1966–67; with the growth for the period 1968–69.

18. How does a polyester fiber differ from a cotton fiber?

19. What does each of these abbreviations stand for? Why is each important?
a. PVC b. DOP c. SBR

20. Draw the complete structure for DIDP plasticizer. How many carbons are there in a nonyl group?

21. Show two chains of Nylon 66 side by side as they would be when connected by hydrogen bonding.

22. a. Polyurethane plastics are made from a difunctional alcohol and a difunctional isocyanate.

$$O=C=N—R—N=C=O \qquad HO—R'—OH$$

Isocyanate   Alcohol

In carrying out polymerization, the alcohol adds to the nitrogen-carbon double bond. The hydrogen from the hydroxyl group attaches to the nitrogen, and the rest of the molecule adds to the carbon atom. Write the basic structure for the polyurethane polymer.

b. Polyurethane is classed as a condensation polymer. Explain how this reaction fits the definition of a condensation but not an addition polymer.

23. Would it be possible to vulcanize silicone rubber? Why or why not?

24. What is an amide linkage? Give an example of a polymer with such a structural arrangement.

25. Will the majority of decomposition of organic matter within a sanitary landfill take place aerobically or anaerobically? Explain.

Study Questions — Group B

1. Try to visit a plastics manufacturer in your area. What are the starting materials at that plant? What processes are used to produce the final plastic product? What are the uses of the product? What is the life expectancy of the product, and where will it likely be disposed of?

2. In 1971, New York City proposed a 2¢ tax on all rigid and semi-rigid plastic containers used for beverage and other nonfood uses. The Society of the Plastics Industry brought suit in the State Supreme Court challenging the legality and constitutionality of the tax. SPI was successful in having the tax ruled invalid, void, and unconstitutional. What were the probable motivations behind the city's proposed tax? What arguments were likely used against the tax? (To check the accuracy of your guesses, consult *The New York Times,* Tuesday, July 27, 1971, p. 14C). Do you feel this approach should be used in your area?

3. Compile a list of common items that used to be made from some other material but that are now often plastic. (The kitchen of your home is a good place to start.) What advantages and disadvantages are there for the plastic version of the item compared with the original?

4. An earnest vacuum cleaner salesman tells you that the hoses to his equipment are far superior to those of Brand X because they are polybutylene, not plastic. How will you handle this opportunity to educate him?

5. A useful reference for additional reading on the disposal of solid wastes is *Solid Wastes,* a collection of twenty-five articles that appeared in *Environmental Science and Technology,* from 1967–71. (This is available from the American Chemical Society as part of their paperback reprint collection.)

The following articles are also recommended, particularly to evaluate the importance of recycling wastes.

> Grinstead, Robert R. "Bottlenecks." *Environment* 14: 3 (April 1972): 2–13.
>
> Grinstead, Robert R. "Machinery for Trash Mining." *Environment* 14: 4, (May 1972): 34–42.
>
> Hannon, Bruce M. "Bottles, Cans, Energy." *Environment* 14: 2 (March 1972): 11–21.
>
> Hershaft, Alex. "Solid Waste Treatment Technology." *Environmental Science and Technology* 6: 5 (May 1972): 412–421.
>
> Ness, Howard. "Recycling as an Industry." *Environmental Science and Technology* 6: 8 (August 1972): 700–704.

Set up a panel discussion for the class in which new approaches as well as the applicability of traditional methods for your area are discussed.

Suggested Readings

"Can Plastics be Incinerated Safely?" *Environmental Science and Technology* 5: 8 (1971): 667–669.

> Overview of incineration problem. Reviews the SPI-sponsored study on incineration of plastics carried out by New York University.

Mark, Herman F. "Giant Molecules," *Scientific American* Offprint #314, 197: 3 (1957): 204–216.

> Introductory article for a series on macromolecules. Contains historical survey of polymer chemistry's development and basic structure of common polymers.

Mark, Herman F. *Giant Molecules*. New York: Time-Life, 1968.

Excellent introduction to polymers and plastics. Written at a popular level yet contains much specific chemistry. Generously illustrated.

Stille, John K. *Introduction to Polymer Chemistry*. New York: John Wiley & Sons, 1962.

Basic textbook introducing the science of polymer chemistry. Early chapters suitable for nonchemistry majors.

Epilogue

Does our spaceship face impending ecological disaster, or will we be wise enough to avoid such a fate? It would surely be a disservice to imply that chemistry alone can decide the issue. The wisdom of science is necessary but far from the only ingredient for successful solutions to the complex environmental problems of our age.

How will man respond to the environmental challenges we face? No doubt some will choose to ignore them out of apathy, ignorance, greed, or fear. The human spirit, however, seems to thrive on creative response to challenge, and therefore there is hope that as the true consequences of environmental disruption become apparent, more appropriate responses will result. It is clear that the effort to maintain a livable environment will require changes in priorities and a personal commitment from everyone.

One overriding problem that affects degradation of our environment is population. It simply is not common sense to think that our finite resources can continue to support an ever-increasing number of people. Since the average citizen of the highly developed United States uses a proportionally large share of our spaceship's supplies, the question of controlling our own population is of major importance. This is partly a problem for chemistry to help solve, but more so, it is a question of society's attitudes. Do we need to work as a society on modernizing present legal restraints on the widespread availability of information and the means of birth control? Could the tax laws which presently encourage large families also be restructured to help them conform with the desirable goal of stable population growth? Recent statistical indications are that the population growth rate is slowing down in the United States.

This is a sign that families, now given a practical choice, are responding by "stopping at two."

We all have to readjust our thinking to avoid the continuation of past short-sightedness. We have been slow to realize the effects of our convenient, disposable, energy-consumptive life style on our finite planetary resources. The growth ethic had never been seriously questioned until it became apparent that conspicuous consumption did not necessarily produce a better quality of life. Perhaps a better attitude in the future would be to "keep *down* with the Joneses" in order to establish a more realistic balance between man and the rest of our spaceship. The rewards of clean air, pure water, and a healthy environment would make the inconvenience of change seem worthwhile.

Each of us has countless opportunities every day to affect the future environment. Hopefully in studying the ideas in this book you have already come up with ways in which you can enjoy better environmental living. Although some suggestions may seem unimportant to you, the effect if magnified by even a fraction of the total population could be quite dramatic. Do not underestimate the power of economics. Every time you spend a dollar, you have an economic vote that can make a difference. You do not have to silently support products that you believe are harmfully affecting your environment, either externally or internally. For some excellent guidance along these lines, try Paul Swatek's *The User's Guide to the Protection of the Environment* (Friends of the Earth/Ballantine, 1970). This handbook will help you to consider the background information necessary to evaluate specific products for their obvious and hidden effects on the environment.

It is usually necessary to work on several levels of a problem simultaneously. For example, keeping your own car in top operating condition so as to minimize emissions is a sensible step, but that must be accompanied by your support of alternate, less polluting modes of transportation in order to have a long-term effect on the problem of air pollution. Production of electric power has been seen to cause major environmental impacts of several kinds, so it makes sense to limit your use of electricity to essential purposes and avoid unnecessary waste. Government and industry can be encouraged to follow the same procedures, and the re-ordering of rate structures might help to accomplish this. Even these changes should not be the full extent of your involvement, for unless alternate and less polluting means of producing electricity are simultaneously explored, we cannot achieve a long-range solution of the problem.

There are other aspects of the over-all picture of environmental degradation that have not been specifically discussed in this book as they are not primarily chemical problems. They are nevertheless important and should be part of your concern. For example, land-use planning is essential to create livable cities. Open space can improve air quality by providing greenery that both absorbs pollutants and produces oxygen, but its role in providing an economic and aesthetic asset to the community is usually underrated. Appropriate uses of land can help to avoid problems of noise, a commonly overlooked but increasingly important problem. Continual exposure to noise can contribute to high blood pressure, irritability, and stress. Hearing damage results from excessively loud noises. Noise abatement procedures are known, but public support is needed for enactment and enforcement of suitable regulations.

The dimensions of our environmental problems are immense, and if you care, the responsibilities are great. It is possible to create change, but you must be well informed, highly involved, and exceedingly persistent. I wish you the best in carrying on the quiet revolution leading to a closer harmony between man and nature.

Glossary

Activation product. A radioactive material produced by neutron bombardment.

Addition polymer. A polymer in which the recurring units have the same composition as the individual monomer units from which it was made. There is no byproduct formed.

Adulteration. The deceptive use of food additives to change the apparent nature or quality of food.

Aerobic decay. The breakdown of organic matter by microorganisms that utilize oxygen.

Aerosol. Small particles of liquid or solid suspended in a gas. Smoke and fog are examples of aerosols.

Algae. Small plants that live in water environments. Carry on photosynthesis.

Alpha particle. A particle emitted when certain unstable nuclei decay. Made up of two protons and two neutrons; identical to the nucleus of a helium atom. Symbols: α, ^4_2He.

Ambient. Surrounding conditions, such as the ambient noise level or the ambient air quality.

Amino acid. Basic building block for proteins. Contains both the typical carboxylic acid group

$$\left(-C\diagup^{\displaystyle O}_{\displaystyle OH}\right)$$ and the amino group ($-\text{NH}_2$).

Amphetamines. Class of drug with stimulant action on the central nervous system.

Anaerobic decay. The breakdown of organic matter by microorganisms in the absence of oxygen.

Angstrom. A unit of length equal to 10^{-10} meter. Symbol: Å

Antioxidants. Class of organic compounds used to prevent oxidation of susceptible substances such as fats, oils, rubber, and lubricants. If used in foods, may be referred to as freshness stabilizers or oxygen interceptors.

Aromatic compounds. Ring-structured hydrocarbons related to benzene (C_6H_6) or its derivatives.

Atom. Smallest unit of an element that still retains all significant properties of that element.

Atomic mass unit. A unit of mass based on one-twelfth the mass of an atom of carbon-12. One atomic mass unit equals 1.66×10^{-27} kg. Abbreviated amu or simply u.

Atomic number. The number of protons in the nucleus of an atom. This value characterizes the atom as one specific element.

Atomic weight. Average relative mass of all isotopes of an element. Based on carbon-12 as exactly 12.000 . . . amu.

Avogadro's number. The constant number of atoms in one mole of an element or molecules in one mole of a compound. Value is 6.023×10^{23}.

Barbiturates. Class of drug with depressant action on the central nervous system.

Beta particle. A particle emitted when certain unstable nuclei decay. Negatively charged beta particles are identical with electrons but come from the nucleus.

Biochemical oxygen demand (BOD). A quantitative measure of the amount of oxygen used by a sample of polluted water during normal decomposition processes.

Biodegradable (degradable). Refers to materials that can be broken apart into smaller chemical units by natural physical, chemical, and biological processes.

Biological magnification (biological concentration). Phenomenon in which successive members of the food chain concentrate and pass on ever-increasing accumulations of a specific substance.

Brackish water. Water ranging from 1000 to 35,000 ppm dissolved solids. Groundwater is brackish in many areas; desalination processes can be used to purify this water.

Carbamates. A class of organic compounds used as pesticides. They are esters of carbamic acid.

Carbohydrates. Class of essential foods; sugar, starch, and cellulose are examples. Carbohydrates are a fundamental food energy source and the most abundant class of organic compounds.

Carcinogen. A substance that causes cancer in living tissues. Such a substance is also referred to as being carcinogenic.

Catalyst. A substance which changes the rate of a chemical reaction but is itself chemically unchanged at the end of the reaction. Most catalysts increase the rate of a reaction.

Catalytic converters. Units added to the exhaust system of an automobile in order to promote complete combustion of hydrocarbons or the breakdown of NO_x into nitrogen and oxygen. Various metals and metallic oxides are commonly proposed as catalysts.

Chain reaction. A reaction that can be repeated many times within a finite period of time. Some aspect of the reaction enables the repetition to occur, such as extra neutrons released in a nuclear chain reaction or free radicals in a polymerization chain reaction.

Chemistry. The study of the composition of substances and the transformations they undergo.

Chemical oxygen demand (COD). A quantitative measure of the amount of oxygen used for oxidizing all wastes in water. The results may include some materials not naturally biodegradable.

Combustion. Rapid oxidation; burning. Accompanied by heat and light production.

Compound. A substance containing two or more elements chemically united.

Condensation polymer. A polymer formed by the repeated combination of two types of monomer units; usually accompanied by the elimination of a small molecule such as water. The polymer's composition is not identical to the monomers from which it was formed.

Copolymer. An addition polymer formed by the repeated combination of two types of monomer units.

Cosmic rays. High-energy particles and gamma rays originating outside the earth's atmosphere.

Covalent bond. A chemical bond in which electrons are shared between atoms. May be polar (unequal sharing of electrons) or nonpolar.

Criteria. Scientific judgments based on experimentation. Give expected effects of a specific concentration of a pollutant, for example.

Defoliation. See herbicides.

Degradable. See biodegradable.

Desalination (desalting). Process of removing salt from seawater (or from brackish water) in order to obtain fresh water.

Detergents. Cleaning agents that emulsify grease and water. Often used to mean newer synthetic materials that, unlike soap, will not form precipitates with hard water.

Disparlure. Common name for the sex-attractant pheromone of the gypsy moth. Useful in achieving biological control of this pest.

Distillation. A process in which a liquid is heated and the resulting vapor is then condensed into pure liquid; less easily vaporized components are left behind. See fractional distillation, flash distillation.

Ecology. A branch of biology. Deals with interrelationships among plants, animals, and their environment.

Effluent. A discharge coming from an identifiable source. Often used to mean a stream of liquid, especially water, carrying various amounts of pollutants.

Electron. A subatomic particle found outside the nucleus. It has an extremely small mass and carries a negative electrical charge. In some cases, an electron may be totally separated from an atom by heat, light, electric energy, or radiation.

Electrophilic. "Electron-loving." Strongly attracts electrons.

Electrostatic precipitator. A device used to remove particulate matter from smoke by application of an electric field.

Element. Substance that cannot be decomposed by ordinary chemical means. Made up of atoms of only one atomic number. 105 elements presently known.

Emissions. Substances given off to the general environment from an identifiable source. Often used to mean pollutants released to the atmosphere.

Emulsifying agent. Substance that temporarily mixes two immiscible materials.

Encapsulation. A fabricating technique useful to prevent chemical deterioration or quick release of an ingredient such as a food flavor, pesticide, or drug. The ingredient is combined with or surrounded by a degradable plastic or natural gum.

Energy level. The energy states of an electron in an atom. The actual description of energy levels varies with the particular model of atomic structure utilized.

Enrichment. (1) A process to produce nuclear fuel with a higher ratio of desired isotopes. Uranium is enriched by gaseous diffusion. (2) Addition of nutrients such as nitrates and phosphates to a water system. See eutrophication.

Environment. All factors in the surroundings with influence upon an organism.

Eutrophication. A process in which a body of water receives excess nutrients, stimulating the abundant growth of algae. The decomposition of algae uses up dissolved oxygen, causing fishkills. Further decay occurs anaerobically, creating unpleasant odors. This process occurs naturally as a body of water ages, but is often accelerated by man's addition of nitrates, phosphates, and other nutrients.

Enzymes. Highly complex protein molecules that act as catalysts in biochemical reactions, such as the digestion of carbohydrates.

Fats. Class of essential foods that supply reserve food energy. Fats are esters often made from glycerol and long-chain organic acids.

Fission. Splitting of a heavy nucleus into two medium-weight nuclei. Accompanied by the release of energy and often one or more neutrons.

Flash distillation. Distillation carried out at less than atmospheric pressure so that less heat energy is needed to cause vaporization. Useful as a desalination process.

Flavor enhancer. A substance that improves the sensation of flavor. Especially useful for enhancing protein flavors of meat, fish, etc.

Fluorescence. Phenomenon in which a substance absorbs energy from ultraviolet light and then immediately gives off energy in the form of visible light.

Food additive. Substance added to food either intentionally or unintentionally during some stage of production, processing, or storage. Not part of the basic foodstuff.

Formula weight. The sum of all atomic weights in a chemical formula for a compound.

Fossil fuel. Fuels such as coal, oil, and petroleum that are thought to be the fossilized remains of plants and animals.

Fractional distillation. A process of separating several components of a mixture based on their differing boiling points. See distillation.

Free radicals. A molecular fragment with an unpaired electron. Extremely reactive species.

Fusion. Joining lightweight nuclei together to form heavier nuclei. Accompanied by the release of energy.

Gamma ray. High-energy radiation emitted when unstable nuclei decay. Similar to x-rays but more penetrating, shorter in wavelength. Travels at speed of light.

Gaseous diffusion. A process used to separate the isotopes of uranium. Based on different diffusion rates through a porous barrier.

Gram-atomic weight. The atomic weight of an element expressed in grams. Also the gram weight of one mole of an element.

Gram-molecular weight. The molecular weight of a compound expressed in grams. Also the gram weight of one mole of a compound.

Grams per mile. A unit used to express the concentration of automotive emissions.

Half-life. Time needed for half the atoms of a radioactive isotope to decay into a different nuclear form. Symbol: $t_{1/2}$.

Hard water. Water containing dissolved calcium, magnesium, and iron salts. Forms an undesirable precipitate with soap.

Herbicide. A chemical agent used to kill unwanted vegetation. If used against woody plants, loss of leaves results (defoliation) and the agent is called a defoliant.

Hydrocarbons. Compounds containing exclusively hydrogen and carbon.

Hydrogen bonding. A weak bond between an electropositive part of a polar molecule and an electronegative part of another polar molecule. May also be between polar regions of the same large molecule. Presence of hydrogen bonds affects boiling points and crystal structure.

Hydrogenation. Adding hydrogen to another molecule. Usually involves the use of a metallic catalyst, heat, and pressure. Important commercial process in the food and petroleum industries.

Hydrological cycle. The cyclic movement of water on earth; includes evaporation, precipitation, underground, and surface movements.

Hydrophilic. "Water-loving" or water-seeking.

Hydrophobic. "Water-fearing" or water repelling.

Induced radioisotope. See activation product.

Insecticide. A pesticide used to kill insects.

Ion. An electrically charged atom. A covalently bonded group of atoms carrying an electrical charge may also be called an ion or a radical ion.

Ionic bonding. A chemical bond in which electrons are transferred between atoms. The result is oppositely charged ions. Also called electrovalent or electrostatic bonding.

Isomers. Compounds containing the same number and types of atoms but differing with respect to their atomic arrangement or orientation in space. Some types are structural isomers, geometric isomers, and optical isomers.

Isotopes. Atoms having the same atomic number but a different atomic mass. They are forms of the same element but differ in the number of neutrons in the nucleus.

Inversion. A reversal of a normal temperature pattern in the atmosphere. Often means a layer of warmer air atop a layer of cooler air; the expected trend is for air to get cooler further from the earth. Inversions may trap layers of pollutants close to the earth's surface and prevent them from dispersing.

LD_{50}. The lethal dose for fifty percent of a given experimental population.

Linear hypothesis. A theory of biological damage. Holds that all doses can cause a harmful effect, even if that effect is not measurable.

Mass. Measures the quantity of matter compared with standard masses. The value of an object's mass is not dependent on its position relative to a gravitational field.

Mass number. The total number of neutrons and protons in the nucleus of an atom. This value is not unique to one element due to the existence of isotopes.

Mole. The amount of a substance containing Avogadro's number of atoms or molecules. Equal to one gram-atomic weight for an element and one gram-molecular or gram-formula weight for a compound.

Molecular weight. The sum of all atomic weights in the molecular formula for a compound.

Molecule. Smallest unit of a compound that still retains all significant properties of that compound.

Monomer. The basic chemical unit from which a polymer is formed. Usually is of low molecular weight and contains carbon.

Nucleus. Dense central region of an atom. Both mass and positive charge are concentrated in the nucleus.

Neutron. A subatomic particle found in the nucleus. It is electrically neutral and approximately equal in mass to a proton.

Octane number. A value assigned to gasoline by comparing the smoothness of combustion with a standard fuel under specified test conditions.

Orbital. Describes a volume in space around a nucleus where an electron has a probability of being found (quantum mechanical model of atomic structure).

Organic chemistry. Branch of chemistry dealing with carbon compounds (excludes simple oxides of carbon and carbonate salts).

Organochlorine compounds. A class of organic compounds containing one or more chlorine atoms per molecule. Members of the class are used as pesticides, plastics, industrial solvents, etc.

Organophosphates. A class of organic compounds containing one or more phosphorus atoms per molecule. Used as pesticides, nerve gases, plasticizers, and flame retardants.

Osmosis. The process of selective movement of ·liquid through a membrane. Normally pure water diffuses faster than solutions so osmosis tends to equalize the concentrations of two solutions separated by a membrane. See reverse osmosis.

Oxidant. A substance that is capable of gaining electrons. An oxidant acts as an oxidizing agent.

Oxidation. Chemically combining with oxygen. In a broader definition, oxidation occurs if electrons are removed, which implies an increase in oxidation number for the element oxidized.

Ozone. A form of oxygen with three atoms per molecule. Very reactive and excellent oxidizing agent.

Pathogenic. Capable of causing disease. Bacteria, fungi, and viruses are examples of agents that can be pathogenic.

Particulates. Small particles of solids or liquids suspended in the atmosphere.

Parts per million. A unit that expresses the concentration of substances present only in small amounts. Commonly used for gaseous or dissolved pollutants. Abbreviation: ppm.

Periodic table. Table that shows all elements arranged in order of increasing atomic number and grouped according to the regular recurrence of their properties.

Pesticide. A material used to kill something identified as a pest. The pest may be an insect, plant, fungus, rodent, etc.

pH. A scale of values used to represent the acidity of a solution. A pH of 7 represents a neutral solution, less than 7 an acid, and more than 7 a basic or alkaline solution.

Pheromones. Chemicals that are used by insects for communication. Mating behavior of insects is controlled by pheromones.

Photochemical smog. The product when sunlight catalyzes chemical changes in the reactive mixture of pollutants in the atmosphere.

Phytoplankton. Unicellular algae at the bottom of the food chain. Capable of photosynthesis.

Plasma. Gaseous mixture in which nuclei have been separated from their electrons. High temperatures are required to produce plasma for controlled fusion.

Plastic. A high molecular weight polymer which has been prepared synthetically to have desirable properties such as flexibility, strength, or inert chemical behavior. It is capable of being molded or shaped.

Plasticizer. Any of a number of chemicals used to improve the processing characteristics or final properties of a plastic.

Pollution. Condition caused by the presence of harmful or objectionable matter or energy forms in our environment.

Polychlorinated biphenyls (PCBs). A class of industrial compounds composed of two attached chlorinated phenyl rings. Recently found to be widespread in the environment. Transport mechanisms and long-term effects similar to those of DDT.

Polymer. A very large molecule made by joining many small chemically similar monomer units. Also called a macromolecule.

Polymerization. The process of forming polymers; repeated joining of individual chemical units into large, complex molecules.

Primary treatment. Simplest type of sewage treatment. Suspended solids are removed by screening or sedimentation.

Proteins. Class of essential foods that provide structural material for life. These large molecules are found in the cells of all living organisms.

Proton. A subatomic particle found in the nucleus. It is electrically positive and approximately equal in mass to a neutron.

Pyrolysis. A process in which heat is applied in the absence of oxygen in order to break down complex substances into smaller chemical units. Also called destructive distillation.

Radiation (nuclear). The emission and movement of energy and fast-moving nuclear particles. May also mean the energy and particles themselves.

Radical ion. See ion.

Radioactivity. A phenomenon in which there is disintegration of an unstable nucleus, resulting in the emission of radiation. This may occur naturally or be stimulated by bombarding a nucleus with particles.

Radioisotope. A radioactive isotope.

Reverse osmosis. The process of applying pressure to reverse the normal diffusion of liquids through a membrane. Useful in desalination and medical purification.

Saline water. Seawater, brine solutions, or brackish water containing at least 1000 ppm dissolved solids.

Sanitary landfill. Disposal area for solid wastes. Formed by making alternate, compacted layers of refuse and earth.

Saturated fat. A fat in which each bond of the carbon atoms present is to a separate atom. There are no double or triple bonds.

Secondary treatment. Use of biological processes to decompose organic matter remaining in sewage after primary treatment.

Septic conditions. Occurs in water in which all dissolved oxygen has been depleted and therefore only anaerobic decay can take place.

Sludge. Waste solids from a sewage treatment plant.

Smog. Originally meant a mixture of smoke and fog. Now used (as an abbreviation) to mean photochemical smog. See photochemical smog.

Soap. Cleaning agent composed of the sodium or potassium salts of long-chain organic acids.

Soft water. Water with low mineral concentration. If produced from hard water by ion exchange, sodium and potassium ions replace the calcium, magnesium, and iron of hard water.

Standards. Legal statements based on criteria and on social judgments of benefit versus risk.

Synergist. A chemical that acts to increase the expected effect of another chemical agent. In a synergistic effect, the total effect is greater than just the sum of the individual effects.

Technology. Applied science. Basic knowledge used to produce new products and processes.

Teratogenic. Property of causing any kind of congenital malformation in the fetus.

Tertiary treatment. Treatment of sewage beyond conventional primary and secondary processes. A variety of processes can be employed to remove a greater proportion of organic matter as well as nutrients, metals, or other specific contaminants.

Thermal pollution. Addition of unwanted heat to the environment.

Thermoplastic. A type of plastic with ability to soften or melt when heated and harden when cooled.

Threshold hypothesis. A theory of biological damage. Holds that dose levels below a certain limit (the threshold) are not necessarily harmful.

Transmutation. Transformation of one isotope to another by means of nuclear reaction. Often changes the identity of the element.

Ultraviolet light. Waves of somewhat greater energy and shorter wavelength than visible light. Our sun emits light in the ultraviolet part of the spectrum.

Unsaturated fat. A fat in which there are some double or triple bonds available for reaction. It does not contain all single covalent bonds.

Volatile. Easily vaporized. A volatile substance normally has a high vapor pressure and a low boiling point.

Vulcanization. A process by which sulfur is added to rubber to improve its properties.

Wankel engine. A rotary combustion engine that is simpler, quieter, less expensive, and has the favorable emissions potential to replace the conventional reciprocating internal combustion engine. Particularly good for reducing NO_x emissions.

Weight. Measures gravitational pull on an object. Dependent on position relative to the gravitational field.

Zeolite. Natural silicate mineral with approximate formula NaH_6AlSiO_7. Used to soften water.

Selected Bibliography

CHAPTER 1

COMMONER, BARRY. *Science and Survival.* New York: Viking Press, 1966.

COOLEY, R. A. and SMITH, G., eds. *Congress and the Environment.* Seattle: University of Washington Press, 1970.

COUNCIL ON ENVIRONMENTAL QUALITY. *Environmental Quality, 1st Annual Report.* Washington, D.C.: U.S. Government Printing Office, 1970.

DEBELL, GARRETT, ed. *The Environmental Handbook.* Pacific Palisades, California: Goodyear, 1970.

DETWYLER, THOMAS. *Man's Impact on Environment.* New York: McGraw-Hill Book Co., 1971.

EHRLICH, PAUL. *Population, Resources, Environment.* San Francisco: W. H. Freeman, 1970.

ENVIRONMENTAL PROTECTION AGENCY. *Don't Leave It All to the Experts. The Citizen's Role in Environmental Decision Making.* Washington, D.C.: U.S. Government Printing Office, 1972.

FISHER, ROBERT B. *Science, Man and Society.* Philadelphia: W. B. Saunders, 1971.

GARVEY, GERALD. *Energy, Ecology, Economy: A Framework for Environmental Policy.* New York: W. W. Norton & Company, 1972.

HARTE, JOHN, and SOCOLOW, ROBERT H. *Patient Earth.* New York: Holt, Rinehart & Winston, 1971.

Man's Impact on the Global Environment: Assessment and Recommendations for Action. Report of the Study of Critical Environmental Problems. Cambridge, Mass.: MIT Press, 1970.

MCKAIN, DAVID W., ed. *The Whole Earth: Essays in Appreciation, Anger, and Hope.* New York: St. Martin's Press, 1972.

MEADOWS, DENNIS L. *The Limits to Growth.* Cambridge, Mass.: MIT Press, 1972.

MONCRIEF, L. W. "The Cultural Basis for Our Environmental Crisis." *Science* 170 (1970):508–12.

MURDOCH, WILLIAM W., ed. *Environment: Resources, Pollution, and Society.* Stamford, Connecticut: Sinauer Associates, Inc., 1971.

NATIONAL GEOGRAPHIC SOCIETY. *As We Live and Breathe: The Challenge of Environment.* Washington, D.C.: The National Geographic Society, 1971.

NOVICK, SHELDON, and COTTRELL, DOROTHY, eds. *Our World in Peril: An Environmental Review*. Greenwich, Conn.: Premier Book Division of Fawcett Publications, 1971.

RIENOW, ROBERT, and RIENOW, LEONA. *Moment in the Sun*. New York: Ballantine Books, 1967.

STROBBE, MAURICE A. *Understanding Environmental Pollution*. St. Louis, Mo.: C. V. Mosby Co., 1971.

UDALL, STEWART L. *1976: Agenda for Tomorrow*. New York: Harcourt, Brace & World, 1968.

WAGNER, RICHARD H. *Environment and Man*. New York: W. W. Norton & Company, 1971.

CHAPTER 2

Note: Many of these basic chemistry references can serve you not only for this chapter but throughout the remainder of the book.

ADLER, IRVING. *Inside the Nucleus*. New York: John Day, 1963.

ASIMOV, ISAAC. *A Short History of Chemistry*. Garden City, New York: Doubleday and Company, 1965.

CHOPPIN, GREGORY R., and JAFFE, BERNARD. *Chemistry*. Morristown, N.J.: Silver-Burdett, 1965.

CHOPPIN, GREGORY R., and JOHNSEN, RUSSELL H. *Introductory Chemistry*. Reading, Mass.: Addison Wesley, 1972.

DILLARD, CLYDE R., and GOLDBERG, DAVID E. *Chemistry: Reactions, Structure, and Properties*. New York: The Macmillan Company, 1971.

KASK, UNO. *Chemistry: Structure and Changes of Matter*. New York: Barnes and Noble, 1969.

LAPP, RALPH E., and the EDITORS OF LIFE. *Matter*. New York: Time-Life Books, 1965.

MASTERTON, WILLIAM L., and SLOWINSKI, EMIL J. *Chemical Principles*. 2nd ed. Philadelphia: W. B. Saunders Co., 1969.

PARTINGTON, J. R. *A Short History of Chemistry*. 3rd ed. New York: Harper & Brothers, 1957.

SIENKO, MITCHELL, and PLANE, ROBERT A. *Chemistry*. 4th ed. New York: McGraw-Hill, 1971.

CHAPTER 3

ABRAHAMSON, DEAN E. *Environmental Cost of Electric Power*. New York: Scientists' Institute for Public Information, 1970.

BEHRENS, CHARLES F.; KING, E. RICHARD; and CARPENTER, JAMES W. J. *Atomic Medicine*. 5th ed. Baltimore: Williams and Wilkins Co., 1969.

BRYERTON, GENE. *Nuclear Dilemma*. New York: Friends of the Earth/Ballantine, 1971.

Disposal of Solid Radioactive Wastes in Bedded Salt Deposits. Report by the Committee on Radioactive Waste Management, National Academy of Sciences, National Research Council, Washington, D.C., 1970.

Environmental Aspects of Nuclear Power Stations. International Atomic Energy Agency, Vienna, 1971. Proceedings of a symposium held in New York, August 10–14, 1970. 58 papers. New York: Unipub., 1971.

Environmental Effects of Producing Electric Power. Hearings before the Joint Committee on Atomic Energy, 91st Congress, Oct.-Nov. 1969, Part I: Jan.-Feb. 1970, Part II, Vol. 1 and 2. Washington, D.C.: U.S. Government Printing Office, 1970.

GILLETTE, ROBERT. Series of articles in *Science* 177 (1972). "Nuclear Safety (I): The Roots of Dissent." pp. 771–75. "Nuclear Safety (II): The Years of Delay." pp. 867–71. "Nuclear Safety (III): Critics Charge Conflicts of Interest." pp. 970–75.

GLASSTONE, SAMUEL. *Sourcebook on Atomic Energy*. 3rd ed. Princeton: Van Nostrand, 1967.

GOFMAN, JOHN W., and TAMPLIN, ARTHUR L. "Radiation: The Invisible Casualties." *Environment* 12:3 (1970): 12–19.

GOUGH, WILLIAM C., and EASTLUND, BERNARD J. "The Prospects of Fusion Power." *Scientific American* 224:2 (1971): 50–64.

HAMMOND, ALLEN L. "Fission: The Pro's and Con's of Nuclear Power." *Science* 178 (1972): 147–49.

HAMMOND, ALLEN L. "The Fast Breeder Reactor: Signs of a Critical Reaction." *Science* 176 (1972): 391–93.

HARVEY, BERNARD. *Introduction to Nuclear Physics and Chemistry*. 2nd ed. Englewood Cliffs, New Jersey: Prentice-Hall, 1969.

MARTELL, E. A., et al. "Fire Damage." *Environment* 12:4 (1970): 14–21.

MORGAN, KARL Z. "Never Do Harm." *Environment* 13:1 (1971): 28–38.

MORGAN, K. Z., and TURNER, J. E. *Principles of Radiation Protection*. New York: John Wiley & Sons, Inc., 1967.

NOVICK, SHELDON. *The Careless Atom*. Boston: Houghton Mifflin Co., 1969.

"Nuclear Power." A series of articles in *Not Man Apart* 2:8 (1972): 1, 9–15.

PITTMAN, FRANK K. "Management of Commercial High-Level Radioactive Waste." Paper presented at MIT, July 25, 1972. Available from the Atomic Energy Commission.

Radioactive Waste Discharges to the Environment from Nuclear Power Facilities. U.S. Department of Health, Education, and Welfare, Public Health Service, Publication No. BRH/DER 70-2. Rockville, Maryland, March 1970.

Radionuclides in the Environment. Advances in Chemistry Series, No. 93. Washington D.C.: American Chemical Society, 1968.

RIVERA-CORDERO, ANTONIO. "The Nuclear Industry and Air Pollution." *Environmental Science and Technology* 4:5 (1970): 392–95.

SEABORG, GLENN T., and BLOOM, JUSTIN L. "Fast Breeder Reactors." *Scientific American* 223:5 (1970): 13–21.

TSIVOGLOU, ERNEST C. "Nuclear Power: The Social Conflict." *Environmental Science and Technology* 5:5 (1971): 404–10.

WEINBERG, ALVIN M. "Social Institutions and Nuclear Energy." *Science* 177 (1972): 27–34.

WOOD, LOWELL, and NUCKOLLS, JOHN. "Fusion Power." *Environment* 14:4 (1972): 29–33.

CHAPTER 4

Chemical Bonding. (Also refer to the general chemistry references listed for Chapter 2.)

BARROW, GORDON M. et al. *Understanding Chemistry*. Vol. I and II. New York: W. A. Benjamin, 1967. *Note:* These are programmed texts dealing with moles and chemical bonding concepts.

COMPANION, A. L. *Chemical Bonding*. New York: W. A. Benjamin, 1964.

GRAY, H. B. *Electrons and Chemical Bonding*. New York: W. A. Benjamin, 1964.

GRISWOLD, E. *Chemical Bonding and Structure*. Boston: D. C. Heath Co., 1968.

LAGOWSKI, J. J. *The Chemical Bond*. Boston: Houghton Mifflin Co., 1966.

PAULING, L. *The Nature of the Chemical Bond*. Ithaca, New York: Cornell University Press, 1960.

RYSCHKEWITSCH, G. E. *Chemical Bonding and the Geometry of Molecules*. New York: Reinhold, 1963.

SISLER, H. H. *Electronic Structure, Properties, and the Periodic Law*. New York: Reinhold, 1963.

Environmental Chemistry References

HILL, JOHN W. *Chemistry for Changing Times*. Minneapolis, Minnesota: Burgess Publishing Company, 1972.

HORRIGAN, PHILIP A. *The Challenge of Chemistry*. New York: McGraw-Hill, 1970.

JONES, MARK M., et al. *Chemistry, Man and Society*. Philadelphia: W. B. Saunders, 1972.

KIEFFER, WILLIAM. *Chemistry, A Cultural Approach*. New York: Harper and Row, 1971.

MACDONALD, MALCOLM M., and DAVIS, ROBERT E. *Chemistry and Society*. Boston: Willard Grant Press, 1972.

MANAHAN, STANLEY E. *Environmental Chemistry*. Boston: Willard Grant Press, 1972. *Note:* This book assumes completion of twenty semester hours in general, analytical, and organic chemistry.

MAXWELL, KENNETH E. *Chemicals and Life*. Belmont, California: Dickenson, 1970.

PETRUCCI, RALPH H. *General Chemistry. Principles and Modern Applications*. New York: Macmillan, 1971.

SCHUBERT, LEO S., and VEGUILLA-BERDECIA, LUIS A. *Chemistry and Society*. Boston: Allyn and Bacon, 1972.

STOKER, H. STEPHEN, and SEAGER, SPENCER L. *Environmental Chemistry: Air and Water Pollution*. Glenview, Illinois: Scott, Foresman and Company, 1972.

CHAPTER 5

Air Pollution Primer. National Tuberculosis and Respiratory Disease Association, New York, 1969.

ALTSHULLER, AUBREY P., and BUFALINI, JOSEPH J. "Photochemical Aspects of Air Pollution: A Review." *Environmental Science and Technology* 5:1 (1971): 39–64.

AYRES, ROBERT U., and McKENNA, RICHARD P. *Alternatives to the Internal Combustion Engine: Impacts on Environmental Quality.* Baltimore, Maryland: Johns Hopkins Press, 1972.

BACH, WILFRID. *Atmospheric Pollution.* New York: McGraw-Hill, 1972.

Biological Aspects of Lead: An Annotated Bibliography. Parts 1 and 2. Washington, D.C.: U.S. Government Printing Office, 1972.

BUFALINI, MARIJON. "Oxidation of Sulfur Dioxide in Polluted Atmospheres—A Review." *Environmental Science and Technology* 5:8 (1971): 685–700.

CHOW, TSAIHWA J., and EARL, JOHN L. "Lead Aerosols in the Atmosphere: Increasing Concentrations." *Science* 169 (1970): 577–80.

COLE, DAVID E. "The Wankel Engine." *Scientific American* 227:2 (1972): 14–23.

COMMITTEE ON BIOLOGIC EFFECTS OF ATMOSPHERIC POLLUTANTS. *Airborne Lead in Perspective.* Washington, D.C.: National Academy of Sciences, 1972.

HALL, HOMER J., and BARTOK, WILLIAM. "NO_x from Stationary Sources." *Environmental Science and Technology* 5:4 (1971): 320–26.

HALL, STEPHEN K. "Lead Pollution and Poisoning." *Environmental Science and Technology* 6:1 (1972): 30–35.

HALL, STEPHEN L. "Sulfur Compounds in the Atmosphere." *Chemistry* 45:3 (1972): 16–18.

"Is Man Changing the Earth's Climate?" *Chemical and Engineering News*, 16 August 1971, pp. 38–40.

JACOBSEN, JAY S., and HILL, A. CLYDE. *Recognition of Air Pollution Injury to Vegetation: A Pictorial Atlas.* Report No. 1, Air Pollution Control Association, Pittsburgh, Pennsylvania, August 1970.

LEES, LESTER, et al. *Smog, A Report to the People.* California Institute of Technology, Environmental Quality Laboratory, Pasadena, California, 1972.

NADLER, ALLEN A., et al. *Air Pollution.* New York: Scientists' Institute for Public Information, 1970.

"New Blueprint Emerges for Air Pollution Controls." *Environmental Science and Technology* 5:2 (1971): 106–108.

NEWELL, REGINALD E. "The Global Circulation of Atmospheric Pollutants." *Scientific American* 224:1 (1971): 32–42.

"Project Threshold: Testing the Tests." *Environmental Science and Technology* 6:1 (1972): 23–24.

STARR, C. "Energy and Power." *Scientific American* 225:3 (1971): 37–49.

U.S. PUBLIC HEALTH SERVICE, U.S. Department of Health, Education, and Welfare. *Air Quality Criteria for Carbon Monoxide,* 1970. *Air Quality Criteria for Hydrocarbons,* 1970. *Air Quality Criteria for Nitrogen Oxides,* 1970. *Air Quality Criteria for Particulates,* 1969. *Air Quality Criteria for Photochemical Oxidants,* 1970. *Air Quality Criteria for Sulfur Oxides,* 1967. Washington, D.C.: U.S. Government Printing Office.

WOHLERS, HENRY C. "Air—A Priceless Resource," in P. Walton Purdom, *Environmental Health.* New York: Academic Press, 1971.

CHAPTER 6

BEHRMAN, A. S. *Water is Everybody's Business: The Chemistry of Water Purification.* Garden City, N.J.: Doubleday and Company, 1968.

BIGGER, J. W., AND COREY, R. B. National Academy of Sciences. *Eutrophication: Causes, Consequences, Correctives.* National Research Council, 1969.

CLARK, J. R. "Thermal Pollution and Aquatic Life." *Scientific American* 220:3 (1969): 18–27.

COUNCIL ON ENVIRONMENTAL QUALITY. *Ocean Dumping: A National Policy.* Washington, D.C.: U.S. Government Printing Office, 1970.

FRANKS, FELIX, ed. *Water—A Comprehensive Treatise. Vol. 1: The Physics and Physical Chemistry of Water.* New York: Plenum Press, 1972.

GRUCHOW, NANCY. "Detergents: Side Effects of the Washday Miracles." *Science* 167 (1970): 151.

GRUNDY, RICHARD D. "Strategies for Control of Man-Made Eutrophication." *Environmental Science and Technology* 5:12 (1972): 1182–90.

McCAULL, JULIAN. "The Black Tide." *Environment* 12:7 (1970): 12–23.

McCAULL, JULIAN. "Who Owns the Water?" *Environment* 12:8 (1970): 30–39.

MARX, WESLEY. *The Frail Ocean.* New York: Balantine Books, 1967.

"Mercury: Anatomy of a Pollution Problem." *Chemical and Engineering News,* 5 July 1971, pp. 22–34.

MILLER, STANTON. "Water Pollution in the States." *Environmental Science and Technology* 5:2 (1971): 120–25.

POPKIN, ROY. *Desalination: Water for Mankind's Future.* New York: Praeger Publishers, 1968.

PUTMAN, JOHN J. "Quicksilver and Slow Death." *National Geographic* 142:4 (October 1972): 507–27.

REY, GEORGE; LACY, WILLIAM J.; and CYWIN, ALLEN. "Industrial Water Reuse: Future Pollution Solution." *Environmental Science and Technology* 5:9 (1971): 760–65.

SAYERS, WILLIAM R. "Water Quality Surveillance: The Federal-State Network." *Environmental Science and Technology* 5:2 (1971): 114–19.

U.S. DEPARTMENT OF INTERIOR. *The Cost of Clean Water. Volumes I–IV.* Federal Water Pollution Control Administration, Washington, D.C., 1968.

"Water Pollution Law – 1972 Style." *Environmental Science and Technology* 6:13 (1972): 1068–70.

WOOD, JOHN M. "A Progress Report on Mercury." *Environment* 14:1 (1972): 33–39.

YEE, WILLIAM C. "Thermal Aquaculture: Engineering and Economics." *Environmental Science and Technology* 6:3 (1972): 232–37.

ZELDIN, MARVIN. "Oil Pollution." *Audubon* (May 1971): 99–119.

ZEMAITIS, WILLIAM L. "Water and Waste Water," in P. Walton Purdom, *Environmental Health.* New York: Academic Press, 1971.

CHAPTER 7

ASHTON, FLOYD M., and CRAFTS, ALDEN S. *The Chemistry and Mode of Action of Herbicides.* New York: Wiley-Interscience, 1972.

BEROZA, MORTON, and KNIPLING, E. F. "Gypsy Moth Control with the Sex Attractant Pheromone." *Science* 177 (1972): 19–27.

BOFFEY, PHILIP M. "Herbicides in Vietnam: AAAS Finds Widespread Devastation." *Science* 171 (1971): 43–47.

CARSON, RACHEL L. *Silent Spring.* Boston: Houghton Mifflin Co., 1962.

DAHLSTEN, DONALD L. *Pesticides.* New York: Scientists' Institute for Public Information, 1970.

DUGGAN, R. E., and DAWSON, KEITH. "Pesticides: A Report on Residues in Food." Reprinted from *FDA Papers* 1:5 (June 1967). Also appears in Maxwell, Kenneth E. *Chemicals and Life.* Belmont, Ca.: Dickenson Publishing Company, 1970.

EPSTEIN, SAMUEL S., and LEGATOR, MARVIN S. *The Mutagenicity of Pesticides: Concepts and Evaluation.* Cambridge, Mass.: MIT Press, 1971.

FERGUSON, DENZEL E. "The New Evolution." *Environment* 14:6 (1972): 30–35.

GRAHAM, FRANK, JR. *Since Silent Spring.* Greenwich, Conn.: Fawcett Publications, 1970.

GUSTAFSON, CARL G. "PCB's – Prevalent and Persistent." *Environmental Science and Technology* 4:10 (1970): 814–19.

HERSH, SEYMOUR M. *Chemical and Biological Warfare.* Garden City, N.J.: Anchor-Doubleday Books, 1969.

HOLCOMB, R. W. "Insect Control: Alternatives to the Use of Conventional Pesticides." *Science* 168 (1970): 1419–24.

JACOBSEN, MARTIN, and CROSBY, D. G., eds. *Naturally Occurring Insecticides.* New York: Marcel Dekker, 1971.

McINTIRE, GREG. "Spoiled by Success." *Environment* 14:6 (1972): 14–22, 27–29.

MAUGH, THOMAS H. "Polychlorinated Biphenyls: Still Prevalent, but Less of a Problem." *Science* 178 (1972): 388.

MILLER, M. W., and BERG, G., eds. *Chemical Fallout – Current Research on Persistent Pesticides.* Springfield, Illinois: Charles C. Thomas, 1969.

MONTAGUE, PETER, AND MONTAGUE, KATHERINE. "The Great Caterpillar War and the Ecopolitics of Pesticides. *Audubon* (January 1971): 50–58.

MRAK, E. M. et al. *Report of the Secretary's Commission on Pesticides and Their Relationship to Environmental Health.* U.S. Department of Health, Education, and

Welfare. Washington, D.C.: U.S. Government Printing Office, 1969.

"Pesticide Regulations Tighten but Choices are in the Offing." *Environmental Science and Technology* 5:5 (1971): 398–403.

PIMENTEL, DAVID. *Ecological Effects of Pesticides on Non-Target Species.* Executive Office of the President, Office of Science and Technology. Washington, D.C.: U.S. Government Printing Office, 1971.

RISEBROUGH, ROBERT, and BRODINE, VIRGINIA. "More Letters in the Wind." *Environment* 12:1 (1970): 16–27.

WHITESIDE, THOMAS. *Defoliation.* New York: Ballantine/ Friends of the Earth, 1970.

CHAPTER 8

Foods:

Chemical Additives in Booze. Washington, D.C.: Center for Science in the Public Interest, 1972.

"Food Additive Makers Face Intensified Attack." *Chemical and Engineering News* (12 July 1971): 16–23.

Food Additives: What They Are/How They Are Used. Washington, D.C.: Manufacturing Chemists' Association, 1971.

"Fortified Foods: The Next Revolution." *Chemical and Engineering News* (10 August 1970): 36–40.

FURIA, THOMAS E., ed. *Handbook of Food Additives.* Cleveland, Ohio: The Chemical Rubber Company Press, 1968.

GUILD, WALTER J. "Theory of Sweet Taste." *Journal of Chemical Education* 49:3 (1972): 171–73.

HUNTER, BEATRICE TRUM. *Consumer Beware! Your Food and What's Been Done to It.* New York: Simon and Schuster, 1971.

KERMODE, G. O. "Food Additives." *Scientific American* 226:3 (1972): 15–21.

MAYER, JEAN. "Toward a National Nutrition Policy." *Science* 176 (1972): 237–41.

WADE, NICHOLAS. "Delaney Anti-Cancer Clause: Scientists Debate on Article of Faith." *Science* 177 (1972): 588–91.

WOLFF, I. A., and WASSERMAN, A. E. "Nitrates, Nitrites, and Nitrosamines." *Science* 177 (1972): 15–19.

Drugs:

BARLOW, RICHARD B. *Introduction to Chemical Pharmacology.* New York: John Wiley & Sons, 1964.

BOGUE, J. Y. "Drugs of the Future." *Journal of Chemical Education* 46:8 (1969): 468–75.

"Consumer Criticism of Drug Industry Mounts." *Chemical and Engineering News* (26 July 1971): 24–28.

Drugs of Abuse. Reprint from the FDA Papers, July-August 1967. Food and Drug Administration, U.S. Department of Health, Education, and Welfare.

LINGEMAN, RICHARD R. *Drugs from A to Z: A Dictionary.* New York: McGraw-Hill, 1969.

Marihuana and Health. Second Annual Report to Congress from the Secretary of Health, Education and Welfare. Washington, D.C.: U.S. Government Printing Office, 1972.

Marihuana: A Signal of Misunderstanding. First Report of the National Commission on Marihuana and Drug Abuse. Washington, D.C.: U.S. Government Printing Office, 1972.

MAXWELL, KENNETH E. *Chemicals and Life.* Belmont, Ca.: Dickenson Publishing Company, 1970. Particularly Chapter 2: Prevention of People, and Chapter 4: Mind Modifiers.

MECHOULAM, RAPHAEL. "Marijuana Chemistry." *Science* 168 (1970): 1159–66.

MULE, S. J., and BRILL, HENRY. *Chemical and Biological Aspects of Drug Dependence.* Cleveland, Ohio: Chemical Rubber Company Press, 1972.

STECHER, P. G., ed. *The Merck Index*, 8th ed. Rahway, N.J.: Merck and Company, 1968.

CHAPTER 9

ANDERSON, EARL V. "Consumer Chemical Specialties." *Chemical and Engineering News* (1 December 1969): 37–64.

"Biodegradability — Lofty Goal for Plastics." *Chemical and Engineering News* (11 September 1972): 37–38.

"Building Bricks from the Waste Pile." *Environmental Science and Technology* 6:6 (1972): 502–503.

HEYLIN, MICHAEL. Series of articles in *Chemical and Engineering News.* "Consumer Packaging." (12 April 1971): 20–23. "Plastics in Construction." (29 March

1971): 16–20. "Reinforced Plastics." (1 February 1971): 14–19.

KIRK, RAYMOND E., and OTHMER, DONALD F., eds. *Encyclopedia of Chemical Technology*. New York: Wiley-Interscience, 1971.

NATTA, GIULIO. "Precisely Constructed Polymers." *Scientific American* 205:2 (1961): 33–41. Available as Offprint #315 from W. H. Freeman and Company, San Francisco.

"Phthalate Effect on Health Still Not Clear." *Chemical and Engineering News* (18 September 1972): 14–15.

SANDERS, HOWARD T. "Artificial Organs." *Chemical and Engineering News* (5 April 1971): 32–49.

Landfill: Alternative to the Open Dump." *Environmental Science and Technology* 6:5 (1972): 406–10.

SARVETNICK, HAROLD A. *Polyvinyl Chloride*. New York: Van Nostrand Reinhold, 1969.

SOLID WASTE MANAGEMENT OFFICE, ENVIRONMENTAL PROTECTION AGENCY. *Disposal of Polymer Solid Wastes by Primary Polymer Producers and Plastic Fabricators*. Washington, D.C.: U.S. Government Printing Office, 1971.

WENDLAND, RAY T. *Petrochemicals: The New World of Synthetics*. Garden City, N.J.: Anchor-Doubleday Books, 1969.